MECHANICS

ADDISON-WESLEY SERIES IN
MECHANICS AND THERMODYNAMICS

Howard W. Emmons, Bernard Budiansky

Consulting Editors

MECHANICS

by

HANS ZIEGLER

Swiss Federal Institute of Technology
Zurich

VOLUME I

STATICS OF RIGID BODIES,
FLUIDS, AND DEFORMABLE SOLIDS

Translated from the German by

D. B. McVEAN

ADDISON-WESLEY PUBLISHING COMPANY, INC.
READING, MASSACHUSETTS

ADDISON-WESLEY PUBLISHING COMPANY, INC.
Palo Alto · READING, MASSACHUSETTS · London
NEW YORK · DALLAS · ATLANTA · BARRINGTON, ILLINOIS

PREFACE TO THE ENGLISH EDITION

This book is the present version of a course given by the author for many years at the Swiss Federal Institute of Technology (Eidgenössische Technische Hochschule, ETH, Zürich). The course is intended for students of civil, mechanical, and electrical engineering. It is the first and also the last compulsory course in mechanics and is preceded by classes in calculus, geometry, and materials. The course is offered in the second and third semesters.

The aim of the course, and hence of this book, is to provide the student with the solid foundation in elementary mechanics which is necessary for subsequent courses in physics, for more specific topics in engineering, and for the pursuit of mechanics itself in its various branches. In particular, the book does not intend to prepare the student in the shortest possible time for a well-defined and accordingly limited field to which he anticipates his future activity will be devoted. I strongly believe, on the contrary, that a truly academic institution should and can provide a reasonably broad education at least in the fundamental topics.

In an introductory text, any attempt to indulge in the axiomatics of the field would be out of place. Even so it is possible and advantageous to stress the logical structure of mechanics, starting from a few convenient basic concepts and axioms. The book makes extensive use of this possibility. In particular, it emphasizes the systematic aspect in the treatment of forces and mechanical systems, and it attempts to put the greatest possible stress on the conditions and suppositions to which the various theorems are subject.

The examples treated in the text and formulated at the end of each section are chosen primarily for their didactic value as applications of the theory and only in the second place for their practical importance. No attempt has been made to restrict the imagination of the reader by figures or examples of an unnecessary specific nature. A student who has learned to correctly use the fundamental laws of particle and rigid body dynamics will have no difficulty in applying these laws if the particle or body happens to be an airplane, missile, or satellite.

With regard to the material covered, this book differs in two respects from similiar texts. It may be surprising, in the first place, that in a text that claims to be modern a few sections are devoted to graphical methods, considered to be out of fashion. I believe, however, that these methods are temporarily underrated and that it might be worthwhile to keep at least a few fundamentals alive. Moreover, and this is the principle reason, I feel that it is advantageous from the didactic point of view to use all approaches at hand to familiarize the student with the process of force reduction. By way of an example: the Maxwell diagram is treated here not so much for its practical value in determining the interior forces in structures; the inclusion seemed justified above all as a nice example for the treatment of rigid systems.

Finally, the present text is not restricted to rigid systems but includes two chapters dealing with deformable media. Historically, this is explained by the fact that, on the European continent, strength of materials has always been an important part of any course in mechanics. The reader will notice, however, that the chapter of deformable solids treats not only elastic but also plastic bodies and that a considerable part of it is conceived as a general introduction to the concepts used in continuum mechanics. The general problem of strength is presented in the only possible way, i.e., in three dimensions, and the applications are reduced to a brief treatment of the methods that use to be described in more detail in subsequent engineering courses.

The book is essentially a translation of the German text published by Birkhäuser Verlag, Basel and Stuttgart. In the English version a section has been added at the end of each volume, containing the solutions of the problems posed at the end of each section. This list has been prepared by my assistant, Mr. Donald McVean, M.A., who also undertook the translation. I gratefully acknowledge the great work done by him as well as the collaboration and the help we have received from the publishers.

It has turned out that with respect to the units, it is still more difficult in this translation to satisfy several divergent demands than it was in the original text. We have made a few choices and tried to maintain consistency throughout the book, assuming that it will not be difficult for anyone preferring different units to translate the numerical data occurring in the examples into the units of his own choice.

The book consists of two volumes. The first one deals with statics of rigid bodies, fluids, and deformable solids. The second volume contains kinematics and kinetics and is essentially restricted to particles, rigid bodies, and rigid systems.

May 1965   H. Z.

CONTENTS

CONTENTS

Introduction

I. Rigid Bodies

II. Statics of Fluids

III. Deformable Solids

INTRODUCTION

Mechanics is the theory of the motion of bodies which are encountered in nature and technology, and of the forces which are regarded as the causes of such motion. Corresponding to this double definition, mechanics can be divided into three subdivisions: *Kinematics*, or the geometry of motion, disregards the forces applied to a given body; it investigates the types of motion of the body and represents the motion as simply as possible. *Statics*, or the geometry of forces, disregards the motion of the body and investigates and reduces the applied forces. Finally, *kinetics* provides the connection between the forces and the resulting motions.

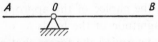

Fig. 0.1

Figure 0.1 shows a lever pivoted at O. The question as to the relation between the velocities of the two points A and B is one of kinematics; the relation between the forces applied to the points A and B of the stationary lever is given by statics; and the determination of the motion of the lever under arbitrarily prescribed forces is a problem of kinetics.

The most important problem of mechanics is concerned with the motion of a body when the forces are at least partially prescribed. This is the *central problem of kinetics*. To solve it, one begins by representing the possible motions in a simple form (by the methods of kinematics) and by reducing the forces (by the methods of statics).

In many cases the body under consideration is at rest. Then there is no kinematic problem and the role of kinetics is limited to the statement that the forces applied to the body can be reduced to the so-called *zero force*, i.e., they must be in *equilibrium*. For the rest, the problem is one of statics: from the equilibrium it is possible to determine the unknown reactions corresponding to the known forces. In this sense *statics* can also be considered as the theory of equilibrium, in contrast to *dynamics*, i.e., the theory of motion (kinematics and kinetics).

If, in Figure 0.1, an arbitrary force is applied at B, then the static problem consists in the determination of those forces at A which maintain equilibrium and of the bearing forces acting at O.

1

Since bodies of different materials react differently to prescribed forces and thus must be treated by different methods, mechanics can also be subdivided according to the objects studied.

Rigid bodies, such as concrete parts of buildings and steel machine components, are characterized by an unchangeable form, independent of the loading. *Elastic bodies*, such as steel springs and rubber, deform under a given loading but resume their original shape after unloading. *Plastic bodies*, like clay, are deformable but do not regain their original shape after unloading. *Fluids*, like water, deform under arbitrarily small forces but have a nearly constant volume, whereas *gases*, like air, have the tendency to fill the greatest available space. Accordingly, there is a mechanics of rigid bodies, of elastic or plastic solids, of fluids, and of gases. The simplest results of the theories of elasticity and plasticity used to be taught under the title *strength of materials*.

The classification given above is incomplete, and, moreover, it represents ideal states which strictly never arise. Under small forces, a steel blade might behave as though practically rigid, but with increasing loading it exhibits elastic and, finally, also plastic behavior. Thus, mechanics is always based on idealizations. Sometimes, the choice of the appropriate idealization is not so much a matter of the magnitude of the loads as of the type of the problem. For instance, in order to determine the forces that a three-legged table exerts on its supports, one can treat the table as rigid, whereas the same problem with a four-legged table is soluble only when the deformations are taken into account.

It will become evident in what follows that mechanics can be built up as an exact science from a small number of fundamental concepts and axioms. In transferring the results to actual situations a certain caution is called for. Since idealizations must always be made in formulating the assumptions, frequent recourse to experience cannot be avoided and, where discrepancies occur, it is generally necessary to correct or refine the assumptions.

The present book is intended to be an introduction to the elementary fields of mechanics. The first volume contains the statics of rigid and fluid bodies as well as an introduction to the theory of deformable solids. The second volume covers the dynamics of rigid bodies and systems. The treatment will be limited to classical mechanics.

I. Rigid Bodies

1. Foundations

Every science, insofar as it is exact, rests on certain *fundamental concepts* that are taken from experience and are not amenable to definition, as well as on elementary principles or *axioms* which cannot be reduced to still simpler ones and which thus cannot be proved. On this foundation, definitions are used to construct higher concepts, and further logical deduction between these leads to the establishment of theorems of a more sophisticated nature.

Among the fundamental concepts of mechanics belongs above all that of *space* as a three-dimensional continuum, which is conveniently illustrated with the aid of a right-handed system of rectangular coordinates (Fig. 1.1). The position of a point P is then described by its three coordinates x, y, z. These are algebraic lengths, i.e., they are either positive or negative.

The unit of length is the meter (m). It is defined as 1,650,763.73 wavelengths of the orange-red spectrum line of the isotope of krypton having a mass number 86. The imperial yard is equivalent to 0.9144004 m. The U.S. yard (yd) is defined as exactly 3600/3937 m. A foot (ft) is $\frac{1}{3}$ yd; an inch is $\frac{1}{12}$ ft, and the (statute) mile is 1760 yd.

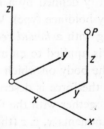

Fig. 1.1

A further fundamental concept, which, however, does not enter into statics, is that of time. It can be represented as a one-dimensional continuum by means of an axis that can be traversed by the image point in but one direction.

The unit of time is the mean solar day (d), which was originally defined as the mean duration of the terrestrial day and is now taken as 1/365·24... of the tropical year 1900. Other units are the year (yr), the hour (hr), the minute (min), and the second (sec).

A *body* is a material configuration in space. The matter in it possesses a definite *mass*, which need not be introduced at this stage. In a *rigid body* an arbitrary pair of points has an invariable distance of separation.

3

If we press our hand against a body (Fig. 1.2), we are applying a *force* to it. In general, forces are applied to a body whenever it comes into contact with other bodies, e.g., a support, a spring, or a cable. Other forces, like the weight of the body or electric and magnetic forces, are applied not by direct contact but act over a distance.

In Fig. 1.2, the behavior of the body under the action of the cable force S produced by the weight and pulley depends on the point A where the cable is attached to the body, on the direction of the part of the cable between A and the pulley, and also on S, the loading of the cable. It can be concluded from this that a force, in general, is determined by three factors, namely, its *point of application*, its *direction* (i.e., its line and sense of action), and its *magnitude*. A measure of the magnitude of the force is provided by the force S exerting the given action on the body by means of the cable and pulley.

Accordingly, the unit of weight, namely the kilogram (kg*), can be used as the unit of force. It is defined conventionally as the weight of a certain body kept under constant conditions in Paris. The (avoirdupois) pound (lb*) is defined as 0.45359 kg*. It is unfortunate that, in dynamics, the kilogram and the pound are also used as units of mass. We use the asterisk to distinguish the force units. In dynamics, we shall use also the Newton (N) as a unit of force:

$$1N = \frac{1}{9.806}\ kg^* = 0.102\ kg^* . \tag{1.1}$$

A quantity defined by a magnitude and a direction is a *vector* (henceforth denoted by boldface type). When the point of application is essential, then we are dealing with a *bound vector*. Consequently, a force is a bound vector, so long as it is applied to an arbitrary body that is not necessarily rigid.

When the body on which the force K acts is referred to a coordinate system (Fig. 1.3), the force is described by the position vector r of its point of application A together with the force vector K. The position vector r can be given by its components x, y, z (the coordinates of the point A), and the components

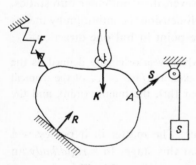

Fig. 1.2

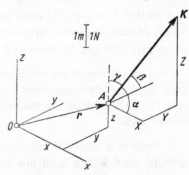

Fig. 1.3

of the force vector K by its components X, Y, Z. Of course, for the representation as shown in Fig. 1.3, a scale for force and length must be introduced. The magnitude $|K| = K$ of the force vector is given in terms of its components by

$$K = \sqrt{X^2 + Y^2 + Z^2},\qquad(1.2)$$

and its direction angles α, β, γ are furnished by

$$\cos\alpha = \frac{X}{K},\qquad \cos\beta = \frac{Y}{K},\qquad \cos\gamma = \frac{Z}{K}.\qquad(1.3)$$

Conversely, we have

$$X = K\cos\alpha,\qquad Y = K\cos\beta,\qquad Z = K\cos\gamma.\qquad(1.4)$$

Analogous expressions also hold, of course, for the corresponding determinatives of the position vector r of A.

In addition to the concentrated forces that have thus far been considered, there are *continuous distributions of force* acting over curves, surfaces, or spatial regions.

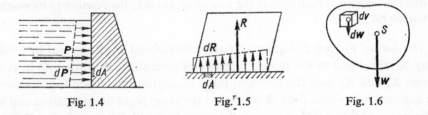

Fig. 1.4   Fig. 1.5   Fig. 1.6

Thus, the action of the water on the wall of the dam (Fig. 1.4) constitutes a *surface force*. On an element of area dA there is a force of magnitude $dP = p\,dA$, where p is the pressure (force per unit area). For many practical purposes these elementary forces can be replaced by a single resultant P. Again, the force dR acting along the supporting surface of a body (Fig. 1.5) is a surface force, and the elementary weights of magnitudes $dW = \gamma\,dv$ acting on an element of volume dv of a body of specific weight γ (Fig. 1.6) define a *body force*, the resultant W of which is the total weight of the body (acting at the center of gravity S).

The first principle of mechanics is the *reaction principle*, which is the third of the three fundamental laws formulated by Newton in 1684 and is also known as the *law of action and reaction*. According to the reaction principle, forces always arise in pairs: if a body 1 (Fig. 1.7) exerts a force R_{21} on a body 2, then body 2 acts back on body 1 with a force R_{12}, and, indeed, in such a way that R_{12} and R_{21} are equal and opposite with a common line of action.

The fact that R_{12} and R_{21} are equal and opposite can be expressed by the vector equation

$$R_{12} = -R_{21}.\qquad(1.5)$$

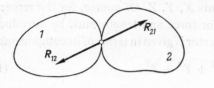

Fig. 1.7

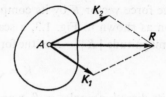

Fig. 1.8

However, the law contains more information, in that it asserts that the lines of action coincide. Either of the two forces is called the *reaction* of the other one. The law always associates forces that act on different bodies. It is valid not only for bodies at rest but also for moving bodies.

Thus, the reaction to the water pressure on the dam in Fig. 1.4 is the pressure (not indicated) of the wall on the water. The reaction to the force that is exerted on a body by its support (see Fig. 1.5) is the force of the body on the support, and the reaction to the weight (see Fig. 1.6) is the force with which the body attracts the earth. This applies in particular in the case of an aircraft; the reaction to its weight is not the lift.

The *law of the parallelogram of forces*, formulated by Robertval in 1650, may be introduced as the second principle of mechanics. According to it, two forces K_1 and K_2 with the common point of application A (see Fig. 1.8) can be replaced by a single force R which has the same point of application and is obtained as the diagonal of the parallelogram formed by the two forces K_1 and K_2. The substitute force R is called the *resultant* of the two forces K_1 and K_2, which in turn are called the *components* of R.

Such a construction for the resultant is tantamount to vector addition of the components. Thus, it follows that

$$K_1 + K_2 = R, \tag{1.6}$$

but, in general, $K_1 + K_2 \neq R$. The fact that R replaces the forces K_1 and K_2, i.e., that it is equivalent to them, can be expressed by the *static equivalence*

$$K_1[A], K_2[A] \sim R[A] \tag{1.7}$$

between the forces acting at A, the law for constructing the resultant being given by (1.6).

Conversely, the equivalence (1.7) indicates the possibility of resolving a given force R into two components K_1 and K_2, with the same point of application, such that their vector sum is equal to the given force vector.

The basic problem of statics consists in the reduction of systems of forces. This can arise as a preparation for deducing the motion of a body from given forces.

On the other hand, bodies at rest are always supported somehow, and in such cases it is a matter of determining the forces in the supports. In order to solve this fundamental problem, a further proposition is required which could be derived from dynamic principles but which in statics, however, must be introduced as an axiom.

This third axiom is the *equilibrium principle*. According to it, the totality of all forces applied to a body at rest is in equilibrium, i.e., the forces cancel each other, having a vanishing resultant. For the n forces $K_1, K_2, \ldots, K_n$ acting on a body at rest, it thus holds that

$$K_1, K_2, \ldots, K_n \sim 0. \tag{1.8}$$

If a *particle m*, i.e., a body whose dimensions are negligibly small, rests on a horizontal plane (Fig. 1.9), then the only two forces acting on the particle, namely, its weight W and the supporting force R, must be in equilibrium. That is, $R = -W$, which means that the supporting force acts vertically upward and has the magnitude W.

More interesting cases will be treated in the following sections. It should be mentioned here that the equilibrium principle cannot be inverted; a body subjected to a self-equilibrating system of forces need not be at rest.

Even when the particle in Fig. 1.9 moves uniformly over the smooth plane, $R = -W$.

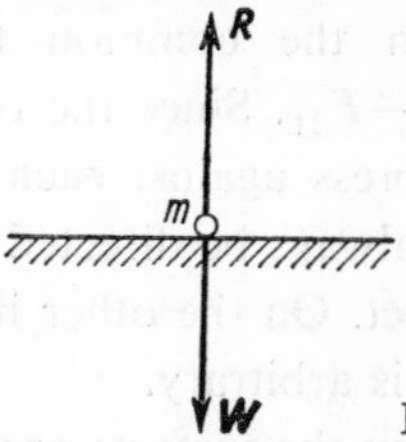

Fig. 1.9

In order to reduce the forces acting on a body and to be able to investigate their equilibrium, it is first necessary to give an exact account of these forces. In addition, it is of primary importance that the limits of the body are defined, i.e., that it is made quite clear what belongs to the body and what to its environment. Then, preferably in a diagram, the so-called *free-body diagram*, the forces are introduced, i.e., all of those acting on the body but none of those acting on the environment. At this stage it is sound practice to consider which of these forces are completely known beforehand and which are at least partially unknown. The known forces are called *loads* and the others *supporting forces* or *reactions*. (The last term is used in a new sense easily distinguished from the earlier one.)

In Fig. 1.10, a body supported by two cables is subjected to three forces: the weight W and the two cable tensions S_1 and S_2. Since only the body is to be considered, none of the forces acting on the cables are to be introduced nor the force with which the body attracts the earth. The force W is a load, whereas S_1 and S_2 are reactions with lines of action along the cables (cf. Section 3 or 12) and with unknown magnitudes.

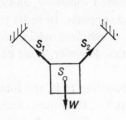

Fig. 1.10

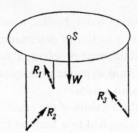

Fig. 1.11

The three-legged table in Fig. 1.11 is subjected to four forces: the weight W as a load and the three supporting forces R_1, R_2, R_3, which are transmitted by the support to the legs and have unknown magnitude and direction.

The forces $R_{12} = -R_{21}$ appearing in the region of contact of two bodies (Fig. 1.12) are called *contact forces*. They can be resolved into the two *normal forces* N_{12} and N_{21} in the contact normal n and the two *friction forces* F_{12} and F_{21} in the common tangent plane t. It is clear that $N_{12} = -N_{21}$ and $F_{12} = -F_{21}$. Since the two bodies, insofar as they merely come into contact, only press against each other without mutual attraction, the normal forces must always be directed toward the interior of the respective bodies on which they act. On the other hand, the direction of the friction force in the tangent plane is arbitrary.

When the surfaces are well finished, the friction forces are small in comparison with the normal forces. The *perfectly smooth surface* is thus defined by the (idealizing) requirement that no friction force can be sustained by it. The contact forces then consist of the normal forces only.

If it is assumed that the table legs in Fig. 1.11 are perfectly smooth and, for the sake of simplicity, that they are rounded off, then each reaction, as shown in Fig. 1.13, will consist in a vertical normal force, the magnitude of which is unknown.

If a body is supported by a hinge, there is always some play between journal and bearing, as shown with great exaggeration in Fig. 1.14. The point of contact

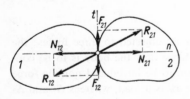

Fig. 1.12

Fig. 1.13

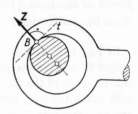

Fig. 1.14

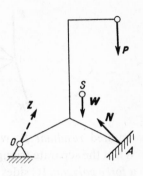

B is not known in advance. Nevertheless, when the hinge is frictionless, the *hinge force Z* must be a normal force, i.e., a force with line of action passing in all cases through the center of the journal and bearing, in short, through the center of the hinge, while the magnitude and direction remain unknown.

When the crane in Fig. 1.15 is hinged without friction at *O* and rests against the smooth support *A*, the weight *W* of the crane and the loading *P* are the loads, and the reactions consist in the normal pressure *N* at *A* as well as the hinge force *Z* at *O*.

Fig. 1.15

2. Concurrent Forces

Systems of forces with a common point of application (concurrent forces) can be reduced either graphically or analytically with the aid of the law of the parallelogram of forces. There is no need to make any assumptions about the nature of the body to which they are applied. Thus it need not be rigid.

When there are only two forces, the *graphical reduction* can be carried out according to Fig. 1.8. However, because of the advantages gained when there are more than two forces, it is expedient, even in this case, to work in two figures, namely, in a *position diagram* (Fig. 2.1 left) in which only the given forces K_1 and K_2 together with their resultant R are shown, and in a *force diagram* (Fig. 2.1 right) in which the construction is carried out. Moreover, it is sufficient to construct the *triangle of forces* in the force diagram (i.e., to use one of the halves of the parallelogram in Fig. 1.8). In this construction the magnitude and direction of the resultant are given by the *closing line*, and, indeed, it is clear that this is independent of the order in which the forces K_1 and K_2 are taken (i.e., which half of the parallelogram is used). In order to also obtain the correct position of the resultant, it must, of course, be transferred to the position diagram.

When there are more than two forces (for example, the four forces in Fig. 2.2), the combination of K_1 and K_2 in the force diagram furnishes a first intermediate resultant R_{12}. Combination of this with K_3 gives a second intermediate resultant R_{123}. The continuation of this process finally leads to the

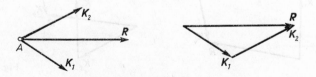

Fig. 2.1

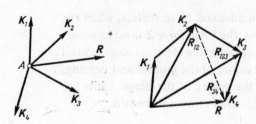

Fig. 2.2

required *resultant* R, which has to be transferred to the position diagram. When the separate triangles are joined together into a single figure, one obtains a *force polygon*. Its sides are formed by the forces, all directed in the same sense of rotation. The *closing line*, with the opposite sense of rotation, represents their resultant, while the diagonals (also those which are not necessary for the construction) represent intermediate resultants.

The result can be expressed by the equivalence

$$K_1, K_2, \ldots, K_n \sim R, \tag{2.1}$$

and the law of construction for the resultant by the vector equation

$$R = \sum_1^n K_i, \tag{2.2}$$

which is a generalization of (1.6).

Usually the intermediate resultants are of no interest and it suffices to use a construction as in Fig. 2.3 which links together the given forces. The resultant given by the closing line is independent of the order of composition, since any sequence can be obtained from another one by permissible, successive interchanges of pairs of forces.

If the forces lie in a plane, as has been tacitly assumed here, then the force polygon is also plane; otherwise it is a spatial polygon and must be constructed in plan and elevation.

The *resolution* of forces can also be carried out in two figures. Thus, for example, a force K (Fig. 2.4) can be uniquely resolved onto two distinct lines g_1 and g_2 coplanar with it and passing through its point of application A. This is effected in the force diagram by constructing the two lines h_1 and h_2

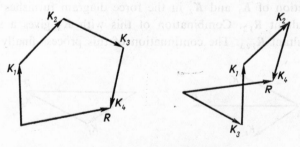

Fig. 2.3

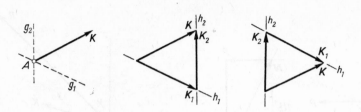

Fig. 2.4

which pass through the end points of K and are parallel to g_1 and g_2, respectively, and by observing the convention for sense of rotation in the resulting triangle of forces. Clearly h_1 can be drawn through either end of K without affecting the result.

Similarly, it can be shown that in three dimensions a force can be uniquely resolved onto three prescibed, noncoplanar lines of action passing through its point of application.

According to the equilibrium principle, the forces applied to a body at rest must be in *equilibrium*. Thus, according to (1.8), they must be equivalent to the zero force. For this, it is necessary and sufficient that the resultant vanishes, and consequently the end point of the last force and the initial point of the first force must coincide in the force diagram. It is then said that the polygon of forces is closed.

In order to bring the system of forces shown in Fig. 2.2 into equilibrium by the addition of one further force, we add the force K_5 which closes the polygon in the force diagram and transfer it to the position diagram (Fig. 2.5).

In order to find the horizontal force P that holds the particle m (Fig. 2.6) at rest on a perfectly smooth inclined plane, we observe that apart from P there is the weight W (with magnitude 2 lb*) and a normal reaction N acting on the particle. Since the lines of action of P and N as well as that of W are known, a closed triangle can be constructed, giving along with the magnitude of P also that of N (to be read off with the chosen scale of forces).

For the *analytical reduction* of n concurrent forces $K_1, K_2, \ldots, K_n$, it is convenient to use a system of coordinates with origin O at the common point of application A. Of the given forces, Fig. 2.7 only shows the ith one, namely, K_i.

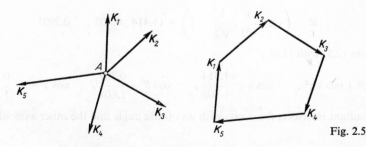

Fig. 2.5

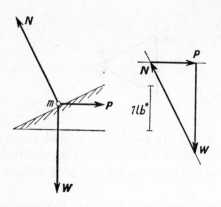

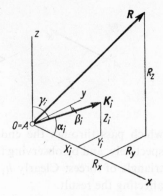

Fig. 2.6   Fig. 2.7

If it is given by its magnitude K_i and the direction angles α_i, β_i, γ_i, then its (algebraic) components are

$$X_i = K_i \cos \alpha_i, \qquad Y_i = K_i \cos \beta_i, \qquad Z_i = K_i \cos \gamma_i. \qquad (2.3)$$

The resultant R is determined by (2.2), and thus has the components

$$R_x = \sum_1^n X_i, \qquad R_y = \sum_1^n Y_i, \qquad R_z = \sum_1^n Z_i. \qquad (2.4)$$

The magnitude of R is

$$R = \sqrt{R_x^2 + R_y^2 + R_z^2}, \qquad (2.5)$$

and its direction angles α, β, γ are given by

$$\cos \alpha = \frac{R_x}{R}, \qquad \cos \beta = \frac{R_y}{R}, \qquad \cos \gamma = \frac{R_z}{R}. \qquad (2.6)$$

Let the three forces with the magnitudes $K_1 = K_2 = K_3 = 1$ kg* be given on a cube as shown in Fig. 2.8. With the coordinate system fixed in the cube and if all forces are understood to be in kg*, it follows from (2.3) that

$$K_1 = \left(\frac{1}{\sqrt{2}}, \frac{1}{\sqrt{2}}, 0 \right), \qquad K_2 = (0, 0, -1), \qquad K_3 = \left(\frac{1}{\sqrt{2}}, 0, \frac{1}{\sqrt{2}} \right),$$

and therefore from (2.4) that

$$R = \left(\sqrt{2}, \frac{1}{\sqrt{2}}, \frac{1}{\sqrt{2}} - 1 \right) = (1.414, 0.707, -0.293)$$

and from (2.5) with (2.6)

$$R = 1.608 \text{ kg*}, \qquad \cos \alpha = \frac{1.414}{1.608}, \qquad \cos \beta = \frac{0.707}{1.608}, \qquad \cos \gamma = -\frac{0.293}{1.608}.$$

The resultant intersects the z-axis with an obtuse angle and the other axes with acute angles.

The addition of the components in the analytical reduction corresponds to the construction of the polygon of forces in the graphical reduction. If the forces are coplanar, the expenditure of labor is about the same with the two methods. However, if they have arbitrary directions in space, as in the last example, the analytical method is more advantageous.

Continuous distributions of forces can be treated exactly only by the analytical method. In this case, integrals occur in place of the sums of components.

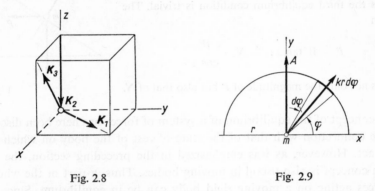

Fig. 2.8   Fig. 2.9

If a semicircular wire (Fig. 2.9) of radius r exerts a force of attraction of magnitude k per unit length on a particle m at the center of the circle, then the element of arc $r \, d\varphi$ exerts a force of magnitude $dA = kr \, d\varphi$ with the components

$$dA_x = kr \cos \varphi \, d\varphi , \qquad dA_y = kr \sin \varphi \, d\varphi , \qquad dA_z = 0 .$$

From (2.4), the resultant has the components

$$A_x = \int dA_x = kr \int_0^\pi \cos \varphi \, d\varphi , \qquad A_y = \int dA_y = kr \int_0^\pi \sin \varphi \, d\varphi , \qquad A_z = \int dA_z = 0 ,$$

and it is thus given by $A = (0, 2kr, 0)$. As could have already been deduced on the grounds of symmetry, it acts along the y-axis and has a magnitude equal to the product of the attraction per unit length and the diameter of the semicircle.

For the *equilibrium* of a system of concurrent forces, the vanishing of the resultant is necessary and sufficient. By (2.2), we thus have the vector equation

$$\sum_1^n K_i = 0 , \tag{2.7}$$

which can be split up into the three scalar equations

$$\sum_1^n X_i = 0 , \qquad \sum_1^n Y_i = 0 , \qquad \sum_1^n Z_i = 0 . \tag{2.8}$$

For equilibrium, the vanishing of the three algebraic sums of components referred to an arbitrary system of coordinates is thus necessary and sufficient.

In order to analytically determine the horizontal force P that holds the particle (Fig. 2.6) at rest on the perfectly smooth inclined plane, the system of coordinates shown in Fig. 2.10 can be used. If the angle of inclination of the plane is denoted by α, it follows from (2.8) that

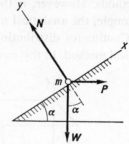

$$P \cos \alpha - W \sin \alpha = 0,$$
$$N - P \sin \alpha - W \cos \alpha = 0,$$

whereas the third equilibrium condition is trivial. The solution

$$P = W \tan \alpha, \qquad N = \frac{W}{\cos \alpha}$$

supplies not only the magnitude of P but also that of N.

Fig. 2.10

The concept of the equilibrium of a system of forces has here been discussed in close connection with that of the state of rest of the body on which these forces act. However, as was emphasized in the preceding section, the equilibrium concept is also useful in moving bodies. Thus, a part or the whole of the forces acting on a moving rigid body can be in equilibrium. Since such systems of forces are equivalent to the zero force, they may be added or removed at will.

Exercises

1. A cylinder (Fig. 2.11) is supported by two smooth, inclined planes. It is subjected to two forces P_1 and P_2 and the weight W, where $W=8$ lb*, $P_1=4$ lb*. $P_2=10$ lb*. Determine the normal forces A and B graphically; they are to be drawn in and their magnitudes read off. In addition, determine A and B analytically. (As will be shown in the next section, the forces may be treated as though they were all applied at O.)

2. Show that a force in three dimensions can be uniquely resolved into three components on prescribed, noncoplanar lines passing through its point of application.

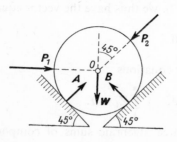

Fig. 2.11

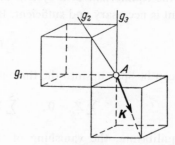

Fig. 2.12

3. Determine analytically the three forces K_1, K_2, K_3 with lines of action g_1, g_2, g_3 (Fig. 2.12), which together with the given force K constitute a self-equilibrating system. Also show how the problem can be solved graphically.

4. The elements of a (unbounded) plane (Fig. 2.13) exert a force of attraction of magnitude $dR = \lambda\, dA/r^2$ on the point O, which is at height h above the plane. Determine analytically the magnitude and direction of the resultant force of attraction.

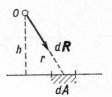

Fig. 2.13

3. Graphical Reduction of Plane Force Systems

By a *plane system of forces* is understood a system of forces all of which lie in a plane, the so-called *plane of the forces*. These forces, together with their points of application, can be arbitrarily distributed in this plane. Their analytic reduction will be treated as a particular case of the reduction in three dimensions in Section 8; here we can limit ourselves to the graphical treatment. Moreover, it will henceforth be necessary to limit ourselves to *rigid bodies*.

Apart from the parallelogram law, the reduction of forces with various points of application is based on a fourth principle, called the *displacement law*. According to this law, a force acting on a rigid body can be displaced along its line of action to any new point of application. Thus, when B in Fig. 3.1 is an arbitrary point in the line of action of the force K acting at A, it is true that $K[B] \sim K[A]$. This means that a force acting on a rigid body is not a bound vector but a *sliding vector*.

The displacement law is not valid for other than rigid bodies. For instance, an elastic helical spring behaves differently under the forces given in Fig. 3.2.

From the parallelogram law and displacement law, it follows that equal and opposite forces with the same line of action (Fig. 3.3) are always in equilibrium. Such pairs of forces may thus be added to, or subtracted from, any system of forces.

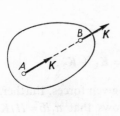

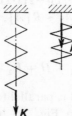

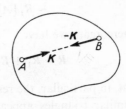

Fig. 3.1   Fig. 3.2   Fig. 3.3

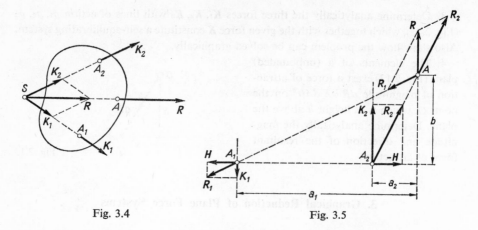

Fig. 3.4   Fig. 3.5

With these two laws it is possible to reduce an arbitrary system of forces. Thus, two forces $K_1[A_1]$ and $K_2[A_2]$ with lines of action intersecting at the point S (Fig. 3.4) can be displaced to this point and added together there. The resultant R can then be displaced to an arbitrary point A on its line of action. Here again the vector of the resultant is given by (1.6) and its line of action is concurrent with the given ones.

In the case of parallel forces the process fails. However, with the aid of auxiliary forces, it is in general possible to effect the reduction. For instance, if there are two forces K_1 and K_2 acting in opposite directions, as shown in Fig. 3.5, it is no restriction in generality to assume that their points of application A_1 and A_2 lie on a normal to the lines of action, and then two equal and opposite auxiliary forces $H[A_1]$ and $-H[A_2]$ can be introduced in this normal. If the forces acting at A_1 and A_2 are then added together separately, two intermediate resultants $R_1[A_1]$ and $R_2[A_2]$ are obtained, the lines of action of which, in general, intersect at a finite distance, and thus the problem has been reduced to the previous one.

The construction carried out in Fig. 3.5 can be described by the chain of equivalences

$$K_1[A_1], K_2[A_2] \sim K_1[A_1], H[A_1], K_2[A_2], -H[A_2] \sim R_1[A_1], R_2[A_2]$$
$$\sim R_1[A], R_2[A] \sim R[A],$$

and here again we have

$$R = R_1 + R_2 = K_1 + H + K_2 - H = K_1 + K_2,$$

so that, in particular, the resultant is parallel to the given forces. Further, from the similar triangles appearing in Fig. 3.5 it follows that $a_1/b = H/K_1$ and $b/a_2 = K_2/H$, and thus that $a_1/a_2 = K_2/K_1$. The line of action of the resultant force thus divides the interval A_1A_2 externally in the inverse ratio of the magnitudes of the forces.

The construction can be carried out similarly for equidirectional forces; the only difference in the result is that the line of action of the resultant then divides the interval A_1A_2 internally.

There is only one case in which even this method fails. Namely, when K_1 and K_2 are equal and opposite, then R_1 and R_2 are equal and opposite and A does not lie in the finite plane. In this case, we speak of a *couple* $K, -K$,* and it is seen from Fig. 3.6 that the above method always leads to another couple. Later on it will be shown that such a couple cannot be further reduced and that it is thus to be regarded, along with the single force, as an element of plane systems of forces. We note further, by letting K_1 tend to K_2 in Fig. 3.5, that the couple can be regarded as the limiting case of a single force moving off to infinity, while at the same time its magnitude tends to zero.

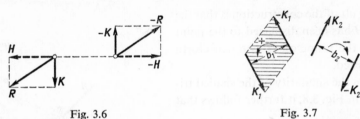

Fig. 3.6   Fig. 3.7

The *arm* of a couple (Fig. 3.7) is defined as the distance b between the two lines of action. The *sense* of the couple is positive or negative according as the body on which it acts tends to be rotated counterclockwise or clockwise. Finally, the *moment* of the couple is understood to be the product

$$M = \pm bK \tag{3.1}$$

of the arm and the magnitude of the force with the sign chosen to agree with the sense of rotation. Its magnitude is given by the area of the parallelogram formed by the two forces.

The moment is thus an algebraic quantity with the dimension $[M]=[FL]$. As a unit one can take, say, 1 lb* ft or 1 kg* m or 1 Joule (J)$=1$ N m.

If the right-hand couple in Fig. 3.7 comprises forces of magnitude 5 lb* and it has an arm of 2 ft, then its moment is $M=-10$ lb* ft.

Two statically equivalent systems of forces remain statically equivalent when one and the same force is added to each system. Hence it follows that any force in an equivalence can be taken over to the other side provided that

---

* Sometimes also referred to as a torque.

the sign is changed, just as is done in an algebraic equation. Further, it can be concluded that two systems of forces each of which is by itself in equilibrium with the same third system are statically equivalent to one and the same system and therefore to each other.

Now, in order to prove that a couple cannot be further reduced, we will combine an arbitrary couple $K[A]$, $-K[A']$(Fig. 3.8) with an arbitrary concentrated force $H[B]$. Because of the possible transformation of a couple as indicated in Fig. 3.6, it may be assumed that the line of action of H intersects those of the couple. Combination of K and H leads to the intermediate resultant P, which, when combined with $-K$, gives the force $H'[B']$ as the result of the reduction. Therefore, we have

$$H[B], K[A], -K[A'] \sim H'[B'],$$ (3.2)

where

$$H' = P - K = H + K - K = H.$$ (3.3)

The result of the construction is that the force H has been displaced to the point B' and the prime on H' can henceforth be omitted.

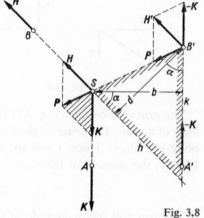

Fig. 3.8

From the similarity of the shaded triangles in Fig. 3.8, it further follows that

$$\frac{K}{H} = \frac{k}{h} = \left(\frac{d}{\cos\alpha}\right) : \left(\frac{b}{\cos\alpha}\right) = \frac{d}{b},$$

and therefore

$$d = \frac{bK}{H} = \frac{M}{H}$$ (3.4)

where M is the moment of the given couple.

Since the combination of a force with a couple always supplies the displaced force and never the zero force, it follows that, at least in a plane, a couple can never be in equilibrium with a single force. Thence it follows, at least in two dimensions, that a couple can never be reduced to a single force. For from

$$K[A], -K[A'] \sim F[D]$$

we would conclude, in contradiction to the last result, that

$$K[A], -K[A'], -F[D] \sim 0.$$

From (3.2) and (3.3) it finally follows that

$$H[B], -H[B'], K[A], -K[A'] \sim 0.$$

The first two forces in this equivalence form a couple which is arbitrary, apart from the condition that its moment $M' = -d \cdot H$ or, by (3.4), that $M' = -M$. Consequently, two arbitrary coplanar couples with a vanishing sum of moments are in equilibrium.

Figure 3.9 shows two arbitrary couples with the same moment $M = bK$. Since both equilibrate an arbitrary couple with moment $M' = -M$, they are statically equivalent to each other. Accordingly, a couple can be displaced and rotated in its plane without restriction, and even the magnitude of the force and arm can be altered provided that the moment is held constant. Thus, in two dimensions, a couple is completely determined by a single algebraic quantity, namely, by its moment.

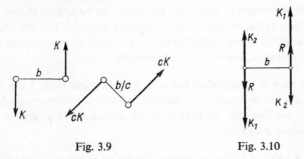

Fig. 3.9   Fig. 3.10

The reduction of two couples with the moments M_1 and M_2 (in Fig. 3.10 it has been assumed that they have opposite signs) can be effected by bringing them to a common arm and making the two pairs of lines of action coincide. Combination of the forces then leads to a *resulting couple* with the moment

$$M = bR = b(K_1 - K_2) = bK_1 - bK_2 = M_1 + M_2. \tag{3.5}$$

Likewise, continued reduction of n couples with the moments $M_1, M_2, \ldots, M_n$ leads to a resultant couple with the moment

$$M = \sum_1^n M_i. \tag{3.6}$$

Further, a couple with moment M can be resolved in its plane into an arbitrary number of couples such that the algebraic sum of the couples is M. Finally, the *equilibrium condition* for a plane system of couples is

$$\sum_1^n M_i = 0. \tag{3.7}$$

In order to apply these results to some simple systems of forces, we first consider the *equilibrium of two forces*. When two such forces are not equal and opposite, they always have a nonzero resultant. Otherwise, they form a couple the moment of which vanishes if and only if its arm is zero, i.e., if the lines of

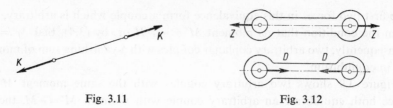

Fig. 3.11   Fig. 3.12

action coincide. Two coplanar forces are thus in equilibrium if and only if they are equal and opposite and have the same line of action.

A *cable* is understood to be a perfectly flexible, one-dimensional body of constant length. If to the ends of a cable (Fig. 3.11) are applied two forces which are large compared with the weight of the cable, the latter can be neglected and we speak of a weightless or light cable. As the forces are applied, the cable tightens, and, since it can sustain only a tensile force, equilibrium requires that the two forces lie in its axis, have equal magnitudes, and be directed outward.

Also, in the case of a weightless bar with smooth joints (Fig. 3.12), it is necessary that the two joint forces are coaxial with the bar. However, they can be directed inward or outward. In the first case we have a tie, or *tension member*, and in the second a strut, or *compression member*.

If a force K with the line of action g is to be resolved into two *components* along the given lines g_1 and g_2, then g must be concurrent with g_1 and g_2, since K is the resultant of K_1 and K_2. The given lines must therefore intersect on the line of action of K. If the point of intersection is in the finite plane, the resolution is carried out as with concurrent forces. The case when g_1 and g_2 are parallel to g will be discussed in the next section.

For the *equilibrium of three forces* K_1, K_2, and K_3 with the lines of action g_1, g_2, g_3, it is necessary that the intermediate resultant R_{12}, the line of action of which passes through the intersection S of g_1 and g_2, must be in equilibrium with K_3. This is possible only when S lies on g_3, i.e., when the three lines of action are concurrent. When S lies in the finite plane, the system of forces can be treated in the same way as a system of concurrent forces. The case of parallel lines of action will also be discussed later.

The above results play an important role in the determination of bearing forces. If no statement to the contrary is made, we will neglect friction until Section 10.

A beam (Fig. 3.13) hinged at A and simply supported at B is loaded by the force P. If the system is at rest, the three forces P, N, and Z must be in equilibrium. The line of action of Z must thus pass through the point of intersection of the other two known lines of action. The three forces can then be treated as three concurrent forces, and N and Z can be obtained from a closed triangle of forces.

In all problems in which normal forces are determined, it is necessary as a last step to check whether they are actually pressing against the body. Otherwise, the body would not remain at rest in spite of the equilibrium of the forces.

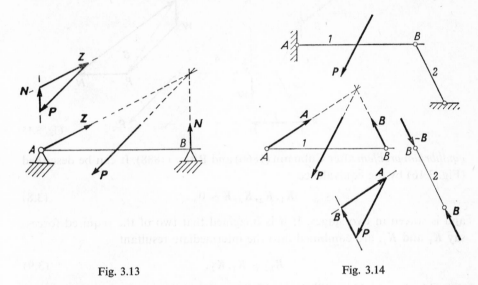

Fig. 3.13   Fig. 3.14

In the last example, N acts upward and thus against the body.

When a beam (Fig. 3.14) is hinged at A and supported at B by the weightless hinged prop, we have a system consisting of two bodies. If the bodies are separated, each one must be in equilibrium under the applied forces. Since the hinges are assumed free of friction, the forces B and $-B$ acting on the hinged prop must be coaxial with it. Hence the line of action of the force B applied to the beam, namely the reaction to the force $-B$ on the prop, is known, and the problem has thus been reduced to the previous one. In practice, the separation of the two bodies as in Fig. 3.14 is carried out only in the imagination.

The structure shown in Fig. 3.15 differs from the beam in Fig. 3.13 only in shape and in the fact that not only the load P but also the weight W is to be considered. If the loads W and P are combined into an intermediate resultant S with the line of action s, the problem reduces to one of only three forces. (In this construction it is best to use a force diagram and transfer only the line of action s to the position diagram.) These three forces must be concurrent and, in the force diagram, they must form a closed triangle that can be appended to the one used to find S. Now the four self-equilibrating forces lie on the sides of a polygon of forces. A check on the normal force N shows that it presses against the structure, which thus will be at rest. If N were directed in the opposite direction, the structure would rotate counterclockwise around the hinge B.

The problem of finding three forces K_1, K_2, K_3 in arbitrarily prescribed lines g_1, g_2, g_3, which equilibrate a given force K in g is called the *Culmann-Ritter*

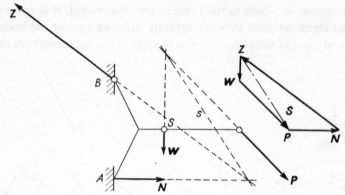

Fig. 3.15

equilibrium problem after Culmann (1866) and Ritter (1888). It can be described (Fig. 3.16) by the equivalence

$$K_1, K_2, K_3, K \sim 0, \tag{3.8}$$

and is solved in two stages. If it is imagined that two of the required forces, say K_1 and K_2, are combined into the intermediate resultant

$$R_{12} \sim K_1, K_2, \tag{3.9}$$

then this must be in equilibrium with K_3 and K, so

$$R_{12}, K_3, K \sim 0. \tag{3.10}$$

It follows from the last two equivalences that the line of action of the intermediate resultant R_{12}, the so-called *Culmann line s*, must pass through the two points of intersection (g_1, g_2) and (g_3, g). When this is found, R_{12} and K_3 can first be determined with the aid of the last equivalence and then, secondly, K_1 and K_2 follow from the first equivalence.

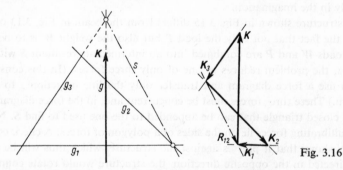

Fig. 3.16

The *Culmann-Ritter resolution problem* is described by the equivalence

$$K_1, K_2, K_3 \sim K \tag{3.11}$$

and can be solved analogously.

In this section we have occasionally (Fig. 3.9 to 3.12) made use of the possibility of indicating a force vector by its magnitude K, instead of by K, as is quite usual in analytical statics. In such cases, of course, the reaction to K or a force $-K$ that equilibrates it (Fig. 3.11) must also be indicated by the magnitude K and not with $-K$.

Exercises

1. Solve the Culmann-Ritter resolution problem for the forces given in Fig. 3.16 by combining K_2 and K_3.

2. The square plate (Fig. 3.17) is hinged at B. It is loaded by its weight W ($W=50$ lb*), which acts at the center of gravity S in the center point, and by the horizontal force P ($P=30$ lb*) applied at A. The plate is held at C by a weightless cable. Determine the hinge force Z and the cable tension S graphically and decide whether the plate will move or not.

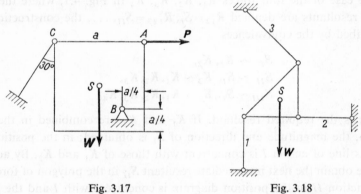

Fig. 3.17   Fig. 3.18

3. A homogeneous plate (Fig. 3.18) of uniform density and weight $W=2$ kg* has the form of a right-angled isosceles triangle. It is supported by three weightless hinged links. Determine the three forces S_1, S_2, S_3 applied to the plate by the links and indicate which are under tension and which under compression.

4. Graphical Statics

An arbitrary plane system of forces can be reduced by reducing two intersecting forces to an intermediate resultant and combining this with a further force and continuing this process until only parallel forces remain. If, of these, the equidirectional ones are combined, then at most there remain two forces with opposite directions. If their magnitudes are different, they can be reduced to a single force; otherwise they form a couple. Thus, the parallelogram and displacement laws allow every plane system of forces to be reduced to a *single force* or to a *couple*.

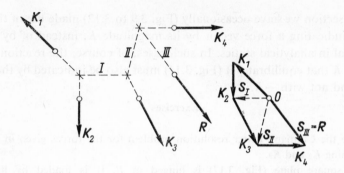

Fig. 4.1

In practice it is convenient to work here also in two figures, namely, in the position diagram, in which it is essential to show only the lines of action, and in the force diagram, in which the forces are joined together.

In the case of the four forces K_1, K_2, K_3, K_4 in Fig. 4.1, where the intermediate resultants are denoted $R_{12} = S_I$, $R_{123} = S_{II}$, ..., the construction can be described by the equivalences

$$S_I \sim K_1, K_2,$$
$$S_{II} \sim S_I, K_3 \sim K_1, K_2, K_3,$$
$$S_{III} \sim S_{II}, K_4 \sim K_1, K_2, K_3, K_4,$$

and S_{III} is the required resultant. If K_1 and K_2 are combined in the force diagram, the magnitude and direction of S_I is obtained; in the position diagram, its line of action I is concurrent with those of K_1 and K_2. By addition of K_3 we obtain the next intermediate resultant S_{II} in the polygon of forces. Its line of action II in the position diagram is concurrent with I and the line of action of K_3. The next step finally yields the resultant $R = S_{III}$ with the line of action III.

This process described for four forces can be carried out for an arbitrary system of coplanar forces, so long as no parallel forces appear during the reduction. Here also the vector of the resultant is given by the sum (2.2) of the given force vectors. The construction described is necessary in order to find also its line of action.

The starting point O of the force polygon is called the *pole*, the diagonals S_I, S_{II}, ... representing the intermediate resultants and usually simply denoted by I, II, ... are called the *pole rays*, the lines I, II, ... parallel to them in the position diagram are called the *funicular lines*, and the polygon formed by them the *funicular polygon* (string polygon).

After some practice, the following procedure can be adopted. In the force diagram, the forces are joined together into a chain and the pole rays are drawn from the pole. The first funicular line passes through the intersection of K_1 and K_2, and then through its intersection with the line of action of K_3 we draw the second funicular line, and so forth. The direction and magnitude of the resultant is given by the last pole ray, and the line of action of the resultant by the last side of the funicular polygon.

If the polygon of the given forces is not closed, the result of the reduction is a single force. If it is closed (whereby the last pole ray disappears), then, in the case of four forces, $S_{II} \sim K_1, K_2, K_3$ is equal and opposite to K_4 or, in general,

$$S_{n-2} \sim K_1, K_2, \ldots, K_{n-1}$$

is equal and opposite to K_n, i.e., the system of forces reduces to the *couple* S_{n-2}, K_n. If the system is to be in *equilibrium*, these two forces must be collinear, i.e., the second last side of the funicular polygon must coincide with the line of action of the last force.

In the general case of n forces, the forces in the polygon of forces lying between the intermediate resultants S_i and $S_k (i < k)$ are $K_{i+2}, \ldots, K_{k+1}$. From the equivalences

$$S_i \sim K_1, K_2, \ldots, K_{i+1},$$
$$S_k \sim K_1, K_2, \ldots, K_{k+1} \sim S_i, R_{i+2\ldots k+1}$$

it follows that the intermediate resultant of these forces in the position diagram is concurrent with the corresponding two sides i and k of the funicular polygon. Thus we have the following *theorem of the intermediate resultants*: Through the point of intersection of any two sides of the funicular polygon passes the line of action of the intermediate resultant of those forces in the polygon of forces that lie between the corresponding pole rays.

If the given forces are nearly or exactly parallel, the above construction will become inconvenient because of the acute intersections, and in the latter case it breaks down completely. In these cases, an *auxiliary force* S_0 is introduced in such a way that its direction deviates as much as possible from those of the given forces. This is then combined step by step with the given forces. In the case of four forces (Fig. 4.2) we then have

$$S_I \quad \sim S_0, K_1,$$
$$S_{II} \quad \sim S_0, K_1, K_2,$$
$$S_{III} \sim S_0, K_1, K_2, K_3,$$
$$S_{IV} \sim S_0, K_1, K_2, K_3, K_4, \sim S_0, R,$$

where R denotes the resultant of the four given forces. The auxiliary force can be represented by a zeroth pole ray and funicular line. The resultant R, which does not include the auxiliary force and thus plays the part of an intermediate resultant, can be gained by the preceding theorem. In the force diagram it is given by the diagonal between the starting point of K_1 and the end point of K_4. Thus its line of action passes through the intersection of sides O and IV of the funicular polygon, since the respective forces lie between the pole rays O and IV.

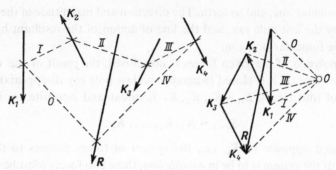

Fig. 4.2

In general, the direction and magnitude of the resultant is given by the join in the polygon of forces from the zeroth to the last pole ray, and the line of action of the resultant in the position diagram passes through the intersection of the zeroth and last side of the funicular polygon.

With parallel forces, the method is analogous. After some practice, it is carried out schematically by first joining the forces into a polygon of forces to give the direction and magnitude of the resultant. When a pole has been chosen, the pole rays can be drawn and the funicular polygon constructed with the parallels to them. The zeroth side, with which the construction is commenced, is arbitrary apart from direction. The intersection of the last with the zeroth side is a point on the line of action of the resultant. The force and funicular polygons turn out differently in accordance with how the pole, the first side of the funicular polygon, and the order of the forces are chosen. It will, however, become evident during the analytical treatment that the result is unique.

The notation "funicular polygon" (or string polygon) is vindicated by the fact that the closed polygon (Fig. 4.2) can be interpreted as the equilibrium configuration of a light rope loaded by the given forces. In fact, the ith segment of the polygon is in equilibrium under the forces S_i and $-S_i$ (the force S_i is always directed away from the pole), and the kth triangle in the polygon of forces embodies the equilibrium of the forces S_{k-1}, K_k, $-S_k$ applied at the kth joint.

In the last section we postponed the resolution of a force into two components parallel to it. Let K in Fig. 4.3 be a force that is to be resolved into components along g_1 and g_2. If K is drawn in the force diagram, a pole O is chosen, and it is observed that K is the resultant of the required forces K_1 and K_2, then the pole rays O and II can be drawn. The two parallel sides O and II of the funicular polygon must intersect on the line of action of K but are otherwise arbitrary. Their intersections with g_1 and g_2 supply the side I of the funicular polygon and thus also the pole ray I. The magnitudes and directions of the forces K_1 and K_2 are given by the intercepts of the pole rays O and I, and I and II, respectively.

In the routine solution of this problem, doubt can arise as to the correct way of assigning the forces found to the given lines of action. A check can be made with

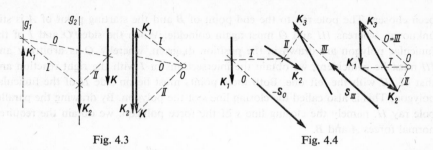

Fig. 4.3   Fig. 4.4

the theorem of the intermediate resultants: since the sides O and I of the funicular polygon intersect on the line of action g_1 of K_1, this force in the force polygon must lie between the pole rays O and I.

If the polygon of the given forces is not closed (Fig. 4.2), the result of the reduction is a *single force*. If it is closed, so that the last pole ray is coincident with the zeroth, we have a case as shown in Fig. 4.4 for three forces. The auxiliary force $S_{III} \sim S_0$, K_1, K_2, K_3 or, in general

$$S_n \sim S_0, K_1, K_2, \ldots, K_n$$

corresponds in magnitude and direction with S_0, and since it follows from the last equivalence that

$$K_1, K_2, \ldots, K_n \sim S_n, -S_0,$$

the given forces have been reduced to a *couple*. If the system is in *equilibrium*, it is necessary that the last and zeroth sides of the funicular polygon should coincide, i.e., the funicular polygon should also be closed.

In the preceding section, the problem of the equilibrium of three parallel forces was set aside. It will be treated here in the case of a horizontal beam simply supported (without friction) at both ends (Fig. 4.5). Since the two normal reactions are vertical and must form a closed triangle with the load P, the beam can remain at rest only under a vertical load. If, of the three self-equilibrating forces P, B, A, we first draw P in the force diagram, the pole rays O and I can be drawn as soon as the pole has

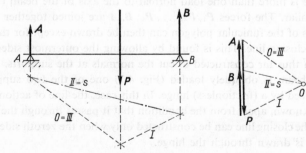

Fig. 4.5

been chosen. The pole ray to the end point of B and the starting point of A is still unknown, whereas III and O must again coincide. When the sides O and I of the funicular polygon are drawn in the position diagram, whereby O is arbitrary and III must be coincident, we obtain the intersections of I with the right reaction and that of III with the left one. Both these points must lie on side II of the funicular polygon. This is also called the closing line s of the polygon. By drawing the parallel pole ray II, namely the closing line s of the force polygon, we obtain the required normal forces A and B.

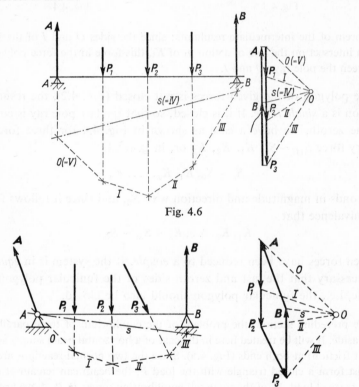

Fig. 4.6

Fig. 4.7

When there is more than one load normal to the axis of the beam (Fig. 4.6), the method is similar. The forces $P_1, P_2, \ldots, P_n, B, A$ are joined together and the pole rays and sides of the funicular polygon can then be drawn except for the second last one, i.e., the closing line. This is found by allowing the outermost sides of the funicular polygon thus far constructed to cut the normals at the supports.

When the beam is obliquely loaded (Fig. 4.7) one of the two supports, say A, must be replaced by a (frictionless) hinge. In this case, the line of action of the hinge force A is unknown, apart from the condition that it passes through the center of the hinge. Thus, the closing line can be constructed only when the zeroth side of the funicular polygon is drawn through the hinge.

Exercises

1. Combine the forces $K_1, \ldots, K_6$ ($K_1=2$ lb*, $K_2=2.5$ lb*, $K_3=1.5$ lb*, $K_4=3$ lb*, $K_5=1.8$ lb*, $K_6=1$ lb*) given on a regular hexagon (Fig. 4.8) without the aid of an auxiliary force first in the sequence 1, 2, 3, 4, 5, 6, and second in the order 3, 6, 2, 1, 4, 5. Determine the resultant R and the two intermediate resultants R_{234} and R_{145}.

2. Reduce with the aid of an auxiliary force the forces K_1, K_2, K_3 shown in the square frame (Fig. 4.9).

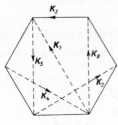

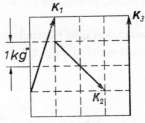

Fig. 4.8   Fig. 4.9

3. What is the result of the reduction of the system of forces given in the regularh exagon shown in Fig. 4.10?

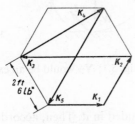

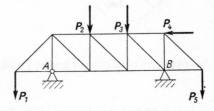

Fig. 4.10   Fig. 4.11

4. Determine graphically the supporting reactions A, B in the truss shown in Fig. 4.11 ($P_1=P_4=3000$ kg*, $P_2=P_3=P_5=1000$ kg*) and decide whether it remains at rest or not. Solve the similar problem for the case when the load P_5 is absent.

5. Systems of Rigid Bodies

A *system* is understood to mean an arbitrary group of bodies, which are here to be regarded as rigid.

Figure 5.1 shows a system of three rigid bodies which are joined with each other and are supported externally in various ways. According to the definition given in Section 1, the forces $P_1, P_2, \ldots, P_n$ and the weights W_1, W_2, W_3 are loads and the remaining forces, such as normal forces, hinge, and cable forces, are reactions. If the cable joining bodies 1 and 2 were replaced by a spring, the forces S_{12} and S_{21} would be known functions of the configuration of the system and thus would be loads.

A force is denoted an *internal* or *external force* according as its reaction acts inside or outside the system.

Thus, in Fig. 5.1, all loads P_i, W_i, the normal forces N_1, N_2, and the hinge force Z are external forces, whereas all the remaining ones are internal.

The classification into internal and external forces naturally depends on the way the system is delimited, i.e., it depends on which bodies are included in the system.

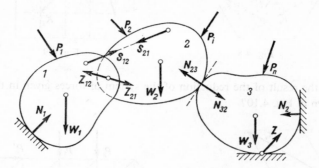

Fig. 5.1

For the subsystem consisting of bodies 1 and 2 in Fig. 5.1, N_{23} would be an external force.

If a system is at rest, so also are all bodies included in it. Then, according to the equilibrium principle, the forces acting on each body are in equilibrium and, therefore, also the totality of the (internal and external) forces acting on the system. The internal forces, however, form a self-equilibrating system by virtue of the reaction principle, so that the external forces applied to a system at rest must also be in equilibrium among themselves.

We have already tacitly made use of this fact in connection with rigid bodies. These could, indeed, be split up into their elements. Between these, we have forces internal with respect to the whole body which act to hold the shape of the body and are thus called the *forces maintaining the rigidity*. Such forces have so far been left out of consideration. When, in a system comprising several bodies, the internal forces are disregarded, the system is being treated as a single rigid body. The fact that the external forces by themselves must be in equilibrium in the case of no motion is not a new axiom but simply a consequence of the reaction principle.

In statics of rigid systems the first problem usually is the determination of the *external reactions*. For example, in order to determine all the forces in the *truss* (Fig. 5.2), i.e., in a system of *bars*, or members, joined together at the so-called *joints*, it is first necessary to determine the external reactions. In many cases this problem can be solved by simply considering the equilibrium of the external forces, i.e., by freezing the truss, as it were. For this reason such a procedure is sometimes called the *freezing method*.

When the truss in Fig. 5.2 is hinged at A and simply supported at B, the external reactions can be determined in the same way as with the beam in Fig. 4.7.

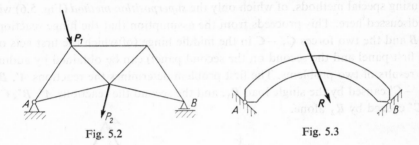

Fig. 5.2   Fig. 5.3

Nevertheless, there are cases where the freezing method does not suffice for the determination of the external reactions. In such cases the system must be divided up into its parts, and the equilibrium of the forces acting on each part must be investigated.

In the case of a beam with a hinged support (Fig. 3.14), subdivision of the system into two parts leads to the solution.

If, after decomposition of the system into its rigid components, it is still impossible to completely determine the reactions, the system is called *statically indeterminate* or *redundant*.

The forces acting on the two-hinged arch in Fig. 5.3 consist of the load R and the two reactions A and B passing through the hinges. Since the arch is at rest, the three forces R, A, B must be concurrent and form a closed triangle of forces. These conditions can be fulfilled in infinitely many ways; the problem is therefore statically indeterminate.

The *three-hinged arch* differs from the two-hinged arch in that it has a (frictionless) hinge C within the arch. It consists of the two *panels* 1 and 2 (Fig. 5.4), which in turn can contain rods, arches, structural frameworks, etc. What

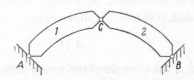

Fig. 5.4

is essential is not their shape but only
their rigidity. Hence, in the future, we
can limit ourselves to indicating the
panels by the lines joining the hinges
(Fig. 5.5). Let the loadings for each
panel be reduced to the two resultants
R_1 and R_2.

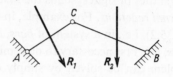

Fig. 5.5

In contrast to the two-hinged arch, the three-hinged arch is *statically determinate*. Decomposition of the system into the two panels is, however, not sufficient for the application of the graphical method. The solution is obtained by using special methods, of which only the *superposition method* (Fig. 5.6) will be discussed here. This proceeds from the assumption that the hinge reactions A, B and the two forces C, $-C$ in the middle hinge (of which the first acts on the first panel and the second on the second panel) can be obtained by adding the results of two problems. The first problem determines the reactions A', B', C', $-C'$ caused by the single load R_1, and the second the reactions A'', B'', C'', $-C''$ caused by R_2 alone.

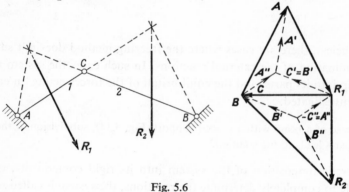

Fig. 5.6

If the second panel is taken to be unloaded, it has the function of a light hinged support and the reactions with single primes can be obtained as in Fig. 3.14. The equilibrium conditions for each of the panels are

$$A', R_1, C' \sim 0, \qquad -C', B' \sim 0, \tag{5.1}$$

and, since B', C' must coincide with the line BC, all reactions with one prime can be determined by a single triangle of forces. If then the first panel is unloaded, it similarly follows that

$$A'', C'' \sim 0, \qquad B'', R_2, -C'' \sim 0, \tag{5.2}$$

and, if the triangle of the forces with double primes is so arranged in the force diagram that the forces C', C'' in the middle joint link up, it is only necessary to complete the parallelogram of forces to obtain the reactions to the total loading:

$$A = A' + A'', \qquad B = B' + B'', \qquad C = C' + C'', \qquad -C \qquad (5.3)$$

The following consideration verifies the correctness of this method. It follows from the equivalences (5.1) and (5.2) that

$$A', A'', R_1, C', C'' \sim 0, \qquad B', B'', R_2, -C', -C'' \sim 0. \qquad (5.4)$$

Since the reactions indicated by the same letter have the same point of application, they may be added together according to (5.3). Then (5.4) becomes

$$A, R_1, C \sim 0, \qquad B, R_2, -C \sim 0. \qquad (5.5)$$

Thus, the reactions have actually been so determined that the forces on each panel are in equilibrium.

This line of argument can be extended to more general systems and is then known as the *superposition principle* for the forces acting on a rigid system. According to it, the reactions can be obtained by superposing the partial reactions caused by different partial loadings of the system.

In order to determine the *internal reactions*, a system must be divided into its components. This procedure will be discussed for a truss.

An *ideal truss* (Fig. 5.2) is understood to be a system of bars satisfying the following conditions: (1) the bars are hinged together (pin jointed) without friction; (2) the bars are so light in comparison with the loads that they may be considered weightless; (3) the external forces (loads and reactions) are applied at the joints only. These assumptions idealize the actual truss (in which the bars can, in particular, be joined together by means of rivets or welding). However, the results so obtained can, if necessary, be easily refined.

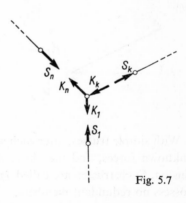

Fig. 5.7

Each bar of an ideal truss (Fig. 5.7) sustains two equal and opposite forces S_i which are coaxial with it and subject it to tension or compression. If the joints are identified with the pins, we have a group of self-equilibrating *joint forces K_k* representing the reactions of the forces in the bars. From the joint forces we can find the forces in the bars and conversely, so it suffices to limit consideration to, say, the joint forces. Indeed, after having determined the external forces, one can often successfully proceed from joint to joint and, with individual equilibrium considerations, step by step determine all joint forces and hence also all forces in the bars.

Figure 5.8 shows a simply loaded ideal truss freely hinged at A and smoothly supported at B. The members are numbered 1 to 7 and the joints are denoted by the letters A to E. The reactions A and B equilibrate the external load and form the first triangle of forces. If the joint A, where only two bars meet, is considered as a free body, the two joint forces K_1 and K_2 can be determined by the triangle of forces A. Then, to joint B is transmitted the force K_1 with opposite direction, and to C is likewise transmitted the force K_2. There now remain only two unknown joint forces at B, which are determined by the polygon of forces B. Then we are in a position to treat joint C, and finally joints D and E. Of these last two triangles, one will contain only a single unknown joint force and the other none. The requirement that the last triangles should be closed provides a check on the accuracy of the construction.

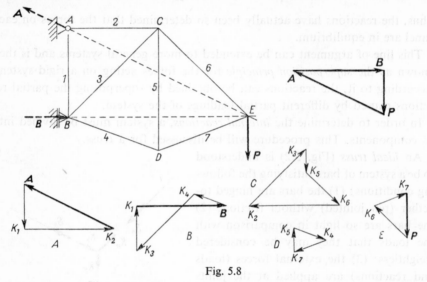

Fig. 5.8

With simple trusses, after each step there always remain joints with only two unknown forces, and the above method can be carried through to the conclusion. Such trusses are called *internally statically determinate*. Clearly they possess no redundant members.

If the truss in Fig. 5.8 were augmented by say a bar AD, it would become *internally statically indeterminate*.

On the other hand, of course, the truss must have enough bars to make it rigid.

Since each joint force must act on two different joints with opposite direction, the process explained by means of the example in Fig. 5.8 has the disadvantage that each joint force must also appear twice in the force diagram, namely with opposite directions in two polygons of force. In many cases, a simplification can be effected by constructing a single force diagram for all joints. This is called the *Maxwell diagram* after its discoverer Maxwell (1864).

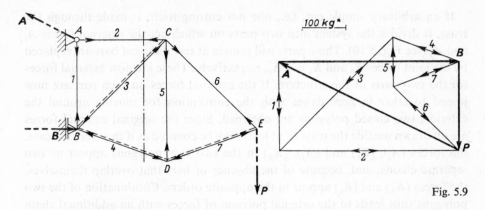

Fig. 5.9

If we start with the polygon of the external forces (Fig. 5.9) for the truss in Fig. 5.8, the triangle of forces for the joint A can be joined onto the force A already drawn. The joint forces obtained are indicated simply by the subscripts 1 and 2 and the small arrows, which are also drawn at joint A in the position diagram. If we then proceed to joint B, use can be made of the fact that the joint force 1 and the reaction B are already correctly joined together in the force diagram, so that it is only necessary to close with 4 and 3. Progressing in this way, a single force diagram is, in fact, obtained. Each joint force appears just once, but, with opposite directions, each belongs to two different polygons of force. Moreover, a check is provided in that the joint force, drawn parallel to the last bar, must close the last polygon.

If the joint forces are read off with the scale shown in Fig. 5.9, in which the load $P=200$ kg*, the forces in the bars are found to be $S_1=200$ kg*, $S_2=400$ kg*, $S_3=-360$ kg*,..., where the negative sign indicates that the force is compressive. In regard to the design of the bars, the distinction between tension and compression members is important; in the position diagram, the compression members can be indicated by an accompanying dashed line.

The *existence of a Maxwell diagram* can be proved for every statically determinate truss that has neither crossed bars nor loaded internal joints. (Internal joints are those that are accessible from the exterior only by crossing some bar.)

If the joints A and D in Fig. 5.9 were joined by a further bar, this would certainly cross bar 3. If these bars were cut at the intersection and the parts tied with a joint, this additional joint would be an internal one.

In order to carry out the existence proof, we imagine all the external forces so drawn in the position diagram that their vectors lie outside the truss. This is in general possible because of the assumption that there are no loaded internal joints. Assuming that all external forces acting on the truss have been determined, we form a closed polygon of the external forces A_i, in the order they appear in moving around the outside of the truss in a definite sense of rotation.

If an arbitrary simple cut, i.e., one not cutting itself, is made through the truss, it divides the system into two parts on which act the external forces A_i' and A_j'' (see Fig. 5.10). These parts will remain at rest if the cut bars are replaced by the joint forces K_k' and $K_k'' = -K_k'$, respectively. These are now external forces for the two parts of the structure. If the external forces on each part are now joined together in accordance with the convention for moving around the exterior, two closed polygons are obtained. Since the original external forces are all drawn outside the truss or at least may be counted as if this were the case, the forces (A_i'), (K_k') and (A_j''), (K_k'') in the two new polygons appear as two separate chains, and, because of the absence of bars that overlap themselves, the forces (K_k'') and (K_k') appear in the opposite orders. Combination of the two polygons thus leads to the original polygon of forces with an additional chain of segments. Each force appears only once.

If each part of the structure is now cut in the same way as the whole structure was, each new polygon is divided into two further ones, and such that, in assembling the polygons, again no force appears twice. After a finite number of further steps the truss will have been divided into its joints, and at the same time the force diagram will have become a Maxwell diagram.

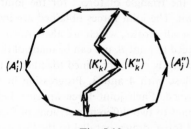

Fig. 5.10

Since each joint force is associated only with two joints, the polygons obtained can be assembled in only *one* way, and it is seen that the *uniqueness* of the Maxwell diagram also follows from the proof of existence. At the same time it is evident that the external forces must be treated as though drawn on the outside of the truss and the convention for proceeding around the force polygons should be adhered to if the construction of the Maxwell diagram is to succeed.

For carrying out the construction we therefore have the following rules: determine the external forces; enter them in the position diagram so that, if ever possible, their vectors lie outside the truss; join them into a polygon of forces in the order given by the convention. Then, beginning with a joint with only two bars, consecutively affix the individual force polygons, always adhering to the chosen convention for the order of entering the forces.

In the example (Fig. 5.9), these rules have been applied. It is easy to check that otherwise a force diagram would have been obtained in which certain forces would appear twice.

It is possible, say when checking a truss, that only the force in one bar is of interest. In such cases, the so-called *Culmann method* (1866), the method of sections, leads to the result quicker than the construction of the Maxwell

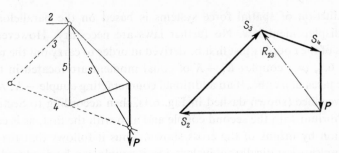

Fig. 5.11

diagram. If the truss is divided into two parts by a cut, both of these are in equilibrium under the external and section forces. If it is possible to make the cut so as to intersect the bar in question and only two others, the problem reduces to the Culmann-Ritter problem (Section 3), since it is now only a matter of determining three joint or bar forces which equilibrate the resultant external force on one of the parts of the truss.

Figure 5.11 shows the construction for bar 3 of the truss from Fig. 5.9. The section is vertical and the only load P on the right-hand part of the truss equilibrates the internal forces S_2, S_3, S_4.

Exercises

1. The three-hinged arch in Fig. 5.12 consists of two trusses formed entirely by isosceles right triangles. It is loaded by the forces $P_1=400$ kg*, $P_2=500$ kg*, $P_3=P_4=P_5=100$ kg*. Determine the hinge forces A, B, C.

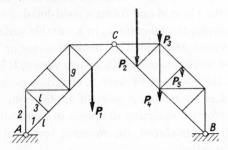

Fig. 5.12

2. Consider the panels of the arch in Fig. 5.12 as ideal trusses and use two Maxwell diagrams to determine the forces in all members. Also determine the force S_9 in bar 9 by means of a Culmann section.

6. Spatial Force Systems

A spatial, or three-dimensional, system of forces consists of arbitrarily directed forces with points of application arbitrarily distributed in space. It represents the most general system of forces, and systems of plane and concurrent forces are special cases.

The reduction of spatial force systems is based on the parallelogram law and the displacement law. No further laws are necessary. However, certain properties of the couple must first be derived in order to carry out the reduction.

In Fig. 6.1, two couples K, $-K$ of equal moment are located in the upper and lower faces of a cube. If an additional counteracting couple $-K$, K is added to the lower face (shown dashed in Fig. 6.1), then according to Section 3 this is in equilibrium with the second couple and also with the first, as is easily seen by reduction by means of the cross shown. Thus it follows that the first and second couples are statically equivalent, i.e., a couple can be displaced not only in its own plane, but also to an arbitrary parallel plane, without affecting its moment M.

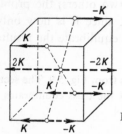

Fig. 6.1

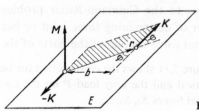

Fig. 6.2

Therefore a *couple* is completely determined by the orientation of its plane E, by its sense of rotation in this plane, and by the magnitude $|M|$ of its moment. It can thus be represented by a *free vector* M (Fig. 6.2). The direction of this vector is normal to the plane E and forms a right-handed screw with the sense of rotation of the couple; the magnitude, in a suitable scale, gives the moment of the couple. This vector M is called the *moment vector* or *vectorial moment* of the couple and is not to be confused with a force vector. It is a coincidence that the force $-K$ and the moment M have a common point of application in Fig. 6.2; the latter has an arbitrary point of application.

If the position vector r connecting the point of application of force $-K$ to that of K (Fig. 6.2) is introduced, the moment vector of the couple can be given by the vector product

$$M = r \times K \qquad (6.1)$$

of the position vector r and the force vector K. In fact, this product is a vector normal to the plane E, forming a right-handed screw with the sense of rotation of the couple and having a magnitude

$$|r \times K| = rK \sin \varphi = bK = |M|.$$

The last relation represents the equality of the areas of the parallelograms formed by r and K, or $-K$ and K.

If two couples lie in intersecting planes E_1, E_2 (Fig. 6.3), they can be combined by expressing them in terms of forces of identical magnitude and then placing two equal and opposite forces in the line of intersection of the planes. Since these cancel each other, there remains just one couple in a new plane. Moreover, if the moment vectors $M_1 = r_1 \times K$ and $M_2 = r_2 \times K$ are added together, we obtain

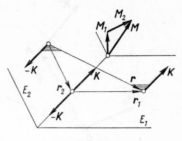

Fig. 6.3

$$M = M_1 + M_2 = (r_1 + r_2) \times K = r \times K,$$

which, by Fig. 6.3, is seen to be the moment vector of the *resultant couple*.

The last result obviously holds also when the couples are coplanar or lie in parallel planes. Further, by means of the formula

$$M = \sum_1^n M_i, \tag{6.2}$$

it can be extended to the case of more than two forces and means that couples acting on a rigid body can be combined by adding their moment vectors. Conversely, a couple with moment vector M can be resolved into an arbitrary number of couples with the total moment M. Finally, the *equilibrium condition for a spatial system of couples* is

$$\sum_1^n M_i = 0. \tag{6.3}$$

If, in Fig. 6.4, O is an arbitrary point in space, A the point of application of a force K, and r the position vector from O to A, then the *static moment of the force* K about point O is understood to be

$$M_O = r \times K. \tag{6.4}$$

This is a vector normal to the plane containing K and O, forming a right-handed screw with the sense of rotation of K around O, and of magnitude

$$M_O = rK \sin \varphi = d \cdot K. \tag{6.5}$$

Thus, M_O is equal to the product of the magnitude of the force and the distance of its line of action from O. It should be noted that the static moment of a force about a point, in spite of the formal analogy between (6.4) and (6.1), is something different from the vector moment of a couple.

However, the dimension of the moment is naturally still $[M_O] = [FL]$, with unsit such as 1 lb* ft.

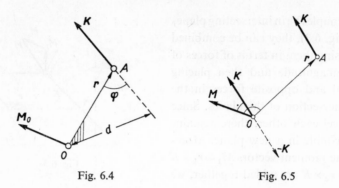

Fig. 6.4   Fig. 6.5

It is evident that the static moment (6.4) of K about O remains unaltered when the force is displaced along its line of action, and that it vanishes if and only if O lies on it. Moreover, a force on a rigid body is fully specified by the vector K and its static moment M_O about O. The vector M_O, in fact, determines a plane through O containing K. The ratio M_O/K gives its distance from O, while the sense of M_O indicates the direction in which this distance is to be measured. Since M_O is independent of a translation of K along the line of action, the representation of a force on a rigid body by its vector K and its static moment M_O about O is more natural than the representation by K and r.

If several forces K_1, K_2, ..., K_n act at a point A, their resultant (2.2), which also acts at A, has about O a static moment

$$M_O = r \times R = r \times \sum_1^n K_i$$

$$= \sum_1^n (r \times K_i) = \sum_1^n M_{Oi},$$

(6.6)

where M_{Oi} is the static moment of K_i. The static moment of the resultant of such a group is thus the vector sum of the static moments of the separate forces.

With this preparation, we are in a position to reduce forces in three dimensions. To a force K acting at a point A of a rigid body (Fig. 6.5) can be added forces K and $-K$ at an arbitrary point O, since these are self-equilibrating. However, the forces $K[A]$ and $-K[O]$ form a couple, so that the given force at A can be replaced by the force K displaced to O together with a couple with moment vector

$$M = r \times K = M_O,$$

(6.7)

which is equal to the static moment of the given force about O and thus is normal to K. It is usual to show also the moment vector M of the *auxiliary couple* in O. Thus a force K in an arbitrary point A is equivalent to the force K acting in O and the auxiliary moment vector (6.7).

If we have the spatial system of forces $K_1[A_1]$, $K_2[A_2]$, ..., $K_n[A_n]$ (Fig. 6.6), and r_i is the position vector from an arbitrary point O of the point of application A_i, then the above process can be applied to each of the forces. The displaced forces $K_i[O]$ can then be compounded into a *resultant force*

$$R = \sum_1^n K_i,\tag{6.8}$$

and the auxiliary couples $M_i = M_{Oi} = r_i \times K_i$ into a *resultant couple* with the moment vector

$$M = \sum_1^n M_i = \sum_1^n M_{Oi} = \sum_1^n (r_i \times K_i),\tag{6.9}$$

which, in general, is no longer normal to R. Thus, an arbitrary system of forces on a rigid body can be reduced at any point O to a resultant force and couple. This force is the vector sum of the given forces, and the moment vector is the vector sum of the static moments about O.

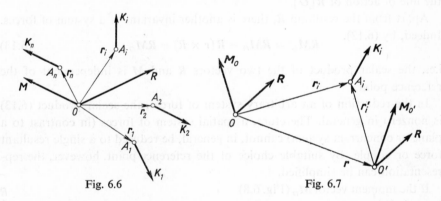

Fig. 6.6   Fig. 6.7

In this reduction the reference point is arbitrary. If a given force system, indicated in Fig. 6.7 by the force K_i, is reduced both at the point O and the point O', then by (6.8) the resultant force is the same. The resultant force is thus independent of the reference point, i.e., it is an *invariant* of the system of forces. If r_i and r_i' are the position vectors of K_i with respect to O and O', respectively, and if r is the position vector of O' relative to O, then, by (6.9), the moment vector at O is given by

$$M_O = \sum_1^n (r_i \times K_i),\tag{6.10}$$

where the subscript O refers to the reference point. Similarly, the moment vector in O' is

$$M_{O'} = \sum_1^n (r_i' \times K_i).\tag{6.11}$$

Since $r_i' = r_i - r$, it follows from (6.11) that

$$M_{O'} = \sum_1^n [(r_i - r) \times K_i] = \sum_1^n (r_i \times K_i) - r \times \sum_1^n K_i,$$

and, by (6.8) and (6.10), this can be replaced by

$$M_{O'} = M_O - r \times R. \tag{6.12}$$

Hence the moment vector is not an invariant but transforms with change of reference point in accordance with (6.12).

The same result would have been obtained by transferring the vectors $R[O], M_O$ to the point O'. The moment vector M_O can simply be shifted to O', but in transferring $R[O]$ to O' we have to add the auxiliary moment $-r \times R$, which combines with M_O to give the couple in (6.12).

If M_O as well as R should remain unaltered at the new reference point O', it is necessary that $r \times R = 0$. That is the case when either $R_O = 0$ or O' lies on the line of action of $R[O]$.

Apart from the resultant R, there is another invariant of a system of forces. Indeed, by (6.12),

$$RM_{O'} = RM_O - R(r \times R) = RM_O, \tag{6.13}$$

i.e., the scalar product of the two vectors R and M is independent of the reference point.

In the reduction of an arbitrary system of forces, the scalar product (6.13) is nonzero in general. Therefore, a spatial system of forces (in contrast to a plane or concurrent system) cannot, in general, be reduced to a single resultant force or couple. By suitable choice of the reference point, however, the representation can be simplified.

If the moment vector M_O (Fig. 6.8) is resolved into the component M_1 in the direction of R and the component M_2 perpendicular to it, we have $RM_O = RM_1$. From the invariance of the left-hand side together with that of R, we conclude that M_1 is also invariant. Thus, with reduction at another point O', only M_2 is altered. If O' is chosen such that

$$M_2 - r \times R = 0, \tag{6.14}$$

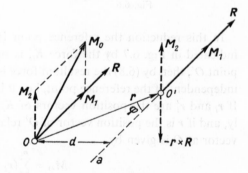

Fig. 6.8

the component M_2 will be cancelled by the auxiliary couple $-r \times R$ at O'. Then the two resultants $R[O'], M_O'$ are collinear with equidirectional or opposite sense. In order to satisfy (6.14), O' must lie on the plane normal to M_2 through O, be at a distance $d=r \sin \varphi=M_2/R$ from the line of action of $R[O]$, and be on that side of O for which the sense of rotation of $R[O']$ about O together with M_2 forms a right-handed screw. Points satisfying these conditions will generally lie on a line a [with the vector equation (6.14)] which is parallel to R. This is called the *central axis* of the system of forces, and such a combination of force and couple is called a *wrench*. It is classified as right-handed or left-handed according as the two vectors are in the same or opposite directions. The construction fails when either $M_2=0$ or $R=0$; in the first case we already have a wrench, and in the second, every line parallel to M_O is a central axis.

In special cases, a system of forces on a rigid body can be reduced further than to a wrench. The necessary and sufficient condition for this is clearly the vanishing of the invariant RM_O. In fact, the condition

$$RM_O = 0 \qquad (6.15)$$

means that

$$R=0, \qquad M_O=0, \qquad \text{or} \qquad M_O \perp R.$$

In the first case, a couple is obtained, and the second and third cases, at least after reduction at a point on the central axis, yield a single force. Thus, if a system of forces is to be reduced to a *couple* or a *single force*, it is necessary that

$$R = 0 \quad \text{or} \quad RM_O = 0 \quad (R \neq 0), \qquad (6.16)$$

respectively.

With a system of concurrent forces, insofar as they are not self-equilibrating, the second condition in (6.16) is satisfied. With a system of coplanar forces, one or the other is satisfied.

If both vectors vanish after reduction of a system at a point O, then they vanish at any point O' by virtue of (6.12) and the invariance of R. The necessary and sufficient *equilibrium conditions* for a spatial system of forces follow from (6.8) and (6.10):

$$\sum_1^n K_i = 0, \qquad \sum_1^n M_{Oi} = \sum_1^n (r_i \times K_i) = 0, \qquad 6.17$$

where O is an arbitrary point. Thus, a system of forces on a rigid body is in equilibrium if and only if the sum of their vectors and that of their static moments about an arbitrary point vanishes.

Now two theorems, proved in Section 3 for plane systems of forces, can be extended to three dimensions. From (6.8) it follows that, also in three dimensions, a single force and a couple can never be in equilibrium. Then, as in Section 3, we have that a couple can never be reduced to a single force.

Exercises

1. Find the resultant force and couple at corner O for the three forces acting on the cube shown in Fig. 6.9 (both intuitively and analytically).

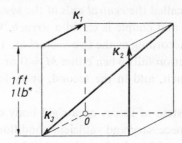

K_1

K_2

$1 ft$
$1 lb^*$

K_3

O

Fig. 6.9

2. Determine the central axis of the force system given in Fig. 6.9, and reduce the forces at a point on it.

7. Analytical Statics in Three Dimensions

The graphical treatment of spatial systems of forces is cumbersome. We will therefore limit ourselves to the analytical evaluation of the results in the last section. For this purpose, a further quantity must first be defined.

Figure 7.1 shows a force K with line of action g and a directed line a which is at a distance d from g. If φ is the angle between K and a, the projection of K onto the normal plane to a is given by $P = K \sin \varphi$; the force P is also at a distance d from a. By the *scalar* or *static moment of the force K about the directed line a* is understood the product

$$M_a = \pm d \cdot P \qquad (7.1)$$

of the distance d of its line of action from a and the magnitude P of its projection on a plane normal to a. It is taken to be positive or negative according as the sense of rotation of P (or K) and the direction of a form a right-handed or left-handed screw.

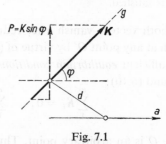

$P = K \sin \varphi$

g

K

φ

d

a

Fig. 7.1

This static moment has the dimension $[FL]$; however, in contrast to the static moment about a point, it is not a vector but a scalar quantity.

From the definition of the scalar moment M_a, it follows immediately that it is invariant with respect to translation of K along g, and that it vanishes if and only if g and a are coplanar (whereby either d or P vanishes).

In analytical statics, the forces are referred to a rectangular system of cartesian coordinates. Figure 7.2 shows a force $K = (X, Y, Z)$ applied to the point A with the position vector $r = (x, y, z)$. Let us calculate its scalar moments about the coordinate axes. For the x-axis, it follows from Fig. 7.3 that

$$M_x = P d = P(y \sin \alpha - z \cos \alpha) = yZ - zY,$$

and cyclic interchange leads to the components

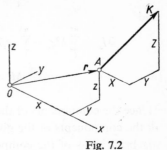

$$M_x = yZ - zY,$$
$$M_y = zX - xZ, \qquad (7.2)$$
$$M_z = xY - yX$$

Fig. 7.2

with respect to the three coordinate axes. The right-hand sides of these expressions can also be interpreted as the components of the vectorial static moment (6.4). Hence, the scalar moments about the three coordinate axes are the components of the static moment for the origin.

In the last section it was shown that the static moment with respect to an arbitrary point O of the resultant of a system of concurrent forces is, by (6.6), equal to the sum of the static moments of the separate forces. From this, it follows by considering components that

$$M_x = yR_z - zR_y = \sum_1^n (yZ_i - zY_i) = \sum_1^n M_{xi}, \qquad (7.3)$$

so that the result is also valid for scalar moments about an arbitrary line. Considering the force K in Fig. 7.2 as the resultant of its components, we obtain from (7.3) a verification of relations (7.2).

In Fig. 7.4, an arbitrary system of forces, represented by the force K_i, is referred to a coordinate system. A reduction at the origin O yields a resultant

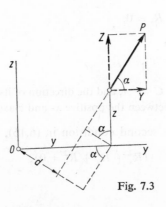

Fig. 7.3

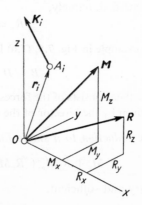

Fig. 7.4

force and couple given by the vectors (6.8) and (6.9), respectively. If these are resolved into their components, we have

$$R_x = \sum_1^n X_i, \qquad R_y = \sum_1^n Y_i, \qquad R_z = \sum_1^n Z_i, \qquad (7.4)$$

and

$$M_x = \sum_1^n M_{xi} = \sum_1^n (y_i Z_i - z_i Y_i), \qquad M_y = \sum_1^n M_{yi} = \sum_1^n (z_i X_i - x_i Z_i),$$

$$M_z = \sum_1^n M_{zi} = \sum_1^n (x_i Y_i - y_i X_i). \qquad (7.5)$$

Hence the components of the resultant force are obtained as the algebraic sums of the components of the given forces, and those of the resultant couple as the algebraic sums of the components of the individual moments about the axes.

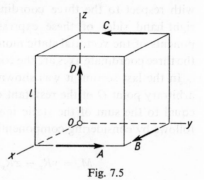

Figure 7.5 shows a cube in which four forces are acting. As is usual in analytical statics, these are indicated by their magnitudes. If they are reduced at the origin of the coordinate system fixed in the edges of the cube, we obtain a single force with components

$$R_x = B, \qquad R_y = A - C, \qquad R_z = D,$$

and a moment vector having the components

$$M_x = lC, \qquad M_y = 0, \qquad M_z = l(A - B).$$

Fig. 7.5

The magnitudes and direction angles of both vectors can be calculated as in (1.2) and (1.3). For example, the magnitude of R is

$$R = \sqrt{B^2 + (A - C)^2 + D^2}.$$

If a spatial system of forces is to *reduce to a couple*, the first condition in (6.16) must be satisfied, namely,

$$R_x = R_y = R_z = 0. \qquad (7.6)$$

For the example in Fig. 7.5, (7.6) leads to

$$B = D = 0, \qquad A = C.$$

The couple then consists of the forces A and $C = -A$, and the direction of its moment vector is given by the bisector of the angle between the positive x- and z-axes.

For the *reduction to a single force* the second condition in (6.16), i.e.,

$$R_x M_x + R_y M_y + R_z M_z = 0 \qquad (R_x^2 + R_y^2 + R_z^2 \neq 0), \qquad (7.7)$$

is necessary and sufficient.

For the example in Fig. 7.5, (7.7) leads to the condition

$$BC + D(A - B) = 0 \qquad [B^2 + (A - C)^2 + D^2 \neq 0],$$

which can be satisfied in infinitely many ways. If, for example, we set $D=C=B\neq 0$, then it is necessary that $A=0$. The resultant lies along the inner diagonal from the corner on the positive y-axis.

The vectorial *equilibrium conditions* (6.17) yield the six scalar conditions

$$\sum_1^n X_i = 0, \qquad \sum_1^n Y_i = 0, \qquad \sum_1^n Z_i = 0, \tag{7.8}$$

and

$$\sum_1^n M_{xi} = \sum_1^n (y_i Z_i - z_i Y_i) = 0, \qquad \sum_1^n M_{yi} = \sum_1^n (z_i X_i - x_i Z_i) = 0,$$

$$\sum_1^n M_{zi} = \sum_1^n (x_i Y_i - y_i X_i) = 0, \tag{7.9}$$

i.e., three *component* and three *moment conditions*. Therefore a spatial system of forces is in equilibrium if and only if its sums of components and static moments for the three coordinate axes vanish.

Returning again to the example in Fig. 7.5, it follows from (7.8) and (7.9) that

$$B = A - C = D = C = A - B = 0,$$

and therefore $A=B=C=D=0$. In this case, equilibrium requires that all forces should vanish.

It has already been mentioned in Section 6 that a force on a body is fully specified by its force vector K together with the static moment M_O about an arbitrary point O, such as the coordinate origin. Since these two vectors are connected by the relation $KM_O=0$, a force has five determinatives. These five quantities are also arrived at by noting that the force vector is given by its three components X, Y, Z and the line of action by two of the three equations (7.2), the third equation following from the other two by virtue of the relation $KM_O=0$. When only the point of application of the force is known, as in the case of the reaction in a smooth ball joint, it represents three unknowns. When the line of action is also known, as in the case of the normal force at a smooth support, it embodies a single unknown.

When a body is at rest, the supporting reactions constitute a series of unknowns between which six equations in the form of the equilibrium conditions (7.8) and (7.9) can be formulated. If these are sufficient for determining the unknowns, the problem is called *statically determinate*, otherwise it is *statically indeterminate*. In the latter case, the formulation of further equilibrium equations, such as component and moment conditions for new axes, does not lead to the goal. Indeed, when the six equilibrium conditions (7.8) and (7.9) are satisfied, the system of forces is in equilibrium and hence satisfies every further equilibrium condition. Mathematically this follows from the fact that the conditions (7.8) and (7.9) are linearly independent and all additional equilibrium conditions are dependent on them. When a problem is statically indeterminate, further equations can be obtained only by taking account of the *deformations* of the body and by expressing what is known about them. We will return to this matter in Chapter III.

The equilibrium conditions (7.8) and (7.9) may, of course, be replaced by six other conditions that are necessary and sufficient for equilibrium and thus linearly independent. For example, use can be made of the component and moment conditions for a system of oblique coordinates [in which the representation (7.2) for the static moments must clearly be dropped]. Also the six moment conditions for the edges of a tetrahedron could be used.

We are now in a position to extend some of the results proved in Section 3 for two-dimensional systems of forces to the general case of three dimensions. Thus, for the *equilibrium of two forces* it is necessary that the moment condition is satisfied for the line of action of one of the forces. Hence, the forces must be coplanar and thus the result of Section 3 applies: the forces must be coaxial, equal in magnitude, and opposite in sense.

For the *equilibrium of three forces* (Fig. 7.6) it is necessary that the sum of the static moments for the joins a_1, a_2, a_3 of the three points of application should vanish, i.e., the forces must again be coplanar. Now the earlier result again applies, whereby, in particular, the three lines of action must be concurrent.

In resolving a force K into *two components* K_1, K_2, use can be made of the fact that K_1, K_2, and $-K$ must be in equilibrium. Thus, the three lines of action must also be coplanar and concurrent.

Let us consider a shaft, i.e., a rigid body that can rotate freely about an axis. If it has two bearings (Fig. 7.7), a system of coordinate axes can be introduced so that the x-axis corresponds with the axis of rotation and the origin can be placed in the center of, say, the left-hand bearing. Further, the loads P_i can be

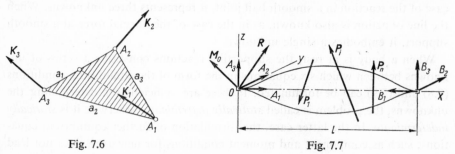

Fig. 7.6   Fig. 7.7

reduced beforehand to a resultant force R and couple M_O in the point O. If the bearings consist of both *thrust* and *transverse bearings*, six reactions appear at each end, namely, three forces and three moment vectors in the directions of the coordinate axes.

If the bearings are frictionless, the moment vectors in the x-axis vanish, and with ideally short or self-aligning bearings the other moment vectors also vanish, so that the reactions reduce to the six forces shown in Fig. 7.7. Now the component conditions are

$$R_x + A_1 - B_1 = 0, \qquad R_y + A_2 + B_2 = 0, \qquad R_z + A_3 + B_3 = 0,$$

and the moment conditions are

$$M_x = 0, \qquad M_y - lB_3 = 0, \qquad M_z + lB_2 = 0.$$

Since the first moment condition contains none of the six unknowns, there are only five equations available for their determination. Hence the problem is statically indeterminate. The last two equations in each line can be solved to give the bearing reactions

$$B_2 = -\frac{M_z}{l}, \qquad B_3 = \frac{M_y}{l}, \qquad A_2 = -R_y + \frac{M_z}{l}, \qquad A_3 = -R_z - \frac{M_y}{l}$$

in terms of the loads. The first component condition,

$$A_1 - B_1 = -R_x,$$

however, only yields the difference of the axial bearing forces.

Fig. 7.8

The problem can be rendered statically determinate by making one of the bearings, for example the right-hand one in Fig. 7.8, only a transverse bearing. Then $B_1 = 0$ and $A_1 = -R_x$, so that equilibrium is possible if $R_x \leq 0$. In any case, the first moment condition, $M_x = 0$, only places a condition on the loading. According to it, the shaft can be at rest only if the sum of the static moments of the loads about the axis of rotation vanishes. On the other hand, the vanishing of this sum of moments does not imply that the shaft remains at rest; as will be shown in kinetics, the shaft could rotate uniformly in this case.

The box shown in Fig. 7.9 is open at the top. A rod of weight W has its lower end in the corner O and the upper end rests against the diagonally opposite corner. The center of mass of the rod is half-way between these points, and the supports are

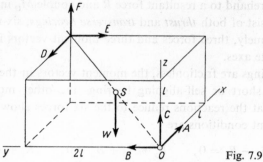

Fig. 7.9

to be assumed frictionless. If we now introduce the six reactions $A, \ldots, F$, the equilibrium conditions in the coordinate axes shown are

$$A - D = 0, \qquad B - E = 0, \qquad C + F - W = 0,$$

$$lE + 2lF - lW = 0, \qquad -lD - lF + \frac{l}{2} W = 0, \qquad 2lD - lE = 0.$$

Their solution yields $B=2A$, $C=W/2+A$, $D=A$, $E=2A$, $F=W/2-A$. Since the moment condition about the axis of the rod is automatically satisfied, only five of the formulated equations are linearly independent, and the reaction A remains unknown. However, the problem is not statically indeterminate because the reactions represent only five unknowns, since, when the contacts are perfectly smooth, the reaction at the upper support must be normal to the direction $(l, 2l, l)$ of the bar. Thus we have the additional equation

$$-lD - 2lE + lF = 0.$$

It yields $A = W/12$ and thus $B=W/6$, $C=7W/12$, $D=W/12$, $E=W/6$, $F=5W/12$.

The procedure in this example can well be taken as a model for the *analytic treatment of equilibrium problems*. First, we isolate the body to be studied. Then, all forces acting on it are introduced, and those with unknown directions are resolved along given directions before formulating the equilibrium and other conditions. Their solution can possibly lead to: (a) requirements to be fulfilled by the loads if the body is to remain at rest, (b) conditions for the determination of the equilibrium configuration, and finally, (c) the reactions.

Since systems will often be encountered in which we have to deal with internal forces and their reactions, it is advisable not to denote the components of the unknown forces as such (i.e., with $X, \ldots,$ or $K_x, \ldots$), but to treat them as independent forces denoted by letters (like $A, B, \ldots$) that have no reference to the coordinate system. Moreover, as has already been remarked, it is usual in analytical statics to denote the forces simply by their magnitudes. We are then really working with algebraic magnitudes of force, and, when a negative value is obtained for a force of initially unknown direction, this means that the true sense of action is opposite to that tentatively assumed.

Exercises

1. Prove that the component and moment conditions for a system of oblique axes are necessary and sufficient conditions for equilibrium.

2. Prove that the moment conditions for the edges of an arbitrary tetrahedron of nonzero volume are necessary and sufficient for the equilibrium of a spatial system of forces.

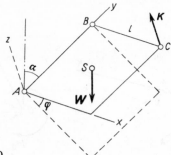

Fig. 7.10

3. The square plate in Fig. 7.10 has its center of gravity at the midpoint and can rotate about the axis AB inclined at an angle α to the vertical. The bearings at A and B are short and free of friction; A is a transverse and thrust bearing, B is a transverse bearing.

Determine the force K applied normally to the plate at C such that the plate is turned an angle φ out of the vertical plane. Also determine the reactions in A and B (resolved into components along the x-, y- and z-axes).

8. Analytical Statics in Two Dimensions

For the reduction of a plane system of forces, it is expedient to choose the coordinates so that the forces lie in the x,y-plane. Figure 8.1 shows one of the forces of such a system. The force vector $K = (X, Y, 0)$ and the position vector $r = (x, y, 0)$ of its point of application A both lie in the x, y-plane. The static moment M_O about O is thus coincident with the z-axis and is given by

$$M_z = xY - yX = \pm d \cdot K, \qquad (8.1)$$

where the sign on the right-hand side is given by the familiar right-handed screw rule.

Since M_O is given by M_z, and on the other hand we gladly do without the z-axis when treating two-dimensional problems, it is advantageous to replace (8.1) by

$$M_O = xY - yX = \pm d \cdot K, \tag{8.2}$$

and to call M_O the *static moment of K about O in the plane*. This new moment, indicated by the curved arrow around O in Fig. 8.2, replaces M_O and M_z; it is given by the product of the magnitude of the force K and the distance of its line of action from the point O. It is positive or negative according as K tends to turn counterclockwise or clockwise about O.

Hence M_O is an algebraic quantity with the dimension $[M_O]=[FL]$.

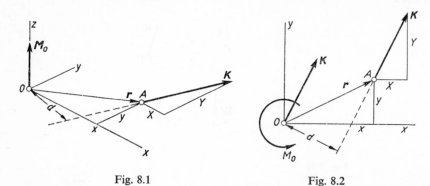

Fig. 8.1   Fig. 8.2

For the static moment of a force about a point we naturally have the same theorems in two as in three dimensions. Thus, M_O is not altered by a translation of the force along its line of action; it vanishes if and only if the latter passes through O, and together with X and Y it completely determines the force on a rigid body. Moreover, the static moment of the resultant of a system of concurrent forces is equal to the algebraic sum of the static moments of the individual forces.

If the *static moment of a couple* (Fig. 8.3) about a point O in its plane is understood to be the sum of the static moments of the two forces, it immediately follows from

$$M_{O1} = d_1 \cdot K \quad \text{and} \quad M_{O2} = -d_2 \cdot K$$

that

$$M_O = (d_1 - d_2)K = bK = M.$$

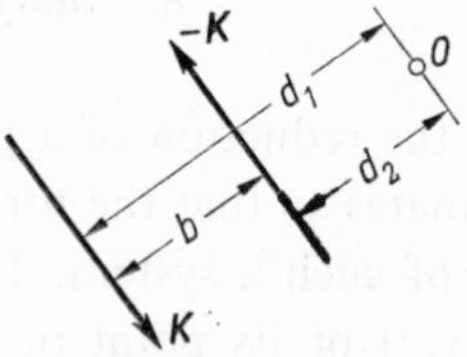

Fig. 8.3

The static moment of a couple is thus independent of the reference point and agrees with that quantity already defined in Section 3 as the moment of the couple.

If the force K (Fig. 8.2) is reduced at the coordinate origin, we obtain the displaced force and a couple with moment M_O, which can be indicated by the curved arrow. Similarly, the reduction of a system of coplanar forces (Fig. 8.4) by (7.4) and (7.5) furnishes a resultant force and couple with the components

$$R_x = \sum_1^n X_i, \qquad R_y = \sum_1^n Y_i, \qquad M_O = \sum_1^n M_{Oi} = \sum_1^n (x_i Y_i - y_i X_i). \qquad (8.3)$$

The components of the resultant force are again obtained as sums of the components of the given forces, and the moment of the resultant couple as the sum of algebraic moments about O.

Since $RM_O = 0$, it is always possible to find positions where the system reduces to either a couple or a single force. If $R = 0$, a couple of moment M_O is obtained. If $M_O = 0$, we have a single force R acting at O. When R and M_O are both nonzero, further reduction leads to a force at a point O' on the central axis a. For this purpose, the vector equation (6.14) for the central axis could be used. The following consideration is just as simple:

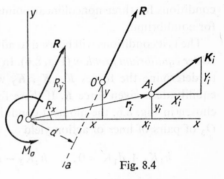

Fig. 8.4

if the displaced force $R[O']$ is to be equivalent to the force $R[O]$ and couple M_O at O, the static moment of $R[O']$ about O must be M_O. Thus

$$xR_y - yR_x = M_O, \qquad \pm d \cdot R = M_O \qquad (8.4)$$

must hold. The first relation (8.4) is the equation of the central axis and hence the line of action of the force $R[O']$; the second shows that R must be displaced a distance $d = |M_O|/R$ and, indeed, to the right or left of R according as $M_O \gtrless 0$.

The reduction at the origin of the forces K_1, K_2, K_3 given on the rectangular lattice of Fig. 8.5 yields, by (8.3), the resultant force and couple

$$R_x = -2\ \text{lb*}, \qquad R_y = 2\ \text{lb*}, \qquad M_O = 8\ \text{lb* ft}.$$

They can be further reduced to a force of magnitude $R = 2\sqrt{2}$ lb* in the central axis. By (8.4), this has the equation $x + y = 4$ ft and the distance $d = 2\sqrt{2}$ ft from O. It is thus given by the diagonal of the outer frame lying parallel to R.

A plane system of forces is in equilibrium if and only if the quantities in (8.3) vanish, i.e., if the two algebraic sums of components for the axes and the sum of static moments about the origin are zero. The *equilibrium conditions* are

$$\sum_1^n X_i = 0, \qquad \sum_1^n Y_i = 0, \qquad \sum_1^n M_{Oi} = \sum_1^n (x_i Y_i - y_i X_i) = 0. \qquad (8.5)$$

They comprise two *component conditions* and one *moment condition*; the remaining three equilibrium conditions (7.8) and (7.9) are here automatically fulfilled.

It is often useful to replace the three equilibrium conditions (8.5) by three others. For example, by the moment conditions relative to two points O_1, O_2 and the component condition for an axis not normal to the join O_1O_2. It is clear that they are necessary; they are also sufficient. In fact, from the first two it follows that the given system of forces can be reduced at most to a single force coaxial with the join O_1O_2, and the third condition requires that its magnitude should vanish. Just as simply it can be shown that the moment conditions for three noncollinear points O_1, O_2, O_3 are necessary and sufficient for equilibrium.

The last conditions will be used to advantage in the treatment of the *Culmann-Ritter equilibrium problem* (Fig. 8.6). In this problem (cf. Section 3), it is required to determine the forces K_1, K_2, K_3 with the lines of action g_1, g_2, g_3 that equilibrate a given force K. If these forces are introduced with the directions chosen in Fig. 8.6, the moment conditions relative to the intersections O_1, O_2, O_3 of pairs of lines of action yield

$$h_1K_1 + d_1K = 0, \qquad h_2K_2 - d_2K = 0, \qquad h_3K_3 + d_3K = 0,$$

and hence the magnitudes of the forces are

$$K_1 = -\left(\frac{d_1}{h_1}\right)K, \qquad K_2 = \left(\frac{d_2}{h_2}\right)K, \qquad K_3 = -\left(\frac{d_3}{h_3}\right)K.$$

The negative signs for K_1 and K_3 indicate that their sense is opposite to that assumed. The *Culmann-Ritter resolution problem* is solved similarly, namely, by setting the sums of moments of K_1, K_2, K_3 about the points O_1, O_2, O_3 equal to the corresponding static moments of K.

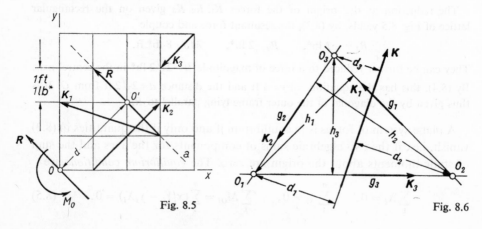

Fig. 8.5   Fig. 8.6

Of course, the Culmann-Ritter problem can also be treated by means of the conditions (8.5) or (8.3). There is then, however, the disadvantage that each equation contains more than one unknown. With other problems also, the amount of calculation can be reduced by a careful choice of the equilibrium conditions and, particularly, of the system of coordinates used.

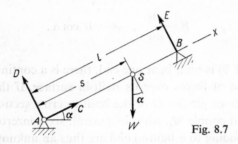

Fig. 8.7

With the beam in Fig. 8.7, freely hinged at A, simply supported at B, and loaded by its own weight, it is expedient to formulate the moment conditions for A and B together with the component condition for the x-axis along the beam. This gives

$$lE - sW \cos \alpha = 0 , \qquad - lD + (l - s) W \cos \alpha = 0 , \qquad C - W \sin \alpha = 0 ,$$

and therefore

$$C = W \sin \alpha , \qquad D = W \left(1 - \frac{s}{l}\right) \cos \alpha , \qquad E = W \left(\frac{s}{l}\right) \cos \alpha .$$

The normal force E is positive when $-\pi/2 < \alpha < \pi/2$.

As has already been remarked at the end of Section 7, the equilibrium conditions can sometimes also be used for the determination of the equilibrium configuration of the body under consideration.

A rod, of which only a part including the center of gravity S is shown in Fig. 8.8, is propped against a vertical wall at A and rests on a pin at B. Both supports are to be assumed frictionless. The equilibrium conditions (8.5), formulated for the system of coordinates introduced in Fig. 8.8, are readily seen to be

$$A - B \cos \alpha = 0 ,$$

$$B \sin \alpha - W = 0 ,$$

$$B \frac{a}{\sin \alpha} - Ws \sin \alpha = 0 .$$

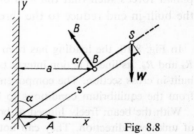

Fig. 8.8

Elimination of B from the last two equations yields

$$\sin \alpha = \sqrt[3]{\frac{a}{s}}$$

giving the position of equilibrium, and then the two reactions are obtained from the first two equations:

$$B = \frac{W}{\sin \alpha}, \quad A = W \cot \alpha.$$

If a beam (Fig. 8.9) is built in at one end, there is a continuous, but not fully known distribution of forces over its built-in surface. If these forces are reduced at the center of gravity O of the built-in cross section, we obtain a resultant force A and couple M_O with, in general, six nonzero components. The reactions corresponding to a built-in end are thus an unknown force A and an unknown moment M_O.

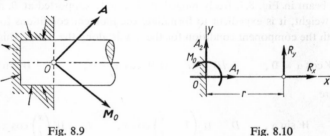

Fig. 8.9   Fig. 8.10

If instead of a beam we have a cylindrical shaft and instead of the built-in end a long (frictionless) *bearing*, the resultant static moment of the surface forces about the axis will be zero. Hence, apart from a *bearing force* of unknown direction, there arises a *bearing moment*, the vector of which is normal to the axis. With a short or self-aligning bearing, it is possible (as in Fig. 7.7) to neglect the bearing moment.

In two-dimensional problems the number of unknown reactions is smaller. For example, if the cantilever beam in Fig. 8.10 is loaded by a system of coplanar forces such that the axis of the beam is also coplanar, the reactions at the built-in end reduce to the three components A_1, A_2, and M_O.

In Fig. 8.10, the loading has been reduced to a single force with the components R_x and R_y. Its line of action intersects the axis at a distance r from the centroid of the built-in cross section. The components of the reactions at the built-in end are found from the equilibrium conditions to be $A_1 = -R_x$, $A_2 = -R_y$, $M_O = -rR_y$.

With the beam freely hinged at both ends (Fig. 8.11), there are two hinge forces of unknown direction. They can both be resolved into two components and hence they represent four unknowns. Since the three equilibrium conditions

$$A_1 + B_1 + R_x = 0, \qquad A_2 + B_2 + R_y = 0, \qquad lB_2 + rR_y = 0$$

are not sufficient for their determination, the problem is statically indeterminate.

In general, an equilibrium problem with n unknowns, between which $r < n$ equations can be set up, is called $(n - r)$-fold statically indeterminate. It has been mentioned in Section 7 that such problems can be solved only by taking the deformations into account.

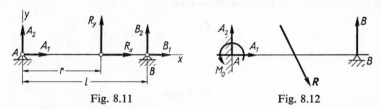

Fig. 8.11   Fig. 8.12

Just as with the problem in Fig. 8.11, the beam built in at one end and smoothly supported at the other (Fig. 8.12) represents a simply statically indeterminate problem. With plane loading, a beam built in at one end and freely hinged at the other is twofold statically indeterminate, and when built in at both ends it is threefold statically indeterminate.

If a system of several bodies is to be considered, caution is required in determining the indeterminacy. As we know from Section 5, the external reactions cannot always be obtained by considering the equilibrium of the external forces. In such cases, we resolve the system into its components and formulate the equilibrium conditions for each of them. Only then, when the number of equations is still insufficient, is the system statically indeterminate.

The external reactions of the *three-hinged arch* in Fig. 8.13 represent four unknowns and cannot be obtained immediately. If the arch is divided into its two panels, there are, with the reactions in the middle hinge, a total of six unknowns. These can be

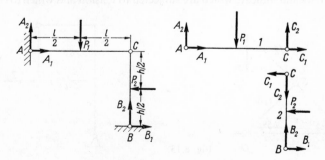

Fig. 8.13

determined, however, with the two times three equilibrium equations for both panels, namely, with the conditions

$$lC_2 - \frac{l}{2}P_1 = 0, \qquad -lA_2 + \frac{l}{2}P_1 = 0, \qquad A_1 + C_1 = 0$$

for the left-hand panel and

$$hB_1 - \frac{h}{2}P_2 = 0, \qquad hC_1 + \frac{h}{2}P_2 = 0, \qquad B_2 - C_2 = 0$$

for the right-hand panel. The solution is then

$$A_1 = B_1 = -C_1 = \frac{P_2}{2}, \qquad A_2 = B_2 = C_2 = \frac{P_1}{2}.$$

Exercises

1. A two-dimensional system of forces has the following sums of moments relative to the vertices of the equilateral triangle shown in Fig. 8.14:

(a) $\sum M_{Ai} = 4\,\text{lb}^*\,\text{ft}, \qquad \sum M_{Bi} = -2\,\text{lb}^*\,\text{ft},$

     $\sum M_{Ci} = -3\,\text{lb}^*\,\text{ft},$

(b) $\sum M_{Ai} = \sum M_{Bi} = \sum M_{Ci} = 4\,\text{lb}^*\,\text{ft}.$

Can it be foreseen that the system will reduce to either a single force or a couple? Give the result of the reduction.

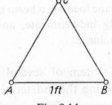

Fig. 8.14

2. A homogeneous prismatic bar (Fig. 8.15) is loaded by its own weight $W = 70\,\text{lb}^*$ at S and by the force $P = 30\,\text{lb}^*$. It is secured by a hinge and a weightless hinged supporting bar. Assume that all hinges are frictionless and determine all reactions acting on the bar.

3. A square plate (Fig. 8.16) is loaded by its own weight $W = 100\,\text{kg}^*$, acting at the center S, and is held by three weightless hinged bars without friction. Determine the forces in these bars and indicate which are subjected to tension and which to compression.

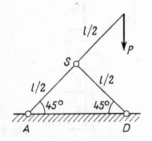

Fig. 8.15

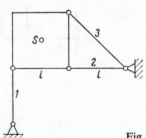

Fig. 8.16

4. The cylinder of radius r shown in Fig. 8.17 has a perfectly smooth surface. On it rests a homogeneous prismatic bar that has been bent into a right angle with sides l, $2l$. The total weight is W. Using the angle φ, determine the position of equilibrium and the reactions. What conditions must r and l fulfil in order that such a position of equilibrium should in fact be possible?

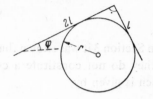

Fig. 8.17

5. Two completely smooth homogeneous circular cylinders (Fig. 8.18) with the weights W_1 and W_2 rest against each other and against two inclined planes. Determine the position of equilibrium and all reactions at the supports.

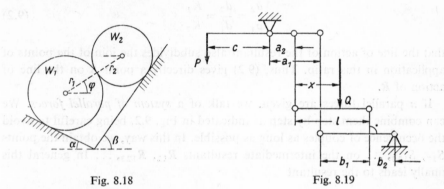

Fig. 8.18   Fig. 8.19

6. Determine the relation between the load Q, its position x, and the weight P for the frictionless balance sketched in Fig. 8.19. How must it be constructed in order that the counterweight P should be independent of the position x of the load? How must it be constructed if it is to be (1) a decimal or (2) a centesimal balance?

7. A weightless rigid frame with $l=10$ ft (Fig. 8.20) is built in at the support and carries three identical weightless rollers of radius 2 ft. The two top rollers can turn without friction, and the lower one is blocked in the bearing. A light cable, one end of which is rolled on the lower roller, runs over the upper rollers and carries the vertical load $P=600$ lb*. Determine the external reactions. Then draw the (whole) frame as well as the rollers separated from each other showing the forces applied to these bodies. Calculate their magnitudes.

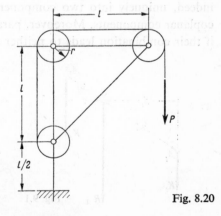

Fig. 8.20

9. Parallel Forces

In Section 3 it was shown that two parallel forces K_1 and K_2 (Fig. 9.1), insofar as they do not constitute a couple, have a coplanar resultant, the vector of which is given by

$$R = K_1 + K_2 \,, \tag{9.1}$$

and the line of action of which divides the distance between the given forces (internally in the case of equidirectional forces, and externally in the other case) in inverse proportion to their magnitudes. If A_1 and A_2 are the points of application of the two forces, it follows from

$$\frac{a_2}{a_1} = \frac{d_2}{d_1} = \frac{K_1}{K_2} \tag{9.2}$$

that the line of action of the resultant also subdivides the join of the points of application in this ratio. Thus, (9.2) gives directly a point S on the line of action of R.

If n parallel forces are given, we talk of a *system of parallel forces*. We can combine them step by step as indicated in Fig. 9.2, being careful to avoid the occurrence of couples as long as possible. In this way, we obtain the points S_{12}, S_{123}, ... on the intermediate resultants R_{12}, R_{123}, ... In general this finally leads to the resultant

$$R = \sum_1^n K_i \tag{9.3}$$

together with a point S on its line of action. However, it is also possible that a couple remains. Thus a system of parallel forces can always be reduced, like a plane system, to either a *single force* or a *couple*.

Conversely, a given force K can be resolved into parallel components and, indeed, uniquely into two components coplanar with K or into three non-coplanar components. Moreover, parallel forces are in *equilibrium* if and only if their combination leads to neither a single force nor a couple.

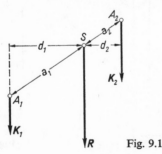

Fig. 9.1   Fig. 9.2

Figure 9.3 shows a three-legged table loaded by its own weight and resting on a smooth horizontal surface. The normal pressures are obtained in the same way as with the Culmann-Ritter equilibrium problem. From

$$N_1, N_2, N_3, W \sim 0 ,$$

by combining two normal pressures, we obtain

$$N_1, N_2 \sim R_{12}, \quad \text{whence} \quad R_{12}, N_3, W \sim 0 .$$

The line of action of R_{12}, which corresponds to the Culmann line, is the line of intersection of the planes containing N_1 and N_2 with that containing N_3 and W. Once this is determined, the problem is solved in two steps corresponding to the last two equivalences.

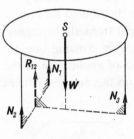

Fig. 9.3

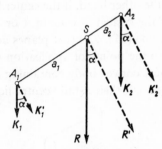

Fig. 9.4

If two parallel forces K_1 and K_2 (Fig. 9.4) are rotated the same angle about their fixed points of application A_1, A_2, two new parallel forces K_1', K_2' are obtained. Since (9.1) remains true for the primed forces, the new resultant R' is parallel to the rotated forces. It is coplanar with K_1' and K_2' so that its line of action cuts the joint $A_1 A_2$, and, since the magnitudes of the forces are unaltered by the rotation, it subdivides the join $A_1 A_2$ in the ratio (9.2) as previously. The resultant thus turns an angle α about a fixed point S which is called the *astatic center* of K_1 and K_2 and is obtained as the intersection of the line of action of R with the transversal $A_1 A_2$.

If all members of an arbitrary system of parallel forces (Fig. 9.5) are rotated in space through the same angle, the intermediate resultant R_{12} rotates about the center S_{12} of the forces K_1 and K_2, R_{123} about the center S_{123} of R_{12} and K_3, which can be regarded as the center of the first three forces, and so on. Finally the resultant R also rotates about a fixed point S, the center of the

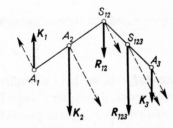

Fig. 9.5

complete system of forces. Consequently every system of parallel forces with fixed points of application has an astatic center, provided that the system does not reduce to a couple. The resultant turns about this point when the given forces are turned through the same angle in space.

If the given forces all have the same direction, we speak of a *system of equidirectional forces*. Such a system reduces to a single force and hence always has an astatic center.

The center of two equidirectional forces (Fig. 9.4) lies between their points of application, because the line of action of R divides the join $A_1 A_2$ internally. Hence it follows that if all the points of application of a system of equidirectional forces are on one side of a plane E (Fig. 9.6), the astatic center is also on this side. On the other hand, if the center lies in the plane E, all the points of application of the system also lie in it or they are distributed on both sides. Now, if we imagine (Fig. 9.7) that planes are brought from all directions as close as possible to the points of application without ever crossing one, they envelop the smallest convex body containing all points of application. If the forces are equidirectional, their astatic center lies in or on this smallest convex envelope.

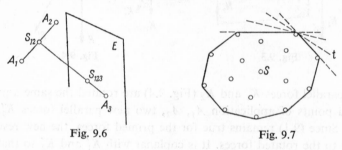

Fig. 9.6   Fig. 9.7

For the analytical reduction of a system of parallel forces, the coordinates shown in Fig. 9.8 can be so chosen that the lines of action are parallel to the z-axis. The forces are then given by the vectors $r_i = (x_i, y_i, z_i)$ and $K_i = (0, 0, Z_i)$. According to (7.4) and (7.5), a reduction at the origin O leads to a force

$$R_z = \sum_{1}^{n} Z_i \tag{9.4}$$

in the z-axis and a couple of moment M_O in the x, y-plane with the components

$$M_x = \sum_{1}^{n} M_{xi} = \sum_{1}^{n} y_i Z_i, \qquad M_y = \sum_{1}^{n} M_{yi} = - \sum_{1}^{n} x_i Z_i. \tag{9.5}$$

Since $RM_O = 0$, we have a confirmation that a system of parallel forces can always be reduced to either a single force or a couple. When $R = 0$, the reduction leads to a couple in a plane parallel to the z-axis; otherwise it leads to a force in the central axis parallel to the z-axis. For equidirectional forces, only the latter case can arise.

The *equilibrium conditions* (7.8) and (7.9) here reduce to

$$\sum_1^n Z_i = 0, \qquad \sum_1^n M_{xi} = \sum_1^n y_i Z_i = 0, \qquad \sum_1^n M_{yi} = -\sum_1^n x_i Z_i = 0, \qquad (9.6)$$

i.e., to one *component* and two *moment conditions*.

In order to determine the astatic center analytically, we make use of an arbitrarily oriented system of coordinates (Fig. 9.9) and introduce a unit vector *e* parallel to the given forces. The latter can then be represented in the form $K_i = K_i e$, where K_i are to be regarded as the algebraic magnitudes of the forces, being positive for forces in one direction and negative for those in the opposite direction. If

$$\sum_1^n K_i \neq 0,$$

then there is a resultant

$$R = Re = e \sum_1^n K_i. \qquad (9.7)$$

Since the static moment of *R* about *O* is equal to the sum of the static moments of the separate forces, the position vector of the point of application *S* of *R* satisfies the relation

$$r_s \times R = \sum_1^n r_i \times K_i,$$

and, by (9.7), this can be put in the form

$$\left(r_s \sum_1^n K_i - \sum_1^n K_i r_i\right) \times e = 0. \qquad (9.8)$$

This equation shows that the vector in the parentheses must be parellel to *e*. Clearly it represents the central axis, i.e., the line of action of *R*.

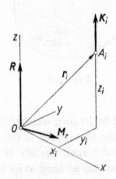

Fig. 9.8

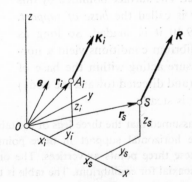

Fig. 9.9

If the given forces are turned about their points of application, e changes direction while K_i and r_i remain constant. In order to obtain the astatic center, we thus demand that equation (9.8) is satisfied for arbitrary directions of e. This requires that the first factor vanishes. Hence the astatic center has the equation

$$r_s \sum_1^n K_i = \sum_1^n K_i r_i, \tag{9.9}$$

and also the coordinates given by

$$x_s \sum_1^n K_i = \sum_1^n K_i x_i, \qquad y_s \sum_1^n K_i = \sum_1^n K_i y_i, \qquad z_s \sum_1^n K_i = \sum_1^n K_i z_i. \tag{9.10}$$

With a system of equidirectional forces, e can be so oriented that all K_i are positive. If, moreover, we have $z_i > 0$ for all i, it follows from (9.10) that $z_s > 0$. This confirms the fact that S lies on the same side of a plane E as the points of application A_i. Conversely, it follows from $z_s = 0$ that not all z_i have the same sign, which means that the A_i lie on, or on both sides of, the plane E.

As an application we will now treat the steadiness of bodies. A body resting on a plane support (Fig. 9.10) is called *steady* when it does not topple over. It makes contact with the support over the *area of contact* of which every element of area dA experiences a normal force dN and a friction force dF. The friction forces dF constitute a plane system, making it difficult or impossible for the body to slide on the support. This matter will not be discussed until Section 11. The normal forces constitute a system of equidirectional forces with points of application in the area of contact. They reduce to a single force, the resultant normal force N, the point of application of which lies within the smallest convex envelope of the area of contact. The surface bounded by this envelope is called the *base of support*. In Fig. 9.10 it is shaded. So long as the equilibrium conditions yield a normal pressure acting within the base of support (and directed toward the body) the body is steady.

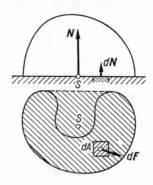

Fig. 9.10

If it is assumed that the three legs of the table loaded by its own weight (Fig. 9.11) touch the horizontal support in three points, the base of support is the triangle having these three points as vertices. The only external forces, namely W and N, must be coaxial for equilibrium. The table is therefore steady so long as its center of gravity is vertically above the base of contact.

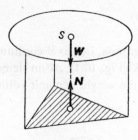

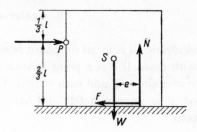

Fig. 9.11   Fig. 9.12

A cube (Fig. 9.12) resting on a rough horizontal plane is subjected to its own weight W along with the horizontal force P, and as reactions we have a normal force N and a friction force F. The equilibrium conditions are

$$P - F = 0, \qquad N - W = 0, \qquad eN - \frac{2}{3}lP = 0,$$

and yield

$$F = P, \qquad N = W, \qquad e = \frac{2}{3} \cdot \frac{P}{W} l.$$

The base of support for the cube is a square with sides of length l. The condition for steadiness is thus $|e| < l/2$ and leads to

$$|P| < \frac{3}{4} W.$$

Exercises

1. Determine graphically and analytically the astatic center for the system of forces shown on the rectangular lattice in Fig. 9.13.

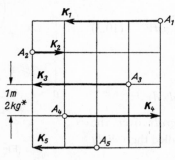

Fig. 9.13

2. Solve the problem given by Fig. 9.12, assuming that the support is inclined at 30° (to the right or left) and that P is parallel to the plane.

10. Center of Gravity

In mechanics it is usual to regard bodies as continua, i.e., as if continuously filled with mass. If P is a point in such a body K (Fig. 10.1), ΔV an element of volume containing P and with weight ΔW, then the weight per unit volume at position P is approximately $\Delta W / \Delta V$, or exactly

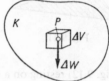

$$\gamma = \lim_{\Delta V \to 0} \frac{\Delta W}{\Delta V} = \frac{dW}{dV}. \qquad (10.1)$$

This limiting value is called the *specific weight* at point P.

Fig. 10.1

The specific weight has the dimension $[FL^{-3}]$ and thus some unit such as lb*/in³, gm*/cm³. In the case of iron we have $\gamma \sim 0.28$ lb*/in³$=7.8$ gm*/cm³.

In general, the specific weight is not constant in the interior of the body but is a scalar function of position, $\gamma(x,y,z)$. The weight

$$dW = \gamma \, dV \qquad (10.2)$$

of a volume element is then more explicitly $dW = \gamma(x,y,z) \, dx \, dy \, dz$. In this case we speak of a *nonhomogeneous body*, and when γ is constant of a *homogeneous body*.

In Fig. 10.2 there is a body K referred to a system of coordinates. The weights of its elements constitute a system of equidirectional forces with fixed points of application. By Section 9, this system has a resultant given by (9.3). Here, however, since the elementary weights form a continuous system of forces, we have

$$W = \int_K dW = \int_V \gamma \, dV \qquad (10.3)$$

or, in detail,

$$W = \iiint \gamma(x,y,z) \, dx \, dy \, dz,$$

which are *volume integrals* over the body. This resultant is called the *weight* of the body.

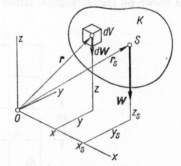

Fig. 10.2

If the body is turned about a point, all the elementary weights turn about their points of application with respect to an observer on the body. According to Section 9, the resultant weight turns about the astatic center, which is called the *center of gravity* of the body. By (9.9), its position vector r_s is given by

$$r_s \int_K dW = \int_K r \, dW,$$

and, by (10.2) and (10.3), can also be written as

$$W r_s = \int_V \gamma r \, dV. \tag{10.4}$$

The coordinates x_s, y_s, z_s thus follow from

$$W x_s = \int_V \gamma x \, dV, \qquad W y_s = \int_V \gamma y \, dV, \qquad W z_s = \int_V \gamma z \, dV, \tag{10.5}$$

and for the calculation the right-hand sides are to be written out as

$$\iiint \gamma(x, y, z) \, x \, dx \, dy \, dz, \ldots$$

Being the astatic center of equidirectional forces acting on points within the body, the center of gravity lies inside the smallest convex envelope of the body. However, as illustrated by Fig. 10.3, it need not lie within the body itself.

For a body K (Fig. 10.4) consisting of n parts K_i with the individual weights W_i at the centers of gravity S_i given by the position vectors r_i, one has

$$W = \sum_1^n W_i \quad \text{and} \quad W r_s = \int_V \gamma r \, dV = \sum_1^n \int_{V_i} \gamma r \, dV = \sum_1^n W_i r_i.$$

$$\tag{10.6}$$

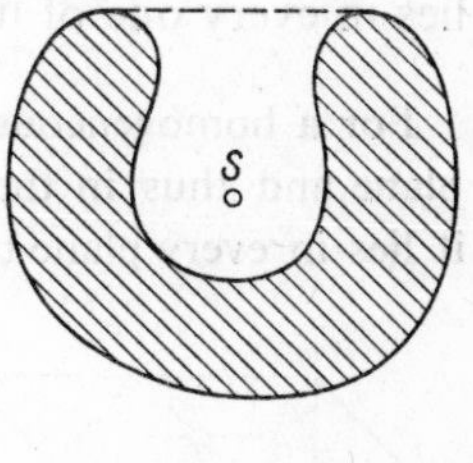

The coordinates of the center of gravity are thus given by

$$W x_s = \sum_1^n W_i x_i, \qquad W y_s = \sum_1^n W_i y_i, \qquad W z_s = \sum_1^n W_i z_i.$$

$$\tag{10.7}$$

Fig. 10.3

With a *homogeneous body*, to which we will henceforth limit ourselves, we have

$$W = \int_V \gamma \, dV = \gamma \int_V dV = \gamma V.$$

Since γ can also be taken outside the integration sign in (10.4) and then cancelled, (10.4) is replaced by

$$V r_s = \int_V r \, dV, \tag{10.8}$$

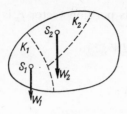

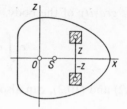

Fig. 10.4　　　　　　　　　　　　Fig. 10.5

and in place of (10.5) we have

$$V x_s = \int_V x \, dV, \qquad V y_s = \int_V y \, dV, \qquad V z_s = \int_V z \, dV. \qquad (10.9)$$

Hence it follows that congruent homogeneous bodies have congruently situated centers of gravity.

Geometric bodies have no weight and therefore have no center of gravity in the strict sense of the word. However, it is quite customary to speak of the *centroid* of these geometric conceptions, meaning by the term the center of gravity of the body if it were occupied by a homogeneous material.

If the homogeneous body in Fig. 10.5 has a plane of symmetry, this can be taken as the x,y-plane. Since the contributions to the third integral in (10.9) cancel each other, $z_s = 0$. The center of gravity of a homogeneous body thus lies in every one of its planes of symmetry.

For a homogeneous cuboid (Fig. 10.6), the center of gravity lies in each middle plane and thus in the center of the cuboid. For a body of revolution (Fig. 10.7), it lies in every plane through the axis of rotation and hence in the latter itself.

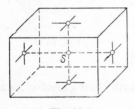

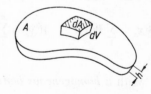

Fig. 10.6　　　　　　　　Fig. 10.7　　　　　　　　Fig. 10.8

If a homogeneous body (such as a sheet) has the form of a shell of constant thickness h and surface area A (Fig. 10.8), it can be treated as a *surface distribution of mass*. The smaller h is compared with the other dimensions, the better is the approximation. Since the volume element $dV = h \, dA$ can be expressed in terms of the element of surface dA, and on substituting into (10.8) the term h

cancels out, the centroid is given by

$$A r_s = \int_F r \, dA, \tag{10.10}$$

and the coordinates of S are given by the components of the position vector.

Correspondingly (Fig. 10.9), a long thin body (like a wire) with constant cross section A, arc element ds, and length l can be idealized as a *lineal distribution of mass*. Substitution of $dV = A \, ds$ reduces (10.8) to

$$l r_s = \int_0^l r \, ds. \tag{10.11}$$

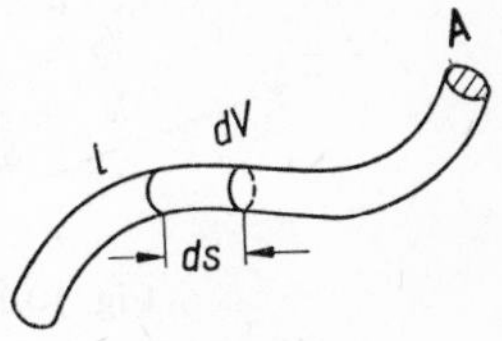

Fig. 10.9

A homogeneous wire of constant cross section and length l is bent as shown in Fig. 10.10 into a right angle with arms of lengths l_1 and l_2. By virtue of symmetry, the centers of gravity of each of the arms must be located at their centers; then the center of gravity of the complete body lies on the join $S_1 S_2$. Since the second condition in (10.6) here reduces to

$$l r_s = l_1 r_1 + l_2 r_2,$$

the coordinates are given by

$$(l_1 + l_2) x_s = \frac{l_1^2}{2}, \qquad (l_1 + l_2) y_s = \frac{l_2^2}{2}.$$

If a homogeneous triangle with altitude h (Fig. 10.11) is divided into elementary strips parallel to the base, these can be regarded as bars of material with centers of gravity in the middle. If the elementary weights are concentrated in these centers, we obtain a distribution of force along the median on the base. This must contain the center of gravity of the body. Accordingly, the center of gravity of the triangle lies in the intersection of the three medians and is thus at a height $h/3$ above the base.

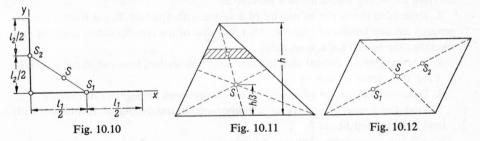

Fig. 10.10   Fig. 10.11   Fig. 10.12

A homogeneous parallelogram (Fig. 10.12) can be divided by a diagonal into two triangles. For these, the second diagonal is a median. It contains the centers of gravity of both parts and thus that of the whole body, which is therefore located at the intersection of the diagonals.

If a homogeneous tetrahedron with altitude h (Fig. 10.13) is divided into elementary laminae parallel to the base, we obtain triangles of mass with centers of gravity lying along the join of the apex O to the center of gravity S_0 of the base triangle.

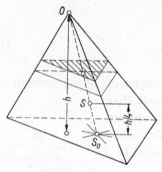

Fig. 10.13

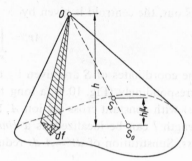

Fig. 10.14

The center of gravity of the whole body is thus located in the intersection of the four transversals, being at a height $h/4$ above the base.

If a homogeneous cone (Fig. 10.14) is similarly subdivided into elementary laminae, it turns out as in the last example that the center of gravity is situated on the join of the apex to the center of gravity S_0 of the base figure. On the other hand, by subdivision into elementary tetrahedra, it follows that it is at a height $h/4$ above the base.

The examples treated here were chosen so that the volume integrals occurring in the formulas for the center of gravity did not have to be calculated. For the evaluation of such integrals (for instance, in connection with the following exercises) the reader should refer to the literature on the integral calculus. Often the calculations can also be simplified by using the theorems of Pappus (Guldin's rules).

Exercises

1. Determine the center of gravity of a homogeneous circular arc of radius r and aperture 2α. Apply the result to a semicircle.

2. Determine the center of gravity of a sector with aperture 2α cut from a homogeneous circular lamina of radius r. Also find that of the corresponding segment and specialize the results for a semicircle.

3. A homogeneous conical shell has circular cross section, base radius r, and height h. Find the center of gravity.

4. Determine the center of gravity of a homogeneous hemisphere of radius r.

5. Find the center of gravity of a homogeneous paraboloid of revolution with base radius r and height h.

6. A thin homogeneous plate (i.e., a lamina) has the form of a quadrant of an ellipse with the sides as shown in Fig. 10.15. Determine its center of gravity. Also find the volume of the figure of revolution formed by rotating it about the side a. Finally determine the tensions in the cables supporting the plate at the corners as shown.

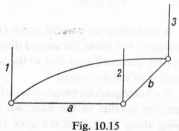

Fig. 10.15

11. Friction

Until now we assumed that bodies in contact were completely smooth so that the reactions consist of normal forces only. However, these surfaces are actually rough to a certain degree. The contact forces $R_{12} = -R_{21}$ are then in general inclined at an angle φ to the contact normal (Fig. 11.1) and can thus be resolved into *normal forces* $N_{12} = -N_{21}$ and *friction forces* $F_{12} = -F_{21}$.

If, for example, a particle rests on an inclined plane (Fig. 11.2), it will remain at rest so long as the angle of inclination φ is sufficiently small. The only two external forces acting are the weight W and the contact force R. When the particle is at rest, these two forces must be in equilibrium. Thus the force R must also have a vertical line of action inclined at an angle φ to the contact normal and can be resolved into the components N and F. Experiment shows that there is a threshold angle φ_0 such that the particle remains at rest on the inclined plane when $\varphi \leq \varphi_0$, the contact force R setting itself automatically so that it remains in equilibrium with W. When $\varphi > \varphi_0$, it is found that the particle slides down the plane. The value of φ_0 depends on the materials of which the "particle" and the inclined plane consist and on the state or nature of both surfaces.

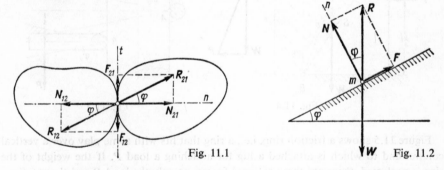

Fig. 11.1   Fig. 11.2

If these results are generalized to the contact of two arbitrary bodies (Fig. 11.1) maintaining contact with each other without slipping (they could be rolling with respect to each other), we can state them thus: the contact forces appearing at the place of contact can be inclined to the contact normal at an angle

$$\varphi \leq \varphi_0 . \tag{11.1}$$

Within the limits given by (11.1), they are free to adjust themselves as required by the conditions of equilibrium (or of motion) for both bodies. However, as soon as these conditions demand an angle φ not satisfying the inequality (11.1), the bodies begin to slide on each other. The inequality (11.1) is called the *condition of static friction* and the angle $\varphi_0 < \pi/2$ which depends on the materials and the nature of the surfaces, is called the *angle of (static) friction.*

The condition of static friction can be interpreted intuitively by the so-called *cone of static friction* (Fig. 11.3), which has apex at the contact point, axis along the contact normal, and apex angle φ_0. If the contact force lies within or on its surface, the two bodies adhere to each other; otherwise they slide.

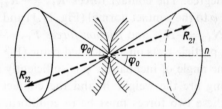

Fig. 11.3

The cube in Fig. 11.4 is subjected to the weight W and the load P. The reaction R is obtained from the force diagram; its line of action s intersects the horizontal support at the point B. Since this is situated inside the base, the body does not tip. Moreover, since s is within the friction cone drawn through B, the cube remains at rest on the support.

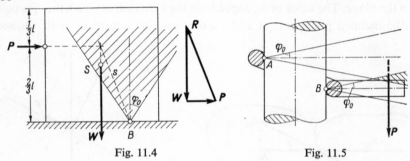

Fig. 11.4

Fig. 11.5

Figure 11.5 shows a friction ring, i.e., a ring that fits with some play over a vertical column and to which is attached a lug for attaching a load P. If the weight of the ring is neglected, there are three external forces, namely the load P and the reactions at the contact points A and B. For equilibrium, they must be concurrent. Since the reactions must lie in or on the appropriate friction cones, their intersection must lie in or on the surface of the region common to the two cones. Thus, the ring grips and does not slip only when the load P is applied far enough away so that its line of action passes through this region. Incidentally, the problem is statically indeterminate, since the reactions cannot be determined uniquely.

The angle φ_0 and also the *coefficient of static friction*

$$\mu_0 = \tan \varphi_0 \qquad (11.2)$$

are material and surface constants.

The coefficient of static friction is dimensionless. For steel on steel with well-finished surfaces, for instance, we have $\mu_0 = 0.15$.

When only the reactions N and $\boldsymbol{F}$ on one body are considered, (11.2) can be used to put the friction condition (11.1) in the form

$$|F| \leq \mu_0 |N|. \tag{11.3}$$

This form is especially suitable for the analytic treatment.

The loading of the cube in Fig. 11.4 is the same as that shown in Fig. 9.12, and in Section 9 the reactions were found to be $N = W$ and $F = P$. Thus the cube will remain at rest on the horizontal support so long as $|P| \leq \mu_0 W$.

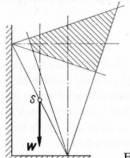

Fig. 11.6

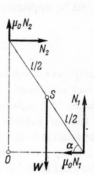

Fig. 11.7

In the last example and in many similar ones, the direction of the static friction force can be given in advance. In such cases, the friction condition can be written down in the form $F \leq \mu_0 N$. However, this direction is often not known *a priori* and, since the equilibrium conditions can yield a negative value for the (algebraic) magnitude of F, it is to be recommended that the condition should be applied in the form (11.3) or at least in the form

$$|F| \leq \mu_0 N. \tag{11.4}$$

Figure 11.6 shows a homogeneous, prismatic bar loaded by its own weight and resting against a rough floor and wall with the same coefficient of static friction. If it is to remain at rest, it must be placed with sufficient slope, because the intersection of the line of action of the weight W with those of the two reactions must lie inside the region common to the two cones of friction. The smallest angle of inclination for which the bar still rests is best determined analytically. Figure 11.7 shows the limiting position in which the friction forces F_1 and F_2 attain their maximum values $\mu_0 N_1$ and $\mu_0 N_2$. The equilibrium conditions are

$$N_2 - \mu_0 N_1 = 0, \qquad N_1 + \mu_0 N_2 - W = 0,$$

$$N_1 l \cos \alpha - W \frac{l}{2} \cos \alpha - N_2 l \sin \alpha = 0,$$

and, solved for the unknowns N_1, N_2, α, yield

$$N_1 = \frac{W}{1 + \mu_0^2}, \qquad N_2 = \frac{\mu_0 W}{1 + \mu_0^2}, \qquad \tan \alpha = \frac{1 - \mu_0^2}{2\mu_0}.$$

In Section 1 it was shown that when a bearing is free of friction, the line of action of the bearing force passes through the center. If, however, the pin and journal are rough and contact occurs at the point B (Fig. 11.8), the bearing force must lie within the cone of friction constructed at B, which in this case is better thought of as a sectoral region. Since B can lie anywhere on the circumference of the bearing, sectors on all points of the circumference must be considered. They envelop the so-called *circle of friction* of radius $\varrho = r_l \sin \varphi_0$, where r_l is the radius of the bearing. Taking account of the fact that φ_0 is always small, this can be approximated by $\varrho = r_l \tan \varphi_0$. Using (11.2), we finally have

$$\varrho = \mu_0 r_l. \tag{11.5}$$

Figure 11.9 shows a weightless unloaded *hinged bar*. When the hinges are free of friction, the two self-equilibrating hinge forces must be coaxial with the bar. However, when friction is taken into consideration, their common line of action has only to pass through the friction circles of the two hinges. Thus it lies in the shaded region between the common tangents to these circles. Consideration of this fact in trusses leads to the so-called *subsidiary forces* which are to be superposed on the forces in the members found for the ideal truss in Section 5.

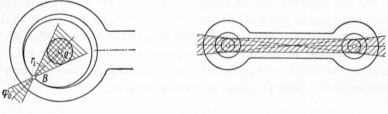

Fig. 11.8   Fig. 11.9

At the beginning of this section it was remarked that two bodies can remain in contact without slipping even when at least one of them is in motion. It is then said that the two bodies *roll* on each other.

The tires of an automobile roll on the road surface so long as they are not made to skid, for instance as a result of too abrupt braking.

It has already been emphasized on several occasions that the external forces on a moving body can be in equilibrium. Thus, it will be shown in kinetics that in the case of uniform rolling of a circular disk on a horizontal plane, for example, all the external forces are in equilibrium. In such cases, the equilibrium conditions can be formulated as with a body at rest.

Figure 11.10 shows the ith wheel pair of a locomotive which is moving uniformly to the right. In the bearing, again assumed frictionless, there acts a force with the two components Z_i and W_i. Here W_i represents the part of the weight of the loco-motive taken up by the ith wheel pair and the reaction Z_i is the contribution of the wheel pair to the total tractive force. More-over, in B there is the normal force N_i and the friction force F_i, and finally from the motor there is the propulsive couple of moment M_i if the axle happens to be a *driving* and not a *free axle*. The equilibrium conditions yield

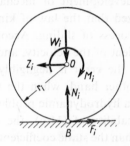

$$F_i = Z_i, \qquad N_i = W_i, \qquad M_i = r_i Z_i,$$

and the friction conditions $F_i \leq \mu_0 N_i$ lead to

$$Z_i \leq \mu_0 W_i.$$

Fig. 11.10

For free axles we have $M_i = 0$. It thus follows from the third equilibrium condition that they contribute nothing to the tractive force. With a driving axle, the contribution of the friction force (and hence also the driving moment M_i) is limited by the coefficient of static friction and the fractional weight W_i. The sum of these weights for the driving axles only,

$$W' = \sum{}' W_i,$$

is the so-called *adhesion* (weight) and represents that part of the total weight carried by the driving axles. Then, for the total traction we have

$$Z = \sum_1^n Z_i \leq \mu_0 W'.$$

In order to make it large, the friction and adhesion must be kept large. It is the practically attainable limit that determines the moments M_i and thus the power of the motors that are to be installed.

This example shows that the static friction forces promote not only braking but also motion. In fact, nearly all vehicles are propelled by means of friction forces.

If the conditions of equilibrium (or the equations of motion) demand re-actions that do not satisfy the conditions of static friction, *slipping* will occur. For simplicity's sake, let us assume that one of the two contacting bodies is at rest. While slipping is taking place, there will act on the moving body at the point of contact a friction force F, with direction against the motion. Its magni-tude was given in terms of a new material and surface constant μ_1 by Coulomb (1736–1806) and Morin (1795–1880) in the form

$$|F| = \mu_1 |N|. \tag{11.6}$$

The relation (11.6) together with the statement of the direction of F is called the *law of kinetic, or sliding, friction* and μ_1 is the *coefficient of kinetic, or sliding, friction*.

The laws of static and kinetic friction will be treated as axioms for the further development of mechanics. However, it must at the same time be emphasized that the law of kinetic friction is only an approximation for the actual process of sliding. According to it, the friction force during sliding is independent of the velocity, and that is only approximately the case. With dry surfaces, the error is negligibly small; in this case we speak of *dry friction*. On the other hand, when the surfaces are lubricated, we have *fluid friction*, which is a hydrodynamic problem strongly dependent on velocity. In the range of applicability of (11.6), the coefficient of kinetic friction μ_1 is somewhat smaller than the static coefficient μ_0; a larger force is required to initiate slipping than that required to maintain uniform sliding. In practice, however, it is often good enough to make the approximation $\mu_1 = \mu_0$.

If N and F are combined into a single contact force R inclined at an angle φ to the contact normal, then (11.6) can also be put in the form

$$\varphi = \varphi_1 \quad \text{where} \quad \tan \varphi_1 = \mu_1 . \tag{11.7}$$

The inclination φ_1 is called the *angle of kinetic friction*. Thus the reaction during sliding lies in the surface of a *cone of friction* having a semi aperture φ_1.

Figure 11.11 shows a *radial bearing* in which a shaft rotates uniformly. If the pin and journal come into contact at B, a reaction Z acts here, which, because of the friction, will be inclined at an angle φ_1 to the radius. If it is reduced at the center of the bearing, we have the displaced force Z, the *bearing force*, and the auxiliary couple of moment M_f that is called the *friction moment of the bearing* and has the value

$$M_f = Z r_l \sin \varphi_1 ,$$

or, approximately,

$$M_f = \mu_1 r_l Z . \tag{11.8}$$

The reactions in a nonideal rotating bearing are thus the bearing force of unknown direction passing through the axis and the friction moment (11.8).

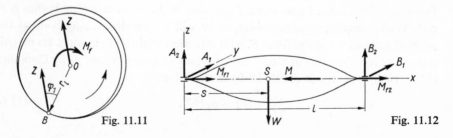

Fig. 11.11   Fig. 11.12

If a uniformly rotating shaft with center of gravity S on the horizontal axis of rotation is loaded by its own weight W and is set in axial bearings at both ends (Fig. 11.12), then the reactions here are bearing forces perpendicular to the axis and axial friction moments. The latter retard the motion; for uniform rotation, the shaft must be driven with a constant moment M. By formulating the five nontrivial equilibrium conditions, we obtain

$$A_1 + B_1 = 0, \qquad A_2 + B_2 - W = 0,$$

$$M_{f1} + M_{f2} - M = 0, \qquad lB_1 = 0, \qquad -lB_2 + sW = 0,$$

or

$$A_1 = B_1 = 0, \qquad A_2 = \left(1 - \frac{s}{l}\right) W, \qquad B_2 = \frac{s}{l} W,$$

and, since by (11.8)

$$M_{f1} = \mu_1 r_\iota A_2 \quad \text{and} \quad M_{f2} = \mu_1 r_\iota B_2,$$

we finally arrive at

$$M = \mu_1 r_\iota W.$$

Since the bearing forces are vertical, the shaft rides up the sides of the bearings against the rotation, as a glance at Fig. 11.11 shows.

In a thrust bearing also, a friction moment accompanies the bearing force. Figure 11.13 shows such a bearing in plan view with a surface element $dA = r \, dr \, d\vartheta$. This element is subjected to an elementary normal force dN and a friction force $dF = \mu_1 \, dN$ in the azimuthal direction. If it is assumed that the pin sits uniformly in the bearing, the forces dN reduce to a resultant *normal force* N along the axis, and we have

$$dN = \frac{N}{\pi r_\iota^2} r \, dr \, d\vartheta; \quad \text{therefore} \quad dF = \mu_1 \frac{N}{\pi r_\iota^2} r \, dr \, d\vartheta.$$

When reduced at the center of the bearing, the friction forces yield a couple of moment

$$M_f = \int_f r \, dF = \mu_1 \frac{N}{\pi r_\iota^2} \int_0^{2\pi} d\vartheta \int_0^{r_\iota} r^2 \, dr,$$

namely, the *bearing friction moment*

$$M_f = \tfrac{2}{3} \mu_1 r_\iota N. \tag{11.9}$$

Thus for uniform seating, the reactions to be introduced are the normal force N in the axis and the bearing friction moment (11.9).

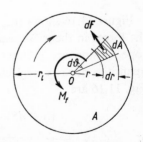

Fig. 11.13

If a uniformly rotating shaft with center of gravity S on the vertical axis of rotation is loaded by its own weight W and is supported by axial and thrust bearings below and by an axial bearing above, then the reactions shown in Fig. 11.14 come into consideration. Once more the uniform rotation must be sustained by a driving couple of moment M. The equilibrium conditions yield

$$A_1 = B_1 = A_2 = B_2 = 0,$$

$$N = W,$$

$$M = M_f,$$

and because of (11.9)

$$M = \frac{2}{3}\mu_1 r_1 W.$$

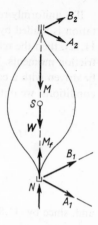

Fig. 11.14

As a further application of the law of kinetic friction we mention *rope friction*. If a rope is placed over a rotating drum (Fig. 11.15) and it is strained by the tensions S_1 and S_2 so that it remains at rest, the drum exerts not only a normal force dN on every element $ds = r\,d\vartheta$ of the rope, but also a friction force dF. In order that the rope is prevented from being carried along by the drum, it is necessary that the rope tension S_2 on the "driving side" should be greater than S_1 on the "slack side."

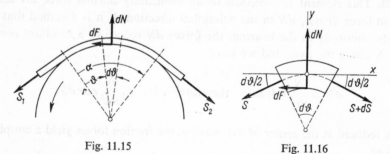

Fig. 11.15   Fig. 11.16

Figure 11.16 shows the forces on an element of rope; here S and $S+dS$ are the forces in the cross sections. Since the angle $d\vartheta$ and the increase dS of the rope tension are infinitesimal, terms of second and higher order in these quantities must be neglected and the component conditions along the axes of Fig. 11.16 are

$$(S + dS) - S - dF = 0, \qquad dN - 2S\frac{d\vartheta}{2} = 0$$

or

$$dF = dS, \qquad dN = S\,d\vartheta.$$

Substitution into the law of kinetic friction (11.6) leads to the differential equation

$$dS = \mu_1 S \, d\vartheta$$

for the rope tension. By integrating this from the radius $\vartheta = 0$ to ϑ, the cable tension is obtained as an exponential function

$$S = S_1 \exp(\mu_1 \vartheta) \tag{11.10}$$

of the angle ϑ. When ϑ is set equal to the so-called *angle of contact* α, the relation

$$S_2 = S_1 \exp(\mu_1 \alpha) \tag{11.11}$$

is obtained between the two extreme tensions. It only determines the ratio between S_1 and S_2; one of the two can still be prescribed at will. Since μ_1 and α are positive, $S_2 > S_1$; moreover, the ratio S_2/S_1 increases exponentially, i.e., very markedly, with increasing angle of contact.

If the tension S_2 is chosen too small, so that

$$S_2 < S_1 \exp(\mu_1 \alpha), \tag{11.12}$$

the cable will be pulled along by the drum.

It is well known that ships are made fast to the shore by means of a rope wrapped several times around a bollard. Since here the angle of contact is very large, a small force S_1, supplied by the friction of the free end of the rope on the ground, suffices to produce a large force S_2 at the other end.

Figure 11.17 shows a *drum brake* which is operated by the force K on the brake lever so that the load Q descends uniformly. If the system is decomposed into the drum with the weight Q hanging from it on the one hand and the brake lever on the other, and it is assumed that the bearing is free of friction, then the two parts are subjected to the forces shown in the figure. The moment conditions for each body, formulated relative to the pivots O_1 and O_2, are

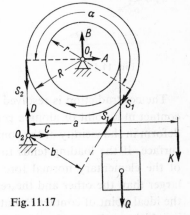

$$(S_2 - S_1) R - Qr = 0 \, ,$$

$$S_1 b - Ka = 0 \, .$$

Fig. 11.17

Introduction of the relation (11.11) and solution for K leads to the braking force

$$K = \frac{b}{a} \frac{r}{R} \frac{Q}{\exp(\mu_1 \alpha) - 1} \, .$$

Here it has been assumed that the slack side is pulled by the brake lever. Since the tension on this side is smaller, braking is achieved with a smaller braking force.

The final form of friction to be discussed is the so-called *rolling friction* that appears with rolling bodies and, in particular, with wheels. The circular disk in Fig. 11.18 has center of gravity at O and stands on a plane inclined at an angle α to the horizontal. It is subjected to its own weight W, a normal force, and a friction force. The equilibrium conditions yield

$$F = W \sin \alpha ,$$
$$N = W \cos \alpha , \qquad\qquad (11.13)$$
$$Wr \sin \alpha = 0 .$$

According to the last condition, the disk cannot remain at rest on the inclined plane. That, however, is contrary to the observed fact that is does remain at rest for sufficiently small angles of inclination α and that it first begins to roll when a certain threshold angle has been attained. Hence it is clear that there is a resistance preventing rolling. This cannot be the static friction force because that has already been taken into consideration in Fig. 11.18.

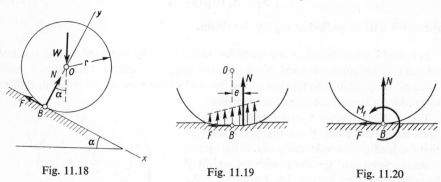

Fig. 11.18   Fig. 11.19   Fig. 11.20

The contradiction is resolved when it is observed that rolling bodies do not contact in a point or along a generator. In reality the bodies are not rigid, but deform in the vicinity of the contact region and are thus in contact over a small surface. If the loading tends to cause rolling away to the right, the intensity of the elementary normal forces (Fig. 11.19) on this side will be somewhat larger than the other and the resulting normal force no longer passes through the ideal point of contact B, but is displaced a small distance e in the direction in which motion tends to take place. An effect like this has already been encountered in the case of the cube in Fig. 9.12.

If the displaced normal force is reduced at B (Fig. 11.20), we obtain, together with the reactions N and F, a couple of moment

$$M_f = eN . \qquad\qquad (11.14)$$

This represents the resistance to rolling and is called the *moment* of *rolling resistance*; it appears as a further resistance in addition to the static friction force. In this connection we have a choice between introducing this moment explicitly as in Fig. 11.20 or representing it by the displacement e of the normal pressure as in Fig. 11.19.

If the forces in Fig. 11.18 are augmented by the rolling moment (Fig. 11.21), only the third equilibrium condition (11.13) is altered. It becomes

$$Wr \sin\alpha - M_f = 0, \tag{11.15}$$

and the disagreement with observation is removed. Now experiment shows that the disk remains at rest only for sufficiently small angles of inclination α. That agrees, of course, with the fact that the eccentricity e of the normal force cannot increase without limit, but must satisfy the inequality

$$|e| \leq \mu_2. \tag{11.16}$$

It is called the *inequality of rolling resistance*, and the constant μ_2 is called the *length of rolling resistance* (and sometimes the coefficient of rolling friction).

In contrast to μ_0 and μ_1, μ_2 has the dimension of length $[L]$; it is not a pure material constant but depends also on the curvature of the two contacting bodies.

If (11.14) is substituted into (11.16), the inequality of rolling resistance assumes the form

$$|M_f| \leq \mu_2 N. \tag{11.17}$$

The analogy between (11.17) and (11.14) on the one hand and (11.16) and (11.1) on the other should be noted.

Finally, in the case of rolling, the conditions (11.16) and (11.17) are to be replaced by the *equations of rolling resistance*,

$$|e| = \mu_2,$$
$$|M_f| = \mu_2 N, \tag{11.18}$$

which are analogous to (11.7) and (11.6), respectively, and are usually formulated with the same length of rolling resistance μ_2 as in equations (11.16) and (11.17).

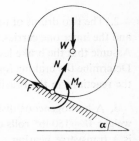

For the disk in Fig. 11.21, the friction condition (11.4), by (11.13), demands that

$$\tan\alpha \leq \mu_0.$$

Fig. 11.21

The inequality of rolling resistance (11.17), with (11.13) and (11.15), yields

$$\tan \alpha \leq \frac{\mu_2}{r}.$$

So long as both conditions are fulfilled, the disk remains at rest. If the inclination of the plane is gradually increased, motion finally begins, and, indeed, the disk will roll or slip according as the second or the first inequality is first violated.

Exercises

1. Figure 11.22 shows a homogeneous circular cylinder of weight $W=50$ lb*, height $h=15$ in, and radius $r=10$ in. It rests on the plane inclined at an angle $\alpha=30°$ to the horizontal, and the force K parallel to the plane is applied half-way up the cylinder opposite the center of gravity S. The coefficient of static friction is $\mu_0=0.2$. Will the cylinder remain at rest when $K=0$? In what interval must K lie in order to prevent slipping? If the cylinder is not to tip over, between what values must K be held? What conditions must be satisfied by r and h if gradual variation of α, either increasing or decreasing, should produce slipping before the body tips over?

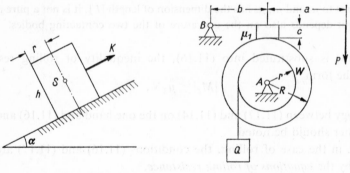

Fig. 11.22   Fig. 11.23

2. The two drums of total weight W in Fig. 11.23 are fixed to a frictionless bearing, and the inner one carries the load Q while the outer one is acted on by a brake-block. Assume that the brake lever has negligible weight and that the hinge B is frictionless. Determine the braking force P that allows the load Q to fall uniformly. Also determine the reactions in the bearings A and B.

3. A homogeneous disk of constant thickness (Fig. 11.24) of radius $r=10$ in. and weight $W=150$ lb* rolls on a rough horizontal plane. At the center of the disk there is a transverse bearing of radius $r_1=1$ in. supporting a homogeneous prismatic rod of weight W and length $3r$. Between the disk and the horizontal plane, we have a coefficient of static friction $\mu_0<0.2$ and of rolling resistance $\mu_2=0.1$ in. The coefficient

of kinetic friction in the bearing is $\mu_1 = 0.2$. Determine the horizontal force P that must be applied to the hub in order to cause the system to roll to the right with constant velocity. Also find the inclination α of the bar during this motion. What is the condition that the disk does not slip?

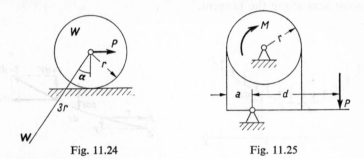

Fig. 11.24   Fig. 11.25

4. A couple of moment M is applied to a pulley (Fig. 11.25) over which runs a brake band that is tensioned by the force P applied to the brake lever. The friction in both bearings as well as the weights of the bodies involved are negligibly small; μ_1 is the coefficient of kinetic friction between brake band and pulley. Determine the braking force P necessary for uniform rotation, as well as all reactions. Is it possible with such a so-called *differential brake* to select the ratio a/r arbitrarily in the interval $0 < a/r < 1$?

12. Statics of Cables

We have already defined a cable in Section 3. It is understood to be a body whose transverse dimensions are so small in comparison with the length that it may be treated as one-dimensional, of invariable length, but perfectly flexible.

As has been pointed out in Section 5, when a body is at rest, the external forces alone must be in equilibrium, i.e., they must be self-equilibrating. This holds in particular for each component cut out of the body, provided that the section forces are introduced as external forces, and it thus also applies for each section of a cable.

When just one force is applied to each end of a light cable, it follows from Section 3 that it assumes the form of a straight line segment coaxial with the common line of action of the end forces. If it is loaded by a two-dimensional system of forces, then, in the case of equilibrium, it will have the form of a polygon. As was shown in Section 4, by means of Fig. 4.2, this polygon can be interpreted as the funicular polygon for the given loads. The cable force at every section and also at the ends always has the direction of the cable segment in question.

If the number of loads is allowed to increase without limit and at the same time their magnitudes and spacing tend to zero, this limit process leads to a continuously loaded cable. In the limiting case it has the form of a curve, which exhibits corners only where concentrated forces are acting, and the cable tension at each point acts along the tangent.

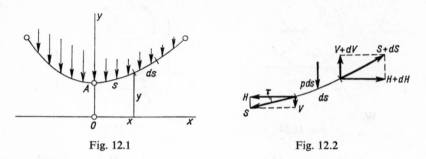

Fig. 12.1   Fig. 12.2

We will limit ourselves to the case of parallel loading as is, for instance, provided by the weight of the cable itself, and it will be assumed that these forces are vertical. The cable will be referred to the coordinate system given in Fig. 12.1 with the y-axis passing through the lowest point A. If then x, y are the coordinates and s the arc length measured from A of an arbitrary section, then the loading is known if the load per unit length, namely the so-called *specific loading* $p(s)$, is prescribed. If, then, an element of cable of length ds is cut out (Fig. 12.2), this is subjected not only to the load $p(s)\,ds$ but also to the tangential section forces, which we resolve into the components H, V and $H+dH, V+dV$. Then the component conditions yield

$$dH = 0, \qquad dV = p\,ds. \tag{12.1}$$

From this it first follows that the horizontal component of the cable tension, the so-called *horizontal tension*, is constant. Secondly, for the angle of inclination τ of an element of the cable, which according to Fig. 12.2 is determined by

$$\tan \tau = \frac{V}{H}, \tag{12.2}$$

we obtain the differential equation

$$d \tan \tau = \frac{dV}{H} = \frac{p}{H}\,ds. \tag{12.3}$$

Provided that H and $p(s)$ are given, (12.3) can be integrated to give the equilibrium shape of the cable.

When p is constant (the cable, e.g., being homogeneous, of uniform cross section, and loaded by its own weight), we can introduce the simplified expression

$$\frac{H}{p} = a, \tag{12.4}$$

and write (12.3) in the form

$$dy' = \frac{1}{a}\sqrt{1 + y'^2}\,dx \tag{12.5}$$

by changing to cartesian coordinates. If this is put in the form

$$\frac{dy'}{\sqrt{1 + y'^2}} = \frac{dx}{a},$$

it is seen that the relation

$$\text{arsinh } y' = \frac{x}{a} + c_1 \tag{12.6}$$

represents a first integral with the constant of integration c_1. This is determined by the boundary condition

$$y'(x = 0) = 0 \quad \text{to be} \quad c_1 = 0,$$

so that (12.6) becomes

$$y' = \sinh\frac{x}{a}. \tag{12.7}$$

Further integration yields

$$y = a\cosh\frac{x}{a} + c_2.$$

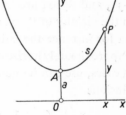

Fig. 12.3

Since the position of the x-axis was not prescribed, there is no boundary condition for c_2. On the other hand, it is possible to set $c_2 = 0$,

$$y = a\cosh\frac{x}{a} \tag{12.8}$$

thus fixing the position of the x-axis. Hence, the cable in equilibrium assumes the form of a *catenary* (Fig. 12.3) with the x-axis as directrix.

Making use of the simplification (12.4), it follows from (12.3) that $ds = a\,dy'$, and then the condition that both s and y' vanish at A leads to

$$s = ay'. \tag{12.9}$$

Thus, by (12.7), the arclength is given by

$$s = a\sinh\frac{x}{a}, \tag{12.10}$$

and then (12.8) and (12.10) lead to the relation

$$y^2 - s^2 = a^2.\tag{12.11}$$

Finally, by (12.4), (12.2), and (12.9), the cable tension S has the components

$$H = pa, \qquad V = Hy' = ps,\tag{12.12}$$

and hence, by virtue of (12.11), the magnitude

$$S = py.\tag{12.13}$$

From this it follows that if a cable (Fig. 12.4) is fixed at P_1 and rests on a small free-running roller at P_2, its free end will hang down till it meets the x-axis.

It should be noted that when a cable is suspended between two points P_1 and P_2, equation (12.8) is not sufficient for finding the equilibrium configuration because the parameter a and the position of the coordinate origin are not yet known. The problem is solved by writing out equations (12.8) and (12.10) for the points P_1 and P_2 and making use of the fact that the differences $x_2 - x_1$, $y_2 - y_1$, and $s_2 - s_1$ are known.

In the vicinity of the vertex A of the catenary, when for instance the cable is highly tensioned and approximately horizontal, we have $x/a \ll 1$. In such cases, use can be made of the power series expansions

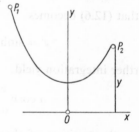

Fig. 12.4

$$y = a \cosh \frac{x}{a} = a\left(1 + \frac{1}{2!} \cdot \frac{x^2}{a^2} + \cdots\right),$$
$$s = a \sinh \frac{x}{a} = a\left(\frac{1}{1!} \cdot \frac{x}{a} + \frac{1}{3!} \cdot \frac{x^3}{a^3} + \cdots\right).\tag{12.14}$$

Retention of terms up to the third power inclusively leads to the approximations

$$y - a = \frac{x^2}{2a}, \qquad s = x + \frac{x^3}{6a^2},\tag{12.15}$$

which mean that to this accuracy, the equilibrium form is a parabola.

Exercises

1. A homogeneous cable of constant cross section and length $s_2 - s_1 = l$ is suspended between the points P_1 and P_2 with the abscissa difference $x_2 - x_1 = d$ and the difference of ordinates $y_2 - y_1 = h$. Show that its equilibrium form is given by (12.8), where the

parameter a and the position of the y-axis are given by the two relations

$$l^2 - h^2 = 4a^2 \sinh^2 \frac{d}{2a}, \qquad \frac{l+h}{l-h} = \exp\left(\frac{2x_1+d}{a}\right).$$

2. A tape rule hangs freely between two points P_1 and P_2 and has a sag f (Fig. 12.5). The actual distance between the two points is d. Show that the measured length l must be corrected by the expression

$$d = l - \frac{8f^2}{3l}$$

in order to obtain the distance d to the accuracy given by the relations (12.15).

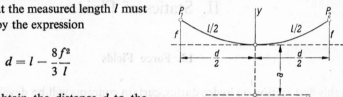

Fig. 12.5

II. Statics of Fluids

13. Force Fields

In this first section on hydrostatics, certain concepts will be developed that are important not only in this chapter but also in later ones. Therefore, more will be undertaken than would otherwise be necessary.

By a *force field* is understood a region in space in which a definite force is associated with every point at every instant of time (Fig. 13.1). This is given by the three scalar functions

$$X = X(x, y, z, t), \qquad Y = Y(x, y, z, t), \qquad Z = Z(x, y, z, t). \quad (13.1)$$

The association of the force with the points in space can be physical or only potential.

The specific weight within a body, considered as a vector, represents a physical force; an electric field, on the other hand, defines a potential force, namely the force that a specified charge would experience if it were placed at a particular point at a particular time.

The force field is only a special case of the more general *vector field*.

The position vectors of the points in an arbitrary spatial region relative to some fixed point also defines a vector field, while their magnitudes represent a *scalar field*.

If the force depends on time, as was assumed in (13.1), the field is called *nonstationary*. Henceforth we limit ourselves, as is proper in statics, to *stationary fields*:

$$X = X(x, y, z), \qquad Y = Y(x, y, z), \qquad Z = Z(x, y, z). \quad (13.2)$$

The elastic force that is applied to the particle m (Fig. 13.2) in the direction of the point O by means of the spring and cable is a (potential) force which is stationary when the extremity A of the spring is fixed. If, say, a prescribed oscillation were imparted to A, the force function would be nonstationary.

When the line of action of the force at each point of the field passes through a fixed *center*, we speak of a field of *central force* or simply a *central field*.

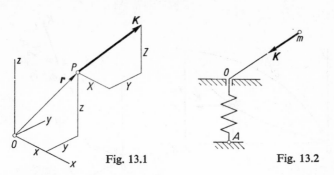

Fig. 13.1   Fig. 13.2

Figure 13.2 defines a central field with center O.

In a central field, the direction of the force is known at every point as soon as the center is given. According to the sense of the force, we talk of *repulsion* or *attraction*. It is customary to treat the magnitude of the force as an algebraic quantity and to take it to be positive when outward, i.e., for a repulsive force. Thus, with the notation in Fig. 13.1, we have the relation $X/K=x/r$ ..., and then the components of the central force are given by

$$X = K\frac{x}{r}, \qquad Y = K\frac{y}{r}, \qquad Z = K\frac{z}{r}. \tag{13.3}$$

Another special case arises when the forces in the field are parallel to a certain plane E and are independent of position along normals to this plane, i.e., when a coordinate system can be chosen so that

$$X = X(x, y), \qquad Y = Y(x, y), \tag{13.4}$$

and $Z=0$. Such cases are called *plane fields of force* and the plane E the *plane of force*.

The force field in Fig. 13.3, having the components

$$X = \lambda y, \qquad Y = Z = 0,$$

is a plane field with the x, y-plane as the plane of force.

If the point of application of the force K in Fig. 13.4 undergoes an infinitesimal displacement AA', this can be represented by the change in the position vector, i.e., by the *displacement vector* $dr = (dx, dy, dz)$. The *elementary work* done by the force K during this displacement is defined as the scalar product

$$dW = K\,dr \tag{13.5}$$

of the force and displacement vector. It can be written in the form

$$dW = |K| \cdot |dr| \cdot \cos\varphi, \tag{13.6}$$

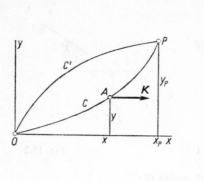

Fig. 13.3   Fig. 13.4

where φ is the angle between these vectors, or, in terms of the components, as

$$dW = X\,dx + Y\,dy + Z\,dz.$$ (13.7)

It is thus an algebraic quantity, positive, negative, or zero according as the angle included between K and dr is acute, obtuse, or right, respectively.

If the point of application A of the force K is displaced from P to Q along a curve C, the total displacement can be imagined as the result of an infinite sequence of elementary displacements dr along C. The *work* done by K in this finite displacement is understood to be the sum of the elementary amounts of work, namely the integral

$$W = \oint_P^Q K\,dr.$$ (13.8)

Work has the dimension $[FL]$ similar to that of a couple. The units are 1 ft lb*, 1 kg* m, 1 J, etc.

The integral (13.8) is called a *line integral* and consequently we say that work is the line integral of the force. In components, (13.8) is written

$$W = \oint_P^Q (X\,dx + Y\,dy + Z\,dz).$$ (13.9)

If the right-hand side is separated into three integrals, the two equations of the curve C can be used to express these in terms of ordinary integrals over x, y, and z, respectively, and then they can be evaluated. However, when the curve C is unknown this method is inapplicable, and it follows that the work between two points generally depends not only on these points but also on the path of integration.

With the plane field of force in Fig. 13.3, the amount of work between the origin O and the point P, by (13.9), is

$$W = \lambda \oint_0^P y \, dx.$$

Since the integral represents the area enclosed by the curve C, the x-axis, and the ordinate of point P, the amount of work is dependent of the displacement path and is different for the curves C and C', for instance. That the work vanishes along the broken path comprising the x-axis and the ordinate of P follows directly from the definition of elementary work and the special components of force in this example.

If the point of application A of the force K (Fig. 13.4) traverses the curve backward from Q to P, then at each step it is only the direction of dr, and hence the sign of the work, that is reversed.

If several fields of force $K_1, K_2, \ldots, K_n$ are prescribed in a given region, it follows from Section 2 that they can be reduced to a resultant

$$R = \sum_1^n K_i$$

at each point in the region. Also R defines a force field, and the amount of work it performs along an arbitrary curve is given by

$$W = \oint_P^Q R \, dr = \oint_P^Q \sum_1^n K_i \, dr = \sum_1^n \oint_P^Q K_i \, dr = \sum_1^n W_i, \qquad (13.10)$$

i.e., by the sum of the amounts of work done by each separate force.

In the case of a central force, the work (13.9), by (13.3), can be written in the form

$$W = \oint_P^Q \frac{K}{r}(x \, dx + y \, dy + z \, dz) = \oint_P^Q \frac{K}{r} d\left(\frac{r^2}{2}\right) = \oint_P^Q K \, dr.$$

When the magnitude K is an arbitrary function of the coordinates x, y, z, the integral on the right-hand side is dependent on the displacement path. However, if K is dependent only on the distance r from the center, i.e., it is of the form $K(r)$, the right-hand side becomes the ordinary integral

$$W = \int_{r_P}^{r_Q} K(r) \, dr, \qquad (13.11)$$

and the work is therefore independent of the displacement path. Force fields for which the work done between two points depends only on these and not on the displacement paths are called *conservative force fields*. They are of particular importance in mechanics. Because of this, we will henceforth limit ourselves to conservative fields.

By definition, the work done in a conservative field of force along the arcs C_1 and C_2 joining the two arbitrary points P_1 and P_2 in Fig. 13.5 are equal. Since reversal of the direction of displacement along one of the two arcs changes the sign of the corresponding work, the work on every closed path is zero. It is obvious that this argument can be inverted so that a conservative force can also be defined by the condition

$$\oint \boldsymbol{K}\, d\boldsymbol{r} = 0, \tag{13.12}$$

i.e., by the vanishing if its *contour integral* over every closed path.

If an arbitrary point in a conservative field (Fig. 13.6) is selected as a fixed reference point O, such as making it the origin of a system of coordinates, then the work done by the force between a free point P and O is a unique function

$$W = V(x, y, z) \tag{13.13}$$

of the coordinates of the point P alone. It is called the *potential* or the *potential energy* at point P. This notation indicates that it is concerned with the capacity to do work.

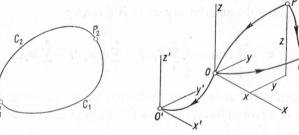

Fig. 13.5   Fig. 13.6

The potential is a scalar quantity and connects the given vector field represented by the force with a *scalar field* having the value zero at the origin.

Other examples of scalar fields are defined by the distance from a fixed point or by the temperature distribution in an arbitrary region; the second of these fields can be nonstationary.

When the reference point is changed from O to O', the potential at point P is altered. Since we can always pass to O' via O, the new value of the potential, with an obvious notation, is

$$V'(P) = V(P) + V'(O).$$

Since $V'(O)$ is a constant, a change in the reference point entails a change of the whole potential field by a constant amount. Hence the potential of a given force field is determined only up to an additive constant; the latter is fixed by the choice of a reference point, and this matter of stipulating the constant is called *normalizing* the potential.

The work of the conservative force between two arbitrary points P and Q can be determined by means of a path via O, and is found to be

$$W = V(P) - V(Q), \qquad (13.14)$$

i.e., the decrease in the potential between the two points. Since any additive constant on the right-hand side cancels out, the work is, as is to be expected, independent of the normalization of the potential, which can hence be carried out according to practical considerations.

If the magnitude of a central force depends only on the distance from the center, the work between two arbitrary points is given by (13.11). By means of the indefinite integral

$$V(r) = - \int K(r)\,dr, \qquad (13.15)$$

it can be written as

$$W = V(r_P) - V(r_Q). \qquad (13.16)$$

In this case, therefore, (13.15) represents the (not yet normalized) potential.

It will be shown in Section 30 that the spring force acting on the particle m (Fig. 13.2) is proportional to the extension of the spring and can thus be set equal to $K(r) = -cr$, when the length of the cable is suitably chosen. Its potential is calculated by (13.15) to be

$$V(r) = \frac{c}{2}r^2 + c',$$

and, when the constant c' is taken to be zero, it is normalized so that it vanishes at the center O. The work done between two points P and Q, by (13.16), is

$$W = \frac{c}{2}(r_P^2 - r_Q^2).$$

A particle m (Fig. 13.7) is attracted by another particle M with a force inversely proportional to the square of the distance. Since

$$K(r) = -\frac{\mu}{r^2},$$

the potential is

$$V(r) = -\frac{\mu}{r} + c.$$

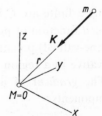

Fig. 13.7

If it is normalized by setting $c = 0$, it vanishes at infinity and tends to $-\infty$ in the vicinity of M. Such a force also occurs between two opposite electric charges.

If several conservative fields of force with the potentials $V_1, V_2, \ldots, V_n$ act in a region, the resultant is also conservative. The amount of work done by it is

$$W = \sum_1^n W_i = \sum_1^n [V_i(P) - V_i(Q)] = \sum_1^n V_i(P) - \sum_1^n V_i(Q),$$

and hence its potential is

$$V = \sum_1^n V_i.$$

If a particle m is attracted to the centers M_i with forces $K_i = -\mu_i/r_i^2$, the resultant has the potential

$$V = -\sum_1^n \frac{\mu_i}{r_i},$$

which again vanishes at infinity.

By means of the potential, the elementary work done by the conservative force K in the displacement dr can be written in the form

$$dW = -dV = -\frac{\partial V}{\partial x} dx - \frac{\partial V}{\partial y} dy - \frac{\partial V}{\partial z} dz. \qquad (13.17)$$

Since (13.7) and (13.17) are valid for arbitrary displacements dr, the coefficients of the right-hand sides must agree. Hence it follows that

$$X = -\frac{\partial V}{\partial x}, \qquad Y = -\frac{\partial V}{\partial y}, \qquad Z = -\frac{\partial V}{\partial z}. \qquad (13.18)$$

Consequently the components of the force in a conservative field can be represented as the negative partial derivatives of the potential. This means that we can speak of a *potential field*.

If, conversely, we start with a potential field, i.e., with a field of force the components of which are derived from a potential according to (13.18), then (13.7) leads to (13.17) and the work

$$W = \oint_P^Q dW = -\int_P^Q dV = V(P) - V(Q)$$

along a finite arc C is thus independent of path when the potential is a one-valued function of position. Thus, whereas a conservative force field is always a (one-valued) potential field, a potential field, on the other hand, is only conservative in a region wherein it is one-valued.

The *gradient* of a function V is understood to be the vector with the components

$$\mathrm{grad}\, V = \left(\frac{\partial V}{\partial x}, \frac{\partial V}{\partial y}, \frac{\partial V}{\partial z} \right). \qquad (13.19)$$

Such a gradient can be formed from any scalar function of position. As will now be proved, it is independent of the coordinate system and hence, in fact, associates a vector field with the scalar field V.

By (13.19), we have

$$dr \text{ grad } V = \frac{\partial V}{\partial x} dx + \frac{\partial V}{\partial y} dy + \frac{\partial V}{\partial z} dz = dV, \qquad (13.20)$$

wherein the right-hand side represents the increase of V along dr. Since dr and dV are not dependent on the choice of the coordinate system, the gradient also is independent of the coordinate system and is thus a vector quantity.

The *level surfaces* of a function $V(x,y,z)$ are defined as the surfaces (Fig. 13.8) connecting points where the function has the same value. If V is a potential, they are also called *equipotential surfaces*. Applying (13.20) to a point P and an arbitrary neighboring point Q_1 in the same level surface, we arrive at

$$d_1 r \text{ grad } V = 0.$$

The gradient is thus everywhere normal to the level surface. If we now select a point Q_2 on the normal to the level surface at P, and, indeed, on the side indicated by the direction of the gradient, (13.20) yields

$$d_2 r \text{ grad } V = |d_2 r| \cdot |\text{grad } V| = dV > 0.$$

Hence it follows that

$$|\text{grad } V| = \frac{dV}{|d_2 r|};$$

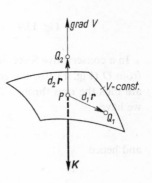

Fig. 13.8

the sense of the gradient points to increasing values of V and the magnitude gives the increase per unit length. With a constant magnitude of dr, the scalar product on the left-hand side of (13.20) assumes a maximum value when the vector dr has the direction of grad V. Thus, the gradient gives the direction and magnitude of the steepest ascent of the function V per unit length.

By means of the potential V, relations (13.18) can be brought together into the one vector equation

$$K = - \text{grad } V. \qquad (13.21)$$

Since the force K is given as the negative gradient of the potential, it is at each point normal to the level surface, has the direction of decreasing potential, and has a magnitude equal to the drop in potential per unit length.

Equidistant level surfaces are potential surfaces on which the potentials differ by a constant amount ΔV, such as (Fig. 13.9) $V_0, V_0 + \Delta V, V_0 + 2\Delta V, \ldots$. The closer they come to each other, the greater is the variation along the direction of their normals and also of the force.

Lines of forces are curves that have at every point the direction of the force. In a conservative field, they are the orthogonal trajectories of the equipotential surfaces.

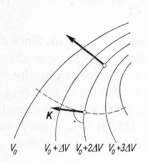

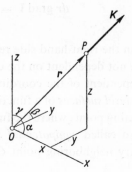

Fig. 13.9   Fig. 13.10

In a conservative force field with a potential $V(r)$ depending only on the distance r from O (Fig. 13.10), the equipotentials are spheres around O and the lines of force are thus the rays through O. This is a central field. With the notation of Fig. 13.10, we have

$$\frac{\partial r}{\partial x} = \frac{\partial}{\partial x} \sqrt{x^2 + y^2 + z^2} = \frac{x}{\sqrt{x^2 + y^2 + z^2}}, \dots,$$

and hence

$$\frac{\partial r}{\partial x} = \frac{x}{r} = \cos \alpha, \qquad \frac{\partial r}{\partial y} = \frac{y}{r} = \cos \beta, \qquad \frac{\partial r}{\partial z} = \frac{z}{r} = \cos \gamma. \qquad (13.22)$$

Since

$$X = -\frac{\partial V}{\partial x} = -\frac{dV}{dr} \cdot \frac{\partial r}{\partial x}, \dots,$$

the components of the force are

$$X = -\frac{dV}{dr} \cos \alpha, \qquad Y = -\frac{dV}{dr} \cos \beta, \qquad Z = -\frac{dV}{dr} \cos \gamma,$$

so that the algebraic magnitude of the force is

$$K = -\frac{dV}{dr}. \qquad (13.23)$$

Thus, the magnitude of the force is also dependent only on r, and, when the potential increases with r, we have a force of attraction.

Sometimes it is necessary to decide whether a given force field is conservative or not. For this purpose, the definition of a conservative field could be used, i.e., the work along arbitrary open or closed paths could be studied. Another method would consist in trying to derive the force vector, in accordance with (13.21), from a single-valued potential function. Both methods are cumbersome in general because they entail integrations. We will now develop a simpler method based on differentiation.

The *curl* or the *rotation* of the force in a field, which here does not have to be conservative, is defined as the vector with the components

$$\operatorname{curl} \boldsymbol{K} = \left(\frac{\partial Z}{\partial y} - \frac{\partial Y}{\partial z}, \quad \frac{\partial X}{\partial z} - \frac{\partial Z}{\partial x}, \quad \frac{\partial Y}{\partial x} - \frac{\partial X}{\partial y} \right). \tag{13.24}$$

Such a curl can be formed from any vector function of position. As will be shown, it is independent of the system of coordinates and thus, in fact, associates with the field $\boldsymbol{K}$ a second vector field. For reasons of terminology we limit ourselves for the time being to fields of force.

Figure 13.11 shows a right triangle with sides $2\,dx$ and $2\,dy$ parallel to the x- and y-axes. Its area is $dA_z = 2\,dx\,dy$. If the force function $\boldsymbol{K}$ is displaced in the indicated sense of rotation once around the perimeter of the triangle, this does an amount of work which is called the *peripheral work* for the triangle. This peripheral work is seen from the figure to be

$$dW_z = \frac{\partial X}{\partial y}\,dy\,(-2dx) + \frac{\partial Y}{\partial x}\,dx\,(2dy)$$

or

$$dW_z = 2\left(\frac{\partial Y}{\partial x} - \frac{\partial X}{\partial y} \right) dx\,dy = (\operatorname{curl} \boldsymbol{K})_z\, dA_z. \tag{13.25}$$

The first factor on the right-hand side denotes the z-component of the curl at point P. If the sloping face of the tetrahedron in Fig. 13.12 has the area dA and the outward unit normal $\boldsymbol{n} = (n_x, n_y, n_z)$, the areas of the other faces are given by

$$dA_x = n_x\,dA, \qquad dA_y = n_y\,dA, \qquad dA_z = n_z\,dA. \tag{13.26}$$

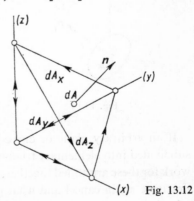

Fig. 13.11   Fig. 13.12

If, then, we add together the peripheral work for each of these three side surfaces, choosing the sense of rotation so as to make a right-handed screw around the respective outward normal, the two contributions along each edge parallel to a coordinate axis cancel. Thus, the addition of the three expressions gained from (13.25) by cyclic permutation yields the peripheral work for the inclined face. This is therefore equal to

$$dW = (\text{curl } K)_x \, dA_x + (\text{curl } K)_y \, dA_y + (\text{curl } K)_z \, dA_z,$$

or, by (13.26),

$$dW = n \, \text{curl } K \, dA. \tag{13.27}$$

It will next be shown that (13.27) is also valid for surface elements with other boundaries but of the same orientation. Thus we can introduce the *specific peripheral work*

$$\frac{dW}{dA} = n \, \text{curl } K, \tag{13.28}$$

which like n is independent of the choice of coordinate axes. Hence the same follows for the curl; it is in fact a vector.

Figure 13.13 shows both an arbitrary element of area dA with the unit normal n and also the curl of the field at a point P. With the sense of rotation shown, the specific peripheral work for this element is given by (13.28). It attains a maximum when n has the direction of the curl, i.e., when the latter is normal to the surface element. Consequently, the direction of the curl at each point of the field of force gives the orientation of the element of area with the greatest specific work, and it also gives the sense of rotation; the magnitude of the curl gives the magnitude of the greatest peripheral work itself.

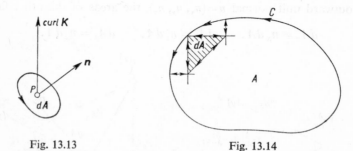

Fig. 13.13   Fig. 13.14

If an arbitrary plane or curved simply connected surface A (Fig. 13.14) is subdivided into elementary triangular loops dA, and the amounts of peripheral work for these are added together, then the contributions along interior boundaries once again cancel and what remains is the work W along the contour C, i.e., only the contour integral of K around C remains. By (13.27), we thus arrive at *Stokes' theorem*:

$$W = \oint_C K\, dr = \int_A n \operatorname{curl} K\, dA. \qquad (13.29)$$

According to this theorem, the amount of work done by the force K around the contour C of the surface A is equal to the surface integral of curl K over this area (i.e., equal to the *flux* of curl K through the surface A), provided that the direction of n and the sense of rotation around C are chosen according to the right-handed screw rule. The theorem is valid for arbitrary force functions K, confirms that relation (13.27) is independent of the form of the surface element, and shows, incidentally, that the surface integral of the curl does not depend on the surface itself but only on its boundary C.

In a conservative field of force, the line integral (13.29) vanishes for every closed curve, and that is possible only if the identity

$$\operatorname{curl} K = 0 \qquad (13.30)$$

holds. Drawing from a concept in hydrodynamics, a field with identically vanishing curl is called *irrotational*. It can thus be said that every conservative field is irrotational. This is confirmed by introducing the potential V. Since, by (13.24), the curl of (13.19) has the components

$$\frac{\partial}{\partial z}\left(\frac{\partial V}{\partial y}\right) - \frac{\partial}{\partial y}\left(\frac{\partial V}{\partial z}\right) = 0, \dots,$$

it follows that

$$\operatorname{curl} \operatorname{grad} V = 0. \qquad (13.31)$$

Conversely, if we have an irrotational field, i.e. a field such that the condition (13.30) is satisfied in the whole region of definition, then the right-hand side of (13.29) vanishes for every surface A in this region, and therefore for each closed curve C that can be shrunk down to a point in this region. Therefore, in every simply connected region, an irrotational field of force is also conservative.

In order to show that a field of force prescribed in a simply connected region is conservative, it is thus sufficient to establish that its curl vanishes in the whole region.

In a region of dimensions small compared with those of the earth, the weight W acting on a given particle is constant in magnitude and direction. In the system of coordinates in Fig. 13.15, it has the components $X = Y = 0$, $Z = -W$. By (13.24), we have curl $K = 0$ everywhere, so the force of gravity is conservative. Its potential, by (13.21), is given by the partial differential equations

$$\frac{\partial V}{\partial x} = \frac{\partial V}{\partial y} = 0, \qquad \frac{\partial V}{\partial z} = W,$$

and is thus

$$V = Wz \qquad (13.32)$$

if it is normalized to vanish in the x, y-plane. In fact, the amount of work done by the weight between the points P and O along the path indicated in Fig. 13.15 is calculated to be $W = Wz$. The lines of force are vertical, the potential surfaces are horizontal planes, and the work between two arbitrary points P and Q is $W = V(P) - V(Q) = W(z_P - z_Q)$.

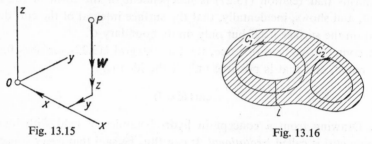

Fig. 13.15   Fig. 13.16

When the curl is used as a criterion that a force field is conservative, the proviso that the region should be simply connected is just as important as the earlier one that the potential should be single valued. For instance, if a plane field of force is irrotational only in the doubly connected region shown in Fig. 13.16, the right-hand side of (13.29) for curves of the type C_1 does not vanish in general. Since, in this case, the left-hand side is also nonzero, we have a non-conservative field with a potential that is multivalued in the region. If, however, the region is made simply connected by a cut along L, then every closed curve such as C_2 can be shrunk down to a point, and for such curves both sides of (13.29) vanish.

Exercises

1. The force in a plane field of force (Fig. 13.17) is one of attraction toward O with a magnitude $A = \lambda ry$. Describe the lines of force and the amount of work expended from A to B, (a) along the circular arc ACB, (b) along the coordinate axes, and (c) along the chord AB. Then determine the work over the closed circuit $ACBOA$ and decide from the information gained whether the field of force is conservative or not. Confirm this conclusion by investigating the curl of A.

2. A particle m is repelled from the origin O of a three-dimensional system of coordinates (Fig. 13.18) by a force K with magnitude equal to λr^2. Show that the

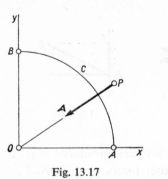

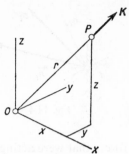

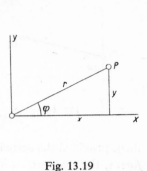

Fig. 13.17   Fig. 13.18   Fig. 13.19

field is conservative. Determine the potential and normalize it to vanish at O. Finally describe the lines of force and the potential surfaces.

3. Show that the multivalued potential

$$V = - \lambda\varphi = - \lambda \arctan \frac{y}{x},$$

which plays an important role in hydrodynamics, determines a plane field (Fig. 13.19) with the components $X=-\lambda y/r^2$, $Y=\lambda x/r^2$, $Z=0$. Discuss the force, the lines of force, and the potential surfaces. Further, demonstrate that the curl of the force vanishes everywhere except on the z-axis, and that the work on every circle about the z-axis is nonzero.

14. Fluid Pressure

Every body (Fig. 14.1) is subjected to external and internal forces. For a rigid body, the external forces are the loads, including the weight, and the reactions, and the internal forces are those maintaining the rigidity. In a fluid, the external forces are the elementary weights and the forces exerted by the walls of the container and by the air over the free surface; the internal forces are the pressures between the individual elements of fluid.

For every body at rest, and in particular for a fluid, the results of Section 5 are applicable: since the internal forces cancel each other in accordance with the reaction law, the external forces alone must be self-equilibrating. If a body is divided into two subsections 1 and 2 by, say, a plane cut as shown in Fig. 14.2,

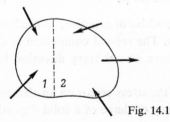

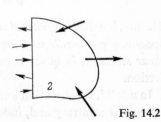

Fig. 14.1   Fig. 14.2

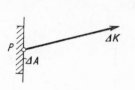

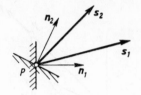

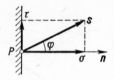

Fig. 14.3   Fig. 14.4   Fig. 14.5

then, provided the actual forces that were acting here are introduced as *section forces*, the two parts will remain at rest. The latter forces were internal with respect to the whole body, but for the parts 1 and 2 they are external forces.

The section forces are distributed continuously over the surface of the cut, and those acting over each element ΔA can be reduced to a concentrated force ΔK (Fig. 14.3) which will be located approximately at the center of gravity of the element. The section force per unit area is given by $\Delta K/\Delta A$ or more exactly by the vector

$$s = \lim_{\Delta A \to 0} \frac{\Delta K}{\Delta A} = \frac{dK}{dA}. \tag{14.1}$$

This is called the *stress vector* or briefly the *stress* on the element ΔA.

The stress on an element is thus a vector, the magnitude of which has the dimension $[FL^{-2}]$ and is measured in such units as lb*/in² (psi), or kg*/cm².

It follows from this definition that the stress within a body is not only dependent on the position P but also on the orientation, determined by the outward normal n, of the elementary surface, whence it follows, in particular, that different stress vectors s_1 and s_2 are to be expected for two surface elements which are defined by n_1 and n_2 but contain the same point P (see Fig. 14.4). The *state of stress* within a body is therefore not defined by a vector function of position, as with a field of force, but by a so-called *tensor function*, i.e., a vector that is a function both of position P and also of direction n.

If φ in Fig. 14.5 is the inclination of the stress vector s to the outward normal n of the corresponding element of surface, resolution onto this normal and perpendicular to it yields the components

$$\sigma = s \cos \varphi, \qquad \tau = s \sin \varphi. \tag{14.2}$$

The first is called the *normal stress*. It can be positive or negative, and is classified accordingly a *tensile* or a *compressive* stress. The second component is called *shear stress*; it is never negative but can have an arbitrary direction in the section.

In a solid, the direction and magnitude of the stress vector on an element are somewhat arbitrary and, indeed, the constancy of shape of a solid depends on this feature. In a liquid or gas at rest, on the other hand, there are no shear stresses, and, apart from side effects like surface tension, the normal stress is always negative, i.e., a compressive stress. This explains why liquids and gases have no definite shape. That shear stresses can arise in moving liquids and that they are accordingly classified as either viscous or nonviscous, need not be taken notice of in statics.

The direction of the stress vector in a fluid at rest is given by that of the surface element, and the magnitude

$$p = |s| = -\sigma \tag{14.3}$$

is called simply the *fluid pressure*. In order to study its dependence on the orientation of the surface element, we will consider the volume element in Fig. 14.6 that has the form of a tetrahedron with three edges parallel to the coordinate axes. If the area of the sloping face, with the outward unit normal $n = (n_x, n_y, n_z)$, is denoted by dA and those of the sides by dA_x, dA_y, dA_z, then these are given, as in Fig. 13.12, by (13.26). If, further, p, p_x, p_y, p_z are the pressures on the four faces, then the resultant section forces

$$p\,dA, \qquad p_x n_x\,dA, \qquad p_y n_y\,dA, \qquad p_z n_z\,dA$$

are second-order small quantities. Since any body forces (such as the weight of the element) are small quantities of third order, these can be neglected for the same reason that the differences in the fluid pressure between parallel surface elements may be overlooked. For instance, to an accuracy of second-order small quantities, the pressure on dA is the same as that on a parallel element through P. The component conditions then yield

$$p_x n_x\,dA - p\,dA n_x = 0, \dots \qquad \text{or} \qquad p_x = p_y = p_z = p.$$

It follows that the fluid pressure is independent of the orientation of the surface element and is thus a scalar function of position. This means that the state of

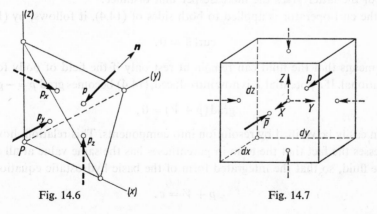

Fig. 14.6   Fig. 14.7

stress in the fluid is known as soon as we have the pressure $p(x, y, z)$ as a function of position.

Figure 14.7 shows an element of fluid in the form of a cuboid with edges dx, dy, and dz. Now we will consider all forces up to the third order of smallness. First of all we must consider the *specific body force* $K = (X, Y, Z)$. To the order of accuracy indicated, this external force per unit volume, which usually consists of the weight alone, will act at the center of gravity of the element. It gives rise to the components

$$X \, dx \, dy \, dz, \qquad Y \, dx \, dy \, dz, \qquad Z \, dx \, dy \, dz.$$

Moreover, we must now take the differences in the pressures on opposite faces into consideration. For example, the forces on the faces normal to the x-axis are

$$p \, dy \, dz \quad \text{and} \quad \bar{p} \, dy \, dz = \left(p + \frac{\partial p}{\partial x} dx \right) dy \, dz.$$

The component condition for the x-axis is

$$X \, dx \, dy \, dz - \left(p + \frac{\partial p}{\partial x} dx \right) dy \, dz + p \, dy \, dz = 0.$$

With the other two component conditions, we are lead to the partial differential equations

$$\frac{\partial p}{\partial x} = X, \qquad \frac{\partial p}{\partial y} = Y, \qquad \frac{\partial p}{\partial z} = Z,$$

which connect the fluid pressure with the body force per unit volume. They can be written as one vector equation

$$\operatorname{grad} p = K, \tag{14.4}$$

which is called the *basic equation of hydrostatics*. It shows that the greatest increase in pressure is in the direction of the specific body force while the magnitude of the latter gives the increase per unit distance.

If the curl operator is applied to both sides of (14.4), it follows, by (13.31), that

$$\operatorname{curl} K = 0. \tag{14.5}$$

This means that the fluid can remain at rest only if the field of body force is irrotational. If a potential V is now introduced, (14.4) becomes $\operatorname{grad} p = -\operatorname{grad} V$ or

$$\operatorname{grad}(p + V) = 0, \tag{14.6}$$

as can easily be verified by resolution into components. This relation, however, expresses the fact that the term in parentheses has the same value at all points in the fluid, so that the integrated form of the basic hydrostatic equation is

$$p + V = c. \tag{14.7}$$

By (14.7), the surfaces of constant pressure are the potential surfaces of the body force. With a fluid having a free surface, this is a surface of constant pressure. It thus corresponds with a level surface of the potential V.

Thus far we have made no use of the incompressibility of the fluid. The results obtained are also applicable to compressible fluids and even to gases. However, it is only for *liquids*, i.e., incompressible fluids, that the specific body force is independent of pressure and thus known at the outset. For the evaluation of (14.7) we will limit ourselves to this simple case.

If the weight is the only body force occurring, the specific body force is directed vertically downward and its magnitude is $K = dW/dV = \gamma$, that is, equal to the specific weight of the liquid. If it is homogeneous, the potential, by (13.32), in the system of coordinates shown in Fig. 14.8 with the z-axis pointing downward, is given by

$$V = -\gamma z.$$

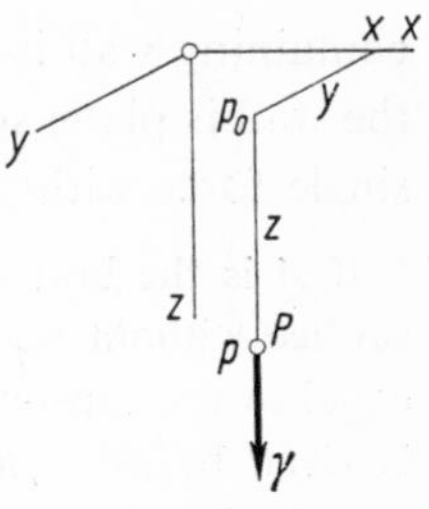

Thus, by (14.7), the pressure is

Fig. 14.8

$$p = \gamma z + c, \qquad (14.8)$$

where c is a constant. The surfaces of constant pressure, and the free surface in particular, are horizontal planes. If the x, y-plane is fixed in the free surface of the liquid and the pressure here is denoted by p_0, then it follows from (14.8) that $c = p_0$, and the basic hydrostatic equation assumes the form

$$p = p_0 + \gamma z. \qquad (14.9)$$

The product γz can be interpreted as the weight of the column of liquid standing above a unit surface area at a depth z; the pressure at this depth consists of p_0 and this weight. For water $\gamma = 10^{-3}$ kg*/cm³, and the normal atmospheric pressure at sea level is $p_0 = 1.033$ kg*/cm². Thus, in round figures, the pressure is 1 kg*/cm² at the free level and increases by the same amount for each additional 10 m depth.

If a container of arbitrary shape (Fig. 14.9) is filled with a liquid, each element of the containing wall at a depth z under the surface experiences two compressive forces along the normal. One is the pressure $p\,dA$ outward and the other is $p_0\,dA$ inward. The resultant is in the outward normal and, by (14.9), it has the magnitude

$$dP = (p - p_0)\,dA = \gamma z\,dA. \qquad (14.10)$$

The forces (14.10) acting on arbitrary elements of the wall represent a spatial system of forces and, by Section 6, can in general be reduced to a resultant force and couple at an arbitrary point. In special cases, namely when the

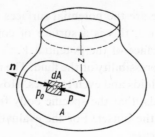

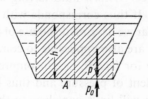

Fig. 14.9

Fig. 14.10

containing wall is spherical so that the forces $d\mathbf{P}$ form a central field or when the wall is plane so that the forces are equidirectional, the reduction leads to a single force without a couple.

If A is the bottom of a freely hanging vessel (or one that rests on a horizontal surface without sealing out the air completely), then, as shown by Fig. 14.10, z is equal to the constant depth h of the liquid and the elementary pressure on the base is given by $dP = \gamma h\, dA$. The resultant pressure on the bottom is vertical, has the magnitude

$$P = \gamma h A,$$

and acts at the center of gravity of the base. The pressure P can be interpreted as the weight of the column of liquid standing above the base; the result remains valid even when the walls taper inward instead of outward. A little reflection shows that this is not so paradoxical as it might seem at first sight.

If A is an area lying on the vertical wall of a container (Fig. 14.11), it is expedient to make use of a system of coordinates with origin at the centroid S of A. Let this point be at a depth h. Then, instead of (14.10), we have

$$dP = \gamma\,(h + z)\,dA,$$

and these forces can be reduced to yield a horizontal wall pressure, which, by (9.4) and (10.10), is given by

$$P = \gamma \int_A (h + z)\,dA = \gamma h \int_A dA + \gamma \int_A z\,dA = \gamma h A.$$

In order to find its point of application, the so-called *center of pressure* D with the coordinates x_D, y_D, we require that the scalar moments of P about the coordinate axes equal the sums of the scalar moments of the dP. Thus

$$x_D P = \int_A x\,dP, \qquad z_D P = \int_A z\,dP$$

or

$$x_D h A = \int_A x\,(h + z)\,dA = h \int_A x\,dA + \int_A xz\,dA = \int_A xz\,dA,$$

$$z_D h A = \int_A z\,(h + z)\,dA = h \int_A z\,dA + \int_A z^2\,dA = \int_A z^2\,dA.$$

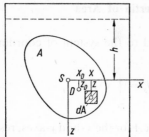

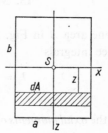

Fig. 14.11   Fig. 14.12

The integrals on the right-hand sides are dependent only on the shape of the surface A and are called the *moment of inertia* of A

$$I_x = \int_A z^2 \, dA > 0$$

about the x-axis and the *product moment*

$$C_{xz} = \int_A xz \, dA$$

about the x- and z-axes, respectively. With these simplifications, we have

$$x_D = \frac{C_{xz}}{hA}, \qquad z_D = \frac{I_x}{hA}.$$

Since I_x is always positive, it follows that the center of pressure is always below the centroid of the surface.

If A is a rectangle with sides a and b (Fig. 14.12), then

$$P = \gamma hab.$$

From symmetry considerations, the center of pressure lies on the z-axis, and since

$$I_x = a \int_{-b/2}^{b/2} z^2 \, dz = \frac{ab^3}{12}, \tag{14.11}$$

we obtain

$$z_D = \frac{b^2}{12h}.$$

Exercises

1. Calculate the resultant wall pressure for a hemispherical bowl filled to the rim.

2. Determine the wall pressure and center of pressure for a vertical circular surface of radius r, which at its highest point touches the surface of the liquid.

3. Determine the wall pressure and the center of pressure for a vertical semicircle of radius r, the straight edge of which lies along the upper surface of the liquid.

15. Moments of Inertia of Area

The plane area A in Fig. 15.1 is referred to the system of coordinates x, y. The surface integrals

$$I_x = \int_A y^2 \, dA, \qquad I_y = \int_A x^2 \, dA \tag{15.1}$$

are called the *axial moments of inertia* of area A for the x- and y-axes, respectively, and the integral

$$C_{xy} = \int_A xy \, dA \tag{15.2}$$

is called the *product of inertia* of the area A relative to the x- and y-axes. Further, the integral

$$J_O = \int_A r^2 \, dA \tag{15.3}$$

is called the *polar moment of inertia* of the area A about the origin O. Since $r^2 = x^2 + y^2$, it follows that

$$J_O = I_x + I_y; \tag{15.4}$$

the sum of the axial moments of inertia is thus invariant with respect to rotation of the coordinate system.

All these quantities have the dimension $[L^4]$ and are usually given in in^4. Moments of inertia are always nonnegative, whereas the product of inertia can be positive, negative, or zero, according to the position of the area in the system of coordinates.

If at least one of the two coordinate axes, like the y-axis in Fig. 15.2, is a symmetry axis of the area A, then the contributions of symmetrically disposed elements of area to the integral (15.2) cancel each other, and the product of inertia vanishes.

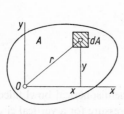

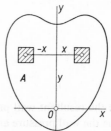

Fig. 15.1   Fig. 15.2

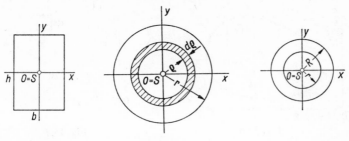

Fig. 15.3   Fig. 15.4   Fig. 15.5

For the rectangle of sides b and h referred to the axes shown in Fig. 15.3, we have, by (14.11),

$$I_x = \frac{bh^3}{12}, \qquad I_y = \frac{b^3h}{12}.$$ (15.5)

By virtue of symmetry it follows that $C_{xy}=0$, and (15.4) yields

$$J_O = \frac{bh}{12}(b^2 + h^2).$$ (15.6)

In particular, for a square of sides a we have

$$I_x = I_y = \frac{a^4}{12}, \qquad J_O = \frac{a^4}{6}.$$ (15.7)

In order to first calculate the polar moment of inertia of the circle in Fig. 15.4, the annulus $dA=2\pi\varrho\,d\varrho$ can be used as the surface element, and then

$$J_O = 2\pi \int_0^r \varrho^3\,d\varrho = \frac{\pi}{2} r^4.$$ (15.8)

It follows that

$$I_x = I_y = \frac{\pi}{4} r^4,$$ (15.9)

and once again $C_{xy}=0$.

Being given by integrals, moments and products of inertia are additive quantities, and those for composite areas can be obtained by addition or subtraction of the values for the parts of simpler shape.

For the annulus with radii R and r (see Fig. 15.5), it follows from (15.8) and (15.9) that

$$I_x = I_y = \frac{\pi}{4}(R^4 - r^4), \qquad J_O = \frac{\pi}{2}(R^4 - r^4).$$ (15.10)

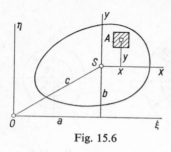 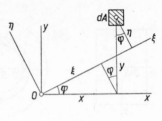

Fig. 15.6   Fig. 15.7

If the x- and y-axes have their origin at the centroid S of the surface A and ξ, η are parallel to x and y, respectively, with an arbitrary origin O, then, with the notation of Fig. 15.6, the coordinate transformation is expressed by the relations

$$\xi = x + a, \qquad \eta = y + b.$$

Thus we have

$$I_\xi = \int \eta^2 \, dA = \int (y + b)^2 \, dA$$
$$= \int y^2 \, dA + 2b \int y \, dA + b^2 \int dA,$$
$$C_{\xi\eta} = \int \xi\eta \, dA = \int (x + a)(y + b) \, dA$$
$$= \int xy \, dA + b \int x \, dA + a \int y \, dA + ab \int dA.$$

Since the middle integrals vanish because of the special position of the centroid, it follows that

$$I_\xi = I_x + Ab^2 \quad \text{and similarly} \quad I_\eta = I_y + Aa^2. \tag{15.11}$$

Moreover

$$C_{\xi\eta} = C_{xy} + Aab, \tag{15.12}$$

and since

$$J_O = I_\xi + I_\eta = I_x + I_y + A(a^2 + b^2),$$

we finally have

$$J_O = J_S + Ac^2. \tag{15.13}$$

These relations, which are attributed to Huygens (1673), allow a transition from one system of axes to any other that can be obtained from the first by parallel displacement. By (15.11), we have $I_\xi \geq I_x$, $I_\eta \geq I_y$, and, by (15.13), it follows that $J_O \geq J_S$. Thus, in comparing various parallel axes, the smallest axial moment of inertia is that relative to the axis through the centroid S, and similarly, the smallest polar moment is that for S.

Figure 15.7 shows a new system of axes ξ, η, obtained by rotating the axes x, y about the origin. The transformation of coordinates reads

$$\xi = x \cos \varphi + y \sin \varphi, \qquad \eta = y \cos \varphi - x \sin \varphi.$$

Whence we have

$$I_\xi = \int \eta^2\, dA = \cos^2 \varphi \int y^2\, dA + \sin^2 \varphi \int x^2\, dA - 2 \cos \varphi \sin \varphi \int xy\, dA,$$

$$I_\eta = \int \xi^2\, dA = \cos^2 \varphi \int x^2\, dA + \sin^2 \varphi \int y^2\, dA + 2 \cos \varphi \sin \varphi \int xy\, dA,$$

$$C_{\xi\eta} = \int \xi\eta\, dA = (\cos^2 \varphi - \sin^2 \varphi) \int xy\, dA + \cos \varphi \sin \varphi \left(\int y^2\, dA - \int x^2\, dA\right),$$

or

$$I_\xi = I_x \cos^2 \varphi + I_y \sin^2 \varphi - 2 C_{xy} \cos \varphi \sin \varphi,$$

$$I_\eta = I_y \cos^2 \varphi + I_x \sin^2 \varphi + 2 C_{xy} \cos \varphi \sin \varphi, \qquad (15.14)$$

$$C_{\xi\eta} = (I_x - I_y) \cos \varphi \sin \varphi + C_{xy}(\cos^2 \varphi - \sin^2 \varphi).$$

Applying the identities

$$\cos^2 \varphi = \tfrac{1}{2}(1 + \cos 2\varphi), \qquad \sin^2 \varphi = \tfrac{1}{2}(1 - \cos 2\varphi),$$

we can rewrite (15.14) as

$$I_\xi = \tfrac{1}{2}(I_x + I_y) + \tfrac{1}{2}(I_x - I_y) \cos 2\varphi - C_{xy} \sin 2\varphi,$$

$$I_\eta = \tfrac{1}{2}(I_x + I_y) - \tfrac{1}{2}(I_x - I_y) \cos 2\varphi + C_{xy} \sin 2\varphi, \qquad (15.15)$$

$$C_{\xi\eta} = \tfrac{1}{2}(I_x - I_y) \sin 2\varphi + C_{xy} \cos 2\varphi.$$

It can be verified directly that

$$I_\xi + I_\eta = I_x + I_y = J_O.$$

The transformations (15.15) or (15.14), together with Huygens' formulas (15.11) to (15.13), put us in a position to recalculate the moments and products of inertia relative to new systems of coordinates, as soon as the area A and the centroid S are known.

The requirement that $C_{\xi\eta} = 0$ leads, by virtue of the last relation (15.15), to

$$\tan 2\varphi = \frac{2C_{xy}}{I_y - I_x}. \qquad (15.16)$$

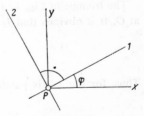

The tangent function has a period π and assumes all real values exactly once, so (15.16) has one solution in each quadrant, provided we do not have simultaneously that $I_x = I_y$ and $C_{xy} = 0$. Thus at each point P in the surface (Fig. 15.8), we have two mutually perpendicular axes 1, 2 for which the product

Fig. 15.8

moment vanishes. These are called the *principal axes* at the point P, and the associated moments of inertia I_1, I_2 are the *principal moments of inertia*. If $I_x = I_y$ and $C_{xy} = 0$, the third equation (15.15) shows that every system of axes at P is a system of principal axes.

Differentiation of the first relation (15.15) with respect to φ yields

$$\frac{dI_\xi}{d\varphi} = (I_y - I_x)\sin 2\varphi - 2C_{xy}\cos 2\varphi = -2C_{\xi\eta}.$$

This expression vanishes if and only if the solution of (15.16) is substituted for φ. Thus, of the moments of inertia of all axes passing through the point P, the principal moments are extremal. One of them is a maximum and the other a minimum. In the special case $I_x = I_y$, $C_{xy} = 0$, the extrema coincide, and the moments of inertia for all axes through P are equal.

If a plane area is axisymmetric, the product moment vanishes for each co-ordinate system with one axis on the symmetry axis. This is thus a principal axis for each point P on it. The other principal axis is the normal through P.

The above-treated areas (rectangle, square, circle, annulus) all had two axes of symmetry passing through the centroid. The moments calculated were thus all principal moments, and, indeed, the product moment in each case was zero. With the square, circle, and annulus the principal moments were equal. In these cases, therefore, every set of axes with origin at S is a set of principal axes.

In order to calculate I_x for a parallelogram as shown in Fig. 15.9, an element of area $dA = b\, dy$ running across the whole width can be used. Now since the integrand in the first relation (15.1) remains unaltered when this strip is so displaced hori-zontally that the parallelogram is changed into the dashed rectangle, we have, as in (15.5), the result

$$I_x = \frac{bh^3}{12}. \tag{15.17}$$

A glance at Fig. 15.9 suffices to show that $C_{xy} > 0$. Therefore the x-axis is not a principal axis and I_x is not a principal moment of inertia.

The triangle in Fig. 15.10 can be regarded as half the parallelogram with centroid at O. It is obvious that I_ξ is a half of (15.17), and therefore

$$I_\xi = \frac{bh^3}{24}.$$

Thus, for the x-axis passing through the centroid parallel to the base, we obtain,

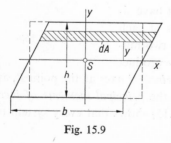

Fig. 15.9

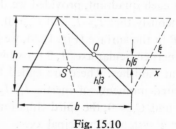

Fig. 15.10

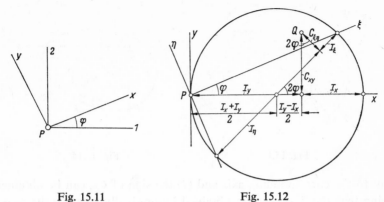

Fig. 15.11   Fig. 15.12

by (15.11), the result

$$I_x = I_\xi - A\left(\frac{h}{6}\right)^2 = \frac{bh^3}{24} - \frac{bh}{2}\cdot\frac{h^2}{36} = \frac{bh^3}{36}.$$ (15.18)

This also, in general, is not a principal moment of inertia.

The two principal axes at a point define a special system of axes (see Fig. 15.11). If we start with these, the transformations (15.14) and (15.15) reduce respectively to

$$I_x = I_1 \cos^2\varphi + I_2 \sin^2\varphi = \tfrac{1}{2}(I_1 + I_2) + \tfrac{1}{2}(I_1 - I_2)\cos 2\varphi,$$

$$I_y = I_2 \cos^2\varphi + I_1 \sin^2\varphi = \tfrac{1}{2}(I_1 + I_2) - \tfrac{1}{2}(I_1 - I_2)\cos 2\varphi,$$ (15.19)

$$C_{xy} = (I_1 - I_2)\cos\varphi\sin\varphi = \tfrac{1}{2}(I_1 - I_2)\sin 2\varphi.$$

The transformations (15.15) can be represented graphically in several ways; for example, by the so-called *inertia diagram* introduced by Mohr (1887). This is shown in Fig. 15.12. If I_y and I_x are measured, one after the other, along the x-axis, then the circle with center on the x-axis and passing through both P and the end point of the second interval has a radius $(I_y + I_x)/2$. The point Q with the coordinates I_y, C_{xy} is called the *pole*; its horizontal distance from the center of the circle is $(I_y - I_x)/2$. Let the ξ,η-axes be a new coordinate system obtained by rotating the axes through an angle φ about the point P. Then the join of the points where the new axes cut the circle will be a diameter inclined at an angle 2φ to the x-axis. The length of the normal from Q to this diameter agrees with the right-hand side of the third relation (15.15), and the two segments of the diameter marked off by this normal are equal to the right-hand sides of the first two relations (15.15). Thus, the length of the normal yields the magnitude of $C_{\xi\eta}$, and the segments of the diameter are I_η and I_ξ. It is to be remarked that (1) the segments giving I_ξ and I_η can be distinguished by the fact that each is

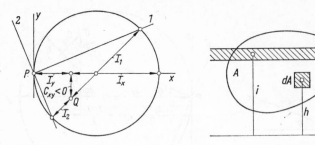

Fig. 15.13   Fig. 15.14

adjacent to the corresponding axis and (2) the sign of $C_{\xi\eta}$ can be obtained by imagining that the ξ, η-axes are obtained by gradually rotating the axes and noting that $C_{\xi\eta}$ undergoes a change of sign each time the diameter, originally along the x-axis, passes through the pole.

Figure 15.13 shows the inertia diagram for the case when $I_y < I_x$ and $C_{xy} < 0$. In order to find the principal axes at P and the principal moments of inertia, we only need to draw the diameter through Q; it is easily verified that I_1 and I_2 are extremal and that the associated product moment vanishes. In the exceptional case $I_x = I_y$, $C_{xy} = 0$, the pole is at the center of the circle and hence each and every system of axes at P is principal.

The *radius of gyration i* of a plane surface relative to an axis g is defined by

$$i = \sqrt{\frac{I}{A}}, \tag{15.20}$$

where I is the moment of inertia relative to the axis g, and A the area of the surface. Then, since

$$I = Ai^2, \tag{15.21}$$

the radius of gyration can be interpreted as that distance from g at which the area A can be concentrated without altering the moment of inertia relative to g (see Fig. 15.14). In particular, the radii of gyration

$$i_1 = \sqrt{\frac{I_1}{A}}, \quad i_2 = \sqrt{\frac{I_2}{A}} \tag{15.22}$$

relative to the principal axes 1, 2 at a point P are called the *principal radii of gyration*.

In order to give a further graphical interpretation of the transformations (15.19), we will mark off on each ray g through P in Fig. 15.15 the so-called *reciprocal radius of gyration*

$$\varrho = \frac{i_1 i_2}{i}. \tag{15.23}$$

This gives the points Q lying on a closed curve C that is symmetric with respect to P. The intercepts on the x- and y-axes will be

$$\varrho_1 = \frac{i_1 i_2}{i_1} = i_2, \qquad \varrho_2 = \frac{i_1 i_2}{i_2} = i_1. \tag{15.24}$$

Thus, the factor in the numerator of (15.23) has been chosen so that the principal reciprocal radii of gyration correspond with the principal radii of gyration.

The equation of the curve C follows from the first relation (15.19), which can be written either as

$$I = I_1 \cos^2 \varphi + I_2 \sin^2 \varphi,$$

or, by use of (15.20) and (15.22), as

$$\frac{i_1^2}{i^2} \cos^2 \varphi + \frac{i_2^2}{i^2} \sin^2 \varphi = 1.$$

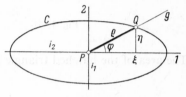

Fig. 15.15

If, then, we use (15.23) to change to reciprocal radii of gyration, we obtain

$$\frac{\varrho^2}{i_2^2} \cos^2 \varphi + \frac{\varrho^2}{i_1^2} \sin^2 \varphi = 1,$$

and, if the coordinates of Q are denoted by

$$\xi = \varrho \cos \varphi, \qquad \eta = \varrho \sin \varphi,$$

the final form of the equation for C is

$$\frac{\xi^2}{i_2^2} + \frac{\eta^2}{i_1^2} = 1. \tag{15.25}$$

The locus C of the point Q is thus an ellipse which is called the *inertia ellipse* for point P. The semiaxes are the principal radii of gyration, but with the axes interchanged.

Let us suppose that the inertia ellipse has been obtained by projection of a circle of radius i_2 (see Fig. 15.16). Then segments parallel to the axis 2 are shortened in the ratio i_1/i_2. The triangle PQT in the ellipse is so constructed that the third vertex T is the point of contact of a tangent t of the ellipse parallel to g. The corresponding figure in the circle is the right isosceles triangle $PQ'T'$ with an area

$$A' = \tfrac{1}{2} i_2^2.$$

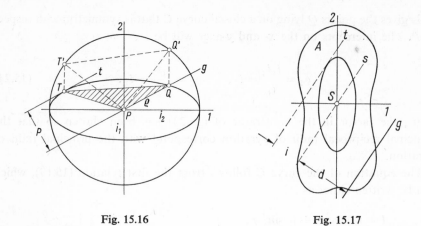

Fig. 15.16   Fig. 15.17

The area of the hatched triangle is

$$A = \frac{i_1}{i_2}A' = \tfrac{1}{2}i_1 i_2,$$

and, if the distance between g and the tangent t is denoted by p, this can, by (15.23), also be written in the form

$$A = \frac{1}{2}\varrho p = \frac{1}{2}\frac{i_1 i_2}{i}p.$$

Hence it follows that $p=i$. Consequently, the radius of gyration for an arbitrary line g through P can be obtained by measuring the distance between P and the tangent line parallel to g.

Such an inertia ellipse can be constructed at each point P of a given surface. Its form and the orientation of the axes vary from point to point. The inertia ellipse at the centroid is called the *central ellipse*. Figure 15.17 shows that when a surface is oblong, the central ellipse will also be oblong and similarly oriented. The central ellipse can also be used to determine the moment of inertia I of the area for a line g not passing through S. Indeed, let s be the line parallel to g through S and let t be the tangent to the ellipse that is parallel to it. With the notation of Fig. 15.17, we have $I_s=Ai^2$ and, by (15.11), $I=I_s+Ad^2$. Thus

$$I = A(i^2 + d^2).$$

The principal moments of inertia of the rectangle with sides b and h are given by (15.5). Since

$$i_x^2 = \frac{h^2}{12}, \qquad i_y^2 = \frac{b^2}{12},$$

the principal radii of gyration are

$$i_x = \frac{h}{2\sqrt{3}} = 0.289\,h\,,$$

$$(15.26)$$

$$i_y = \frac{b}{2\sqrt{3}} = 0.289\,b\,,$$

and the central ellipse has the form given in Fig. 15.18.

Similarly, for the circle of radius r it follows from (15.9) that

$$i_x = i_y = \frac{r}{2}\,;$$

$$(15.27)$$

the central ellipse in this case is thus a circle of radius $r/2$.

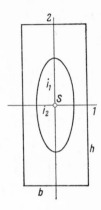

Fig. 15.18

For the usual standard sections (I, channel, T, etc.) which are of importance as cross sections of rolled steel beams (cf. Section 25), the principal radii of gyration are included with the other data in the tables contained in handbooks.

Exercises

1. Determine the values of I_x, I_y, C_{xy}, and J_S for the I-section shown in Fig. 15.19.

2. Determine the moments of inertia I_ξ, I_η, $C_{\xi\eta}$, J_O of the segment of a parabola shown in Fig. 15.20. Then calculate the corresponding moments for the parallel x- and y-axes through the centroid S.

3. Construct the central ellipse for the rectangle (Fig. 15.21) of sides $b=6$ in., $h=8$ in. and use it to determine I_ξ and I_η for the ξ, η-axes with the ξ-axis passing through two corners. Also determine I_ξ, I_η, and $C_{\xi\eta}$ with the aid of the inertia diagram.

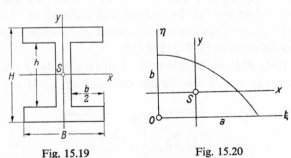

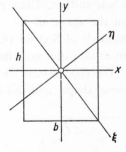

Fig. 15.19   Fig. 15.20   Fig. 15.21

4. Determine I_ξ, I_η, and $C_{\xi\eta}$ for the ξ, η-axes which are the perpendicular bisectors of the sides $a=5$ in, $b=10$ in of the right triangle in Fig. 15.22. Then determine I_x, I_y, and C_{xy} for the parallel x,y-axes that pass through the centroid S, and further

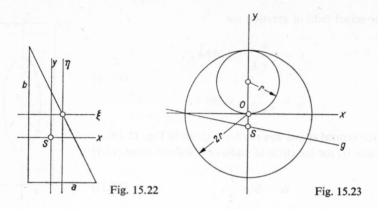

Fig. 15.22   Fig. 15.23

the principal axes and moments of inertia at S by means of the inertia diagram. Finally construct the central ellipse and use it to confirm the values for I_ξ, I_η.

5. Figure 15.23 shows a circle of radius $2r$ from which has been cut a circle of radius r. Determine for such a surface and with the system of coordinates indicated (a) the area, (b) the coordinates x_s, y_s of the centroid, (c) the moments of inertia I_x, I_y, C_{xy}, and J_O, (d) the principal axes 1, 2 at the centroid, (e) the corresponding principal moments of inertia I_1 and I_2, and (f) the moment of inertia I for the line g by means of both the inertia ellipse and the inertia diagram.

16. Floating Bodies

Figure 16.1 shows a rigid body which is poised, fully immersed, in an incompressible fluid (i.e., a liquid) of specific weight γ. The external forces consist of the elementary weights, which can be compounded into the resultant weight W at the center of gravity S of the body, and also the pressures $d\mathbf{P}$ over the whole surface. These pressures depend only on the position of the body and on the shape of the surface. They can be determined and reduced by the methods of Section 14. However, the problem can be solved more simply by an artifice that goes back to *Archimedes* (287–212 B.C.).

The *displacement D* of a body K (Fig. 16.2) is defined to be a body of the same shape and position made up of the liquid surrounding K. It has

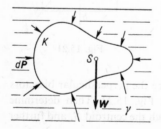

Fig. 16.1

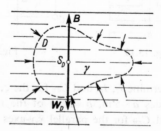

Fig. 16.2

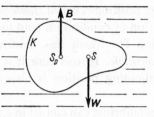

Fig. 16.3

the same volume v_D as K and a weight $W_D = \gamma v_D$, but it is possible that its center of gravity S_D differs from S, namely when K is nonhomogeneous. Since the displacement can be at rest in the liquid, the surface pressures, which are the same for D and K, can be reduced to a single force in S_D, the so-called *buoyancy* B, directed vertically upward and of magnitude

$$B = \gamma v_D. \tag{16.1}$$

Thus the forces acting on the body K (Fig. 16.3) have been reduced to W at S and B at S_D.

The equilibrium of the body K requires that $B = W$ and that the points S and S_D lie on a vertical line. When the first condition is satisfied, the body will be poised anywhere in the liquid. When S and S_D are distinct, there are two equilibrium positions (Fig. 16.4); otherwise there are infinitely many. In the first position (S beneath S_D), as soon as the body is slightly rotated, W and B form a couple counteracting the direction of the rotation; such a configuration is called *stable*. In the second position (S above S_D), a couple arises that tends to rotate the body further out of the equilibrium position. In this case, the equilibrium position is called *labile*. If S and S_D coincide, every position in the vicinity of the equilibrium position is also one of equilibrium; the equilibrium is then called *indifferent* or *neutral*.

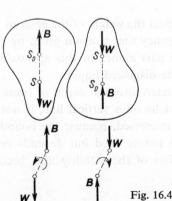

Fig. 16.4

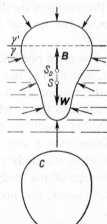

Fig. 16.5

In general, an equilibrium position is called *stable* when the forces that result from an arbitrary perturbation of equilibrium tend to return the body. If there is at least one perturbation for which this tendency does not arise, then the equilibrium is called *unstable*. In this case it is designated *indifferent* or *labile* according as any adjoining position is also an equilibrium position or not.

The perturbation of the equilibrium can consist in either a small displacement of the body or in a small impulse. If the equilibrium is stable, the body executes a small vibration about the position of equilibrium. If it is indifferent, it either remains stationary or it gradually moves away from the equilibrium position. Also when it is labile there are perturbations that send it far away from the equlibrium position.

If the condition $B = W$ is not satisfied, the body either sinks to the bottom where new forces in the form of reactions appear and make equilibrium possible, or it emerges partially from the liquid. The fact that certain bodies can be in equilibrium when fully immersed at a quite definite depth depends on the compressibility of the body or of the fluid, i.e., on effects that are not admitted here.

When a body floats on the surface (Fig. 16.5), the plane curve C where the surface of the liquid and that of the body intersect is called the *water line*. The part of the surface of the body above the water line is subjected to the pressure of the surrounding gas (i.e., atmospheric pressure in general) which can usually be regarded as constant; below the water line, however, there is the liquid pressure, increasing with depth. The buoyancy can be determined in the same way as for the fully immersed body, whereby it is to be noted that the displacement now consists of two different media. Below the water line it consists of a liquid of specific weight γ, and above of a gas of specific weight γ'. Since $\gamma' \ll \gamma$, the weight of the displacement decreases the more the body emerges from the liquid. The normal floating position is again characterized by the condition $B = W$.

In practice it is often possible to neglect the weight of the gaseous part of the displacement, and then it has a buoyancy that is again given by (16.1), with v_D denoting the volume of the liquid part alone. In this approximation, the buoyancy is equal to the weight of the displaced liquid.

The equilibrium condition $B = W$ determines the depth of immersion. The second condition, that S and S_D must lie on a vertical line, is not so simple to discuss as when the body is fully immersed, because the boundary of the fluid displacement of the body is no longer fixed but depends on position. For the same reason, the investigation of the stability also becomes more complicated.

The cross section of a body consisting of four long floats is shown in Fig. 16.6. There are at least eight equilibrium positions of which four are stable and four labile.

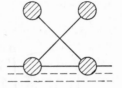

Fig. 16.6

The stability problem is particularly important for ships, and therefore we will next consider bodies that have a large dimension normal to the plane of the diagram and a vertical plane of symmetry when floating in the normal position. If the body in Fig. 16.7 executes an infinitesimal rotation about the line of intersection of the symmetry plane and the free surface of the liquid, the displacement experiences an increase on the side toward which the body inclines and a reduction on the other side. The position of its center of gravity is thereby displaced, i.e., the point of application of the resultant buoyancy moves from S_D to a new position S_D'.

If the center of gravity S of the body lies below that S_D of the displacement (as is the case with yachts), the weight W of the body and the displaced buoyancy for B always form a couple acting against the rotation; the normal floating position is thus stable. Insight into this can also be gained by starting with the buoyancy force at the center of gravity S_D of the displacement. Then its variation resulting from the shifting of the displacement can be expressed by the two forces δB and $-\delta B$ (see Fig. 16.8). The first corresponds to the increase in displacement on the immersing side and the second to the reduction on the other side. In this way one obtains two couples W, B and $\delta B, -\delta B$, both tending to right the boat.

For most boats (such as jolly boats) the center of gravity S of the body lies above that S_D of the displacement. If again W, B is the couple formed by the buoyancy force at S_D and $\delta B, -\delta B$ is that describing the shifting of the displacement, then the second alone has the tendency to right the boat, and the stability now depends on which has the larger moment. If a moment righting

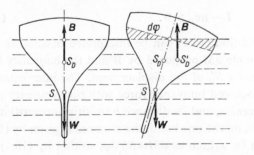

Fig. 16.7

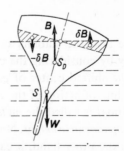

Fig. 16.8

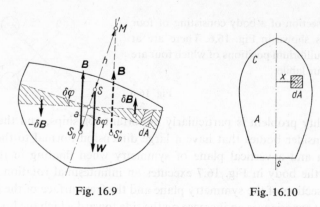

Fig. 16.9   Fig. 16.10

the body is called positive, then the moment of the couple W, B is

$$\delta M_1 = -Ba\delta\varphi = -\gamma v_D a\delta\varphi, \tag{16.2}$$

where a is the distance between S and S_D. The change in the displacement can be represented by volume elements which, by Figs. 16.9 and 16.10, has the volume $\delta v_D = x\delta\varphi\,dA$. Their buoyancy forces, by (16.1), are given by $\gamma\,\delta v_D = \gamma x\,\delta\varphi\,dA$, and when the static moment about the axis of rotation s is formed, we obtain the moment

$$\delta M_2 = \int_A \gamma x \delta v_D = \gamma\delta\varphi \int_A x^2\,dA \tag{16.3}$$

of the couple δB, $-\delta B$. The integral is to be taken over the interior A of the water line and represents the moment of inertia of area A about the symmetry axis s. If this is denoted by I, combination of (16.2) and (16.3) leads to the resultant moment

$$\delta M = \delta M_1 + \delta M_2 = \gamma(I - av_D)\delta\varphi, \tag{16.4}$$

and the condition that it is positive, i.e., that the boat rights itself, is

$$I - av_D > 0. \tag{16.5}$$

Here also the stability condition (16.5) can be interpreted in another way, namely by considering the couple δM produced by W and the buoyancy force B in the shifted center of gravity S_D' of the displacement. The intersection M of the line of action of the displaced buoyancy force with the symmetry plane of the boat is called the *metacenter*, and its distance h (positive upward) above S, the *metacentric height*. Now, on the one hand, the moment is given by (16.4), but on the other hand, it can be written as $\delta M = Bh\,\delta\varphi$, so that by (16.1) and (16.4) we have

$$\delta M = \gamma v_D h\delta\varphi = \gamma(I - av_D)\delta\varphi,$$

from which it follows that

$$h = \frac{I}{v_D} - a.$$ (16.6)

The stability condition (16.5) can now also be interpreted as the condition that the metacentric height must be positive.

Finally, the stabilizing moment (16.4), with (16.6) and $\gamma v_D = B = W$, can be brought into the form

$$\delta M = W h \delta \varphi.$$ (16.7)

Accordingly it is proportional to the metacentric height. In practice this is not made too large so as to reduce as much as possible the vibrations of the boat in the waves.

Exercises

1. A homogeneous beam (Fig. 16.11), with an equilateral triangular cross section of side c, small compared with the length, has a specific weight γ_b and floats on a liquid of specific weight γ_l. Calculate the metacentric height for the equilibrium position shown. Then indicate for which ratios $\lambda = \gamma_b/\gamma_l$ this equilibrium is stable. How large is the associated depth x of immersion?

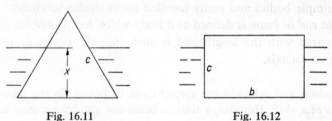

Fig. 16.11   Fig. 16.12

2. The prismatic block shown in Fig. 16.12 is very long in the direction normal to the plane of the figure. Its specific weight is γ_b, and it floats in the indicated equilibrium position on a liquid of specific weight γ_l. Determine the metacentric height h. With a prescribed ratio $\lambda = \gamma_b/\gamma_l$, what conditions must the ratio of sides b/c fulfill in order that the equilibrium position should be stable? For what ratios b/c can λ be chosen in the interval $0 < \lambda < 1$ so that the equilibrium is unstable? Then, for what values of λ is the equilibrium unstable?

III. Deformable Solids

17. Stress Resultants in Beams and Shafts

In elasticity and plasticity, solid bodies are treated in a manner similar to that used for fluids in hydrostatics. In each case, the problem consists in determining not only the external reactions to the loading of a body of arbitrary form and shape, but also the inner forces, i.e., the stresses, as well as the deformations and the allowable loading.

Since a solid, in contrast to a fluid, can sustain shearing stresses as well as the normal stresses, the problem is much more involved than the corresponding one in hydrostatics. Therefore we limit ourselves in one part of the chapter to especially simple bodies and easily handled approximate solutions.

A straight *rod* or *beam* is defined as a body which has transverse dimensions small compared with the length and is such that the centroids of all cross sections lie on an axis.

Slender prisms and cylinders are special cases of beams; in the latter case one often speaks of a *shaft*. However, a straight beam can also have a cross section that is not constant along its axis.

In the sequel, only beams (or rods, or shafts) that are in a state of rest will be studied. In such cases, the equilibrium principle from Section 1 implies that the external forces (see Fig. 17.1) are in equilibrium. If the beam is cut into two parts by a section normal to the axis as in Fig. 17.2, these two parts will also remain at rest under the action of the external forces $(A_i)_1$, or $(A_i)_2$, and

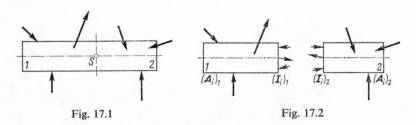

Fig. 17.1   Fig. 17.2

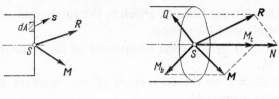

Fig. 17.3   Fig. 17.4

the respective forces $(I_i)_1$ or $(I_i)_2$ acting over the section. From the equivalences

$$(A_i)_1, (A_i)_2 \sim 0, \qquad (A_i)_1, (I_i)_1 \sim 0, \qquad (A_i)_2, (I_i)_2 \sim 0,$$

it follows, however, that

$$(I_i)_1 \sim (A_i)_2, \qquad (I_i)_2 \sim (A_i)_1; \qquad\qquad (17.1)$$

the forces on each face of the section are thus statically equivalent to the external forces on the other part of the body.

If s is the stress vector on an element of surface dA of the section (Fig. 17.3), this element experiences a force $s\,dA$. If these elementary forces are reduced at the centroid S of the section, we will have there a resultant force R and a resultant couple M, which will be designated the *stress resultants* of the section. They depend on the location of the section and consist of two vectors. According to the reaction principle, they are respectively equal and opposite on both faces of the section. The distribution of the stresses s over the cross section is not known *a priori*. However, these resultant vectors are given in each section as soon as the external forces have been determined. By (17.1), they are found by reducing the external forces acting on the discarded part of the beam at the centroid of the cross section in question.

We have already used the concept of the stress resultant without giving it an exact definition. For example, when it is stipulated that a weightless cable is subjected to tension or that an unloaded link is subjected to tension or compression, that is to be understood to mean that the stress resultants in an arbitrary cross section reduce to a single force acting outward or inward, respectively.

In general, namely when the external forces are arbitrary, the forces acting in a section (Fig. 17.4) reduce to two arbitrarily directed vectors. Resolution of these along the axis (the direction outward from the section being taken positive) and in the normal plane leads to:

1. *Tension* or *compression* by the axial component of the resultant force. This is called the *normal* or *axial force* N ($N > 0$ for tension and $N < 0$ for compression).

2. *Shear* by the *shearing force Q*, which is the component of the resultant force lying in the plane of the section.

3. *Torsion* (twisting) by the axial component of the resultant couple, the *torsion moment M_t*.

4. *Bending* or *flexure* by the component of the resultant couple in the section, the *bending moment M_b*.

If more than one of these components arises, we usually speak of *complex resultants*; on the other hand, the stress resultant is *simple* when, as we will now assume, only one component is nonzero. Then the concepts defined here for individual sections can be carried over to the whole beam particularly when the stress resultants of every section are of a similar nature.

A shaft is subjected to pure *torsion* when the stress resultants in each section reduce to a torsion moment M_t. This is the case when all external forces are applied in the form of couples in planes normal to the axis as shown in Fig. 17.5 (i.e., when, in particular, the weight of the shaft can be neglected). The only nontrivial equilibrium condition for the external forces then is

$$\sum_1^n M_i = 0, \qquad (17.2)$$

provided that the external moments are treated as algebraic quantities which are positive in one sense of rotation and negative in the other.

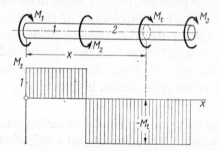

Fig. 17.5

In a section at, say, a distance x from the left-hand end we have a torsion moment M_t, which is also to be considered as an algebraic quantity and is given by the algebraic sum of all external moments to the left of the section. Its sign is best determined from case to case so that, for example, the torsion moment M_t is considered positive when it has the sense of rotation of M_1 on the right-hand face of the section (and thus the opposite sense on the left-hand face). In the kth field, i.e., between the kth and $(k+1)$th external moment, we have

$$M_t = \sum_1^k M_i,$$

or, making use of the equilibrium condition (17.2),

$$M_t = - \sum_{k+1}^{n} M_i.$$

If the torsion moment is plotted on the x-axis with a suitable scale, then, because the moment is constant in each field, we obtain a step curve, called the *torsion-moment diagram*.

A column is subjected to pure *tension* or *compression* if the stress resultant in each section reduces to a single normal force N. That is the case when, for example, all external forces are coaxial with the column (see Fig. 17.6). If they are treated as algebraic quantities by taking, say, downward as positive, the equilibrium condition is

$$\sum_{1}^{n} K_i = 0. \tag{17.3}$$

The normal force N of a section at a height x above the lower end is given by the algebraic sum of the external forces below the section, and is taken to be positive in the case of tension. In the kth field, we have

$$N = \sum_{1}^{k} K_i,$$

or, by virtue of (17.3),

$$N = - \sum_{k+1}^{n} K_i.$$

Plotting N against the x-axis produces a *normal-force diagram*, which is again a step curve.

The axial force can also be distributed continuously along the axis. In this case, the normal-force diagram is a curve with a continuous tangent.

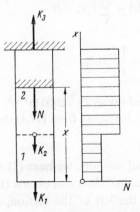

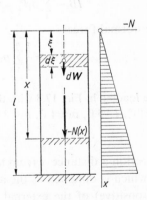

Fig. 17.6   Fig. 17.7

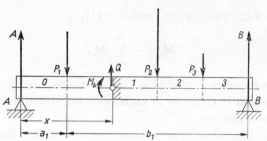

Fig. 17.8

Figure 17.7 shows a homogeneous prismatic column fixed at the base and loaded by its own weight. A slice of thickness $d\xi$ has a weight $dW = (W/l)\,d\xi$, and the normal force in section x is thus given by

$$N(x) = -\int_{\xi=0}^{x} dW = -\frac{W}{l}\int_{0}^{x} d\xi = -\frac{W}{l}x.$$

The normal-force diagram is a triangle and the greatest compressive force $|N|_{max} = W$ appears in the lowest section.

Bending and *shearing* nearly always appear simultaneously, when the external forces intersect the axis normally. In this case also, one speaks of simple stressing. If further the external forces lie, as will henceforth be assumed, in a plane (the so-called loading plane), the determination of the reactions is a two-dimensional problem in statics. For instance, they will be determined analytically by means of moment conditions at the two supports in the case of the simply supported beam shown in Fig. 17.8. If l is the length of the beam between the two supports, and a_i, b_i the distances of the ith force from these, then $a_i + b_i = l$. The moment conditions

$$lB - \sum_{1}^{n} a_i P_i = 0, \qquad -lA + \sum_{1}^{n} b_i P_i = 0$$

yield the normal forces

$$A = \frac{1}{l}\sum_{1}^{n} b_i P_i, \qquad B = \frac{1}{l}\sum_{1}^{n} a_i P_i. \tag{17.4}$$

For the loading in Fig. 17.8 with the numerical values $P_1 = 2000$ lb*, $P_2 = 3000$ lb*, $P_3 = 1000$ lb*, $l = 5$ ft, $a_1 = 1$ ft, $a_2 = 3$ ft, $a_3 = 4$ ft, it follows from (17.4) that $A = B = 3000$ lb*.

At a section a distance x from the left-hand support, we have (1) a shearing force Q which is obtained as the algebraic sum of the components (taking upward as positive) of the external forces to the left of the section, and (2) a bending moment M_b that is given by the algebraic sum of the moments of these

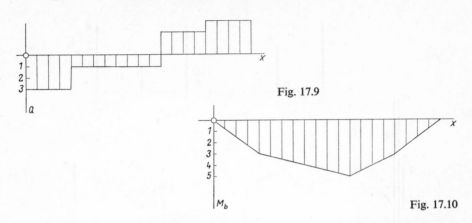

Fig. 17.9

Fig. 17.10

forces about the centroid of the cross section. Conventions have to be introduced from case to case; for example, Q and M_b can be taken positive when
they act on the right-hand face of the cut as indicated in Fig. 17.8. In the kth
field, we then have

$$Q = A - \sum_0^k P_i, \qquad M_b = Ax - \sum_0^k P_i(x - a_i), \tag{17.5}$$

if the enumeration of the fields begins with 0 and we set $P_0 = 0$. The *shearing-
force diagram* (Fig. 17.9) is a step curve and the *bending-moment diagram*
(Fig. 17.10) a chain of straight lines.

From (17.5) it follows incidentally that in each field the derivative of the
bending moment with respect to x agrees with the shearing force. Thus we have

$$\frac{dM_b}{dx} = \pm Q, \tag{17.6}$$

where the appropriate sign depends on the convention chosen. Each zero of
the shearing force corresponds to an extreme value of the bending moment.
If this fact is used to locate the greatest absolute value of the bending moment,
caution is called for, since in general the proposition cannot be inverted. For
example, the bending moment M_b in a cantilever beam may be greatest at the
fixed end without the shearing force vanishing. This is because the functions
$M_b(x)$ and $Q(x)$ can be continued past the ends of the beam without these con-
tinuations having any practical significance. In this connection, it is also to be
remarked that at sections where couples, instead of concentrated forces, are
applied, the bending moment is discontinuous.

From the data given above, Figs. 17.9 and 17.10 can be obtained numerically.
In particular, it can be verified that the greatest bending moment $|M_b|_{max} = 5000$ lb* ft
actually appears at the section $x = 3$ ft, where the shearing force passes through the
x-axis.

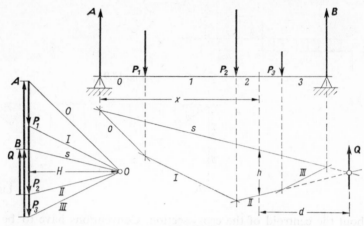

Fig. 17.11

The graphical determination of the reactions for the beam in Fig. 17.8 leads to a closed force and funicular polygon (Fig. 17.11). If x is a section in the kth field (in Fig. 17.11 we have chosen $k = 2$), in which field the funicular polygon is bounded by the pole ray k and the closing line s, the external forces $P_{k+1}, \cdots, P_n, B$ lying to the right of this section can be reduced to a resultant Q. According to the rules in Section 4, this appears in the force diagram between the pole ray k and the closing line; its line of action in the position diagram passes through the intersection of the closing line and the kth side of the funicular polygon. The force Q represents the shearing force in section x. If its magnitude is multiplied by the distance d of its line of action from the section, we obtain the bending moment

$$M_b = Q\,d. \tag{17.7}$$

Let h be the height of the funicular polygon between the sides k and s measured at the section x, and let H be the so-called *pole distance*, i.e., the distance of the pole O from the polygon of forces. Then the similarity of the triangle formed by k, s, and h in the position diagram and the triangle k, s, Q in the force diagram means that $d/h = H/Q$ or $Qd = Hh$. Whence (17.7) can be put in the form

$$M_b = Hh. \tag{17.8}$$

Since H is constant, it follows that the vertical heights in the closed funicular polygon represent the bending-moment diagram for the beam. In fact, it is a parallel projection of the diagram in Fig. 17.10. It is to be noted that the pole distance H is a force that is measured according to the scale in the force diagram; multiplying it with the height of the funicular polygon at section x yields, by (17.8), the bending moment.

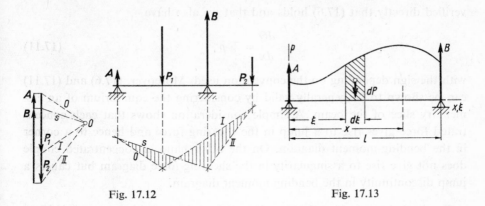

Fig. 17.12   Fig. 17.13

Figure 17.12 shows the bending-moment diagram for a beam simply supported at one end and overhanging the other simple support. Corresponding to the two zeros in the shearing force, the bending moment has two extrema of opposite sign and a zero between them.

A continuous loading (Fig. 17.13) is prescribed by the *specific load* $p(\xi)$, i.e., by the loading per unit length, as a function of position ξ.

The specific load has the dimension $[FL^{-1}]$ and such units as lb*/ft.

An element of length $d\xi$ experiences a load $dP = p(\xi)d\xi$, acting at the centroid of the strip $p(\xi)d\xi$ of the loading diagram. For a beam simply supported at both ends, the moment conditions at either support is

$$lB - \int_0^l \xi p(\xi)\,d\xi = 0, \qquad -lA + \int_0^l (l - \xi)p(\xi)\,d\xi = 0,$$

so that the reactions are

$$A = \frac{1}{l}\int_0^l p(\xi)(l - \xi)\,d\xi, \qquad B = \frac{1}{l}\int_0^l p(\xi)\xi\,d\xi. \tag{17.9}$$

The shearing force and bending moment at a section x can be obtained by reduction from the left, for instance, and are

$$Q(x) = A - \int_0^x p(\xi)\,d\xi, \qquad M_b(x) = Ax - \int_0^x p(\xi)(x - \xi)\,d\xi. \tag{17.10}$$

The similarity of these expressions with those in (17.5) is evident, and it can be verified directly that (17.6) holds and that we also have

$$\frac{dQ}{dx} = \mp p, \tag{17.11}$$

with the sign depending on the convention used. Moreover, (17.6) and (17.11) can be shown to be generally valid by considering the equilibrium of an elementary slice of the beam. A simple consideration shows that each concentrated force gives rise to a jump in the shearing force and hence to a corner in the bending-moment diagram. On the other hand, a concentrated couple does not give rise to a singularity in the shearing-force diagram but causes a jump discontinuity in the bending-moment diagram.

The simple beam in Fig. 17.14 is uniformly loaded by a load P. The specific load $p = P/l$ is constant. The reactions are $A = B = P/2$. The shearing force and bending moment can be gained without evaluating the integrals (17.10). By observing that the continuous loading to the left of section x can be reduced to a concentrated force Px/l at a distance $x/2$ from the section, it immediately follows that

$$Q(x) = A - \frac{P}{l}x = \frac{P}{2l}(l - 2x), \qquad M_b(x) = Ax - \frac{P}{l}x\frac{x}{2} = \frac{P}{2l}x(l - x).$$

The latter is bounded by a parabola, and the greatest absolute value of the bending moment $|M_b|_{max} = Pl/8$ occurs at the middle.

For a graphical treatment of continuous loadings it is necessary to approximate by subdividing the beam into fields of suitable length and replacing the loading in each by a concentrated force.

Figure 17.15 illustrates the graphical treatment of the last example by a subdivision into four fields.

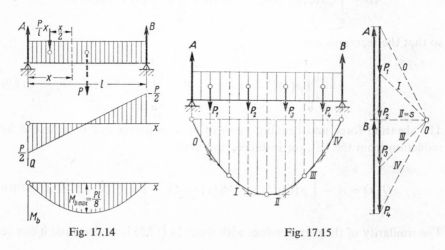

Fig. 17.14   Fig. 17.15

The construction provides the exact values of the reactions. The loading of the sections will, however, be correct only where two fields meet, because it is only in these sections that the actual external loading and the approximate one on each side of the section are statically equivalent. It follows by noting (17.6) that the sides of the funicular polygon at these same sections, and only here, are tangential to the curve $M_b(x)$, which is thus circumscribed by the (approximate) funicular polygon.

In the case of more *complex stress resultants*, the first step, as usual, is to determine the reactions, and then each partial stress resultant is treated separately (as was done with the shearing force and the bending moment associated with pure flexure).

A frequent combination is that of *bending and torsion*. It occurs, along with a shearing force that is usually neglected, when the external forces cross the axis perpendicularly.

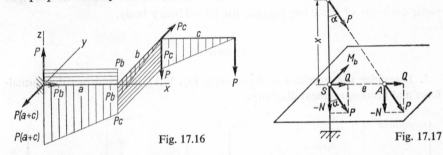

Fig. 17.16   Fig. 17.17

The crank handle in Fig. 17.16 lies in a horizontal plane and is fixed at the left. With the x,y,z-axes as shown, the equilibrium conditions yield a fixing force $A_z=P$ and two fixing moments $M_x=Pb$, $M_y=-P(a+c)$. The arm c is subjected to bending alone if the shearing force is neglected, and the bending-moment diagram is a triangle. If the force P is reduced at the joint between c and b, it is found that the latter is subjected to bending and torsion; the corresponding moment diagrams are hatched vertically and horizontally, respectively. The arm a is treated similarly. Then, we finally have a check in that the loading in the root section must agree with the reactions there.

The consideration of the weight, which even in Fig. 17.5 would alter the stress resultants, modifies the internal forces without altering them fundamentally.

Another combination is that of *bending with tension or compression*. It arises, again neglecting the shearing forces, when the lines of action of the external forces intersect, or are parallel to, the axis.

The bar shown in Fig. 17.17 is fixed at the lower end and is loaded by an oblique force at the other. The stress resultants at a section x are given by

$$N = -P\cos\alpha, \qquad Q = P\sin\alpha, \qquad M_b = Px\sin\alpha,$$

and consist, when the shearing force is neglected, in a normal force and a bending moment. Let the reduction in a section be carried out by displacing the load P along its line of action until it acts at the point A in the plane of the section and then resolving it into the components $-N$ and Q. Now the assumption that Q can be neglected leaves only the eccentric force $-N$ at a distance $e = x \tan \alpha$ from S. It is called an *eccentric compressive force* and the distance e the *eccentricity*.

A complex loading consisting of bending and axial force can hence always be considered as *eccentric tension or compression*. In contrast to this, we refer to cases like those in Figs. 17.6 or 17.7 as *concentric compression or tension*.

If the stress resultants in the section of a bar are known, it is next a matter of using them to find the internal forces, i.e., the state of stress within the body, which in turn makes it possible to determine the deformations. This will be carried out in later sections, subject to the usual simplifying assumptions made in strength of materials. To begin with, however, we will discuss in full rigor some concepts of basic importance for an arbitrary body.

Exercises

1. Determine the reactions in the example Fig. 17.17, and construct the normal-force and bending-moment diagrams.

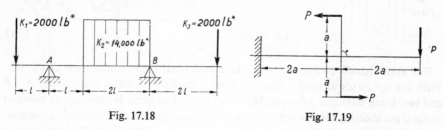

Fig. 17.18   Fig. 17.19

2. The beam in Fig. 17.18 consists of six fields of length $1 = 3$ ft. The loading and support are as shown. Determine both analytically and graphically the supporting reactions and the shearing-force and bending-moment diagrams. Then use both methods to locate the zeros and extrema of the bending-moment diagram, as well as the greatest absolute value of this moment.

3. Determine the reactions, the shearing-force diagram, and the bending-moment diagram for the beam shown in Fig. 17.19.

18. State of Stress

If P is an arbitrary point in the interior of a body and dA is an arbitrary element of area through P with the outward unit normal n (Fig. 18.1), then the stress vector s, by Section 14, represents the internal force per unit area acting

on the hatched face of the element dA. It is dependent
on both the position of point P and the orientation n
of the surface element dA and can be resolved into a
normal stress σ and a shearing stress τ. Whereas in a
fluid at rest we have $\tau=0$ and $\sigma<0$, both components
of stress with arbitrary sign occur inelastic or plastic
bodies.

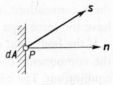

Fig. 18.1

Let an elementary cuboid with edges dx, dy, dz and containing the neighbor-
hood of P be cut out of a body as shown in Fig. 18.2. Then the stresses acting
on the visible faces can each be resolved into a normal and a shearing stress. If
the latter are represented by their components in the directions of the axes, we
obtain the nine components of stress in Fig. 18.2. If, for the equilibrium considerations that are to be carried out later, we limit ourselves to forces which
have second order of smallness, it is possible to neglect not only any possible
volume forces but also the differences in the stresses on opposite faces. Thus,
each face that is not visible in Fig. 18.2 is subjected to stresses equal and
opposite to those shown on the respective face lying opposite it. For the same
reason, the stress components may be imagined to be acting at the centroids
of the faces.

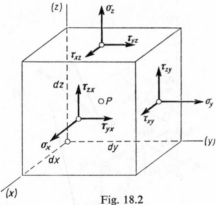

Fig. 18.2

The state of stress at point P is accordingly given by the nine components

$$\sigma_x \; \tau_{xy} \; \tau_{xz}, \qquad \tau_{yx} \; \sigma_y \; \tau_{yz}, \qquad \tau_{zx} \; \tau_{zy} \; \sigma_z, \qquad (18.1)$$

where the first subscript in the shearing stress indicates the direction of the
component, and the second indicates the normal to the appropriate face.
Normal stresses are taken to be positive when they act outward, i.e., when they
are tensile stresses. A shearing force is taken to be positive when the component
on an element with normal in the direction of a positive, or negative, axis also
has the direction of a positive, or negative, axis, respectively. According to

these conventions, the corresponding components of stress on opposite faces have the same sign in spite of the reversed direction of action.

If the body is at rest, the forces acting on sections, obtained by multiplying the components of stress by the corresponding dA element of area, must be in equilibrium. The component conditions for the cuboid in Fig. 18.2 are (to the degree of approximation introduced here) satisfied automatically. The moment condition for the middle line parallel to the z-axis is

$$(\tau_{yx}\,dy\,dz)\,dx - (\tau_{xy}\,dx\,dz)\,dy = 0,$$

and similarly for the x- and y-axes. Thus we have

$$\tau_{zy} = \tau_{yz}, \qquad \tau_{xz} = \tau_{zx}, \qquad \tau_{yx} = \tau_{xy}. \tag{18.2}$$

The matrix (18.1) is thus symmetric about the leading diagonal. Hence only six of the nine components of stress are independent. Moreover, since the choice of the coordinate system and thus the orientation of the cuboid is arbitrary, we have the *theorem of the reciprocity of the shearing stresses*. This theorem states that for any two perpendicular sections, the components of shearing stress perpendicular to the common edge have equal magnitudes and are both directed either toward or away from this edge.

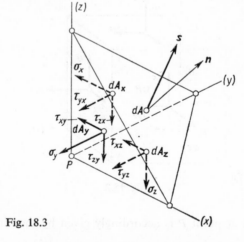

Fig. 18.3

In order to prove that the six independent stress components in (18.1) completely describe the state of stress at the point P, we will investigate the equilibrium of a volume element in the form of a tetrahedron (Fig. 18.3) with three edges parallel to the coordinate axes. If dA is the area of the sloping face with the outward unit vector $n = (n_x, n_y, n_z)$, then the areas of the other faces, as in (13.26), are given by

$$dA_x = n_x\,dA, \qquad dA_y = n_y\,dA, \qquad dA_z = n_z\,dA. \tag{18.3}$$

Let the stress vector on the sloping face be denoted by $s = (s_x, s_y, s_z)$, whereas the stress components (18.1) act on the other faces. The first component condition is

$$s_x \, dA - \sigma_x \, dA_x - \tau_{xy} \, dA_y - \tau_{xz} \, dA_z = 0 \,.$$

Noting (18.3) and using cyclic interchange of subscripts, we see that the components of the stress vector on the sloping face are

$$\begin{aligned}
s_x &= \sigma_x n_x + \tau_{xy} n_y + \tau_{xz} n_z \,, \\
s_y &= \tau_{yx} n_x + \sigma_y n_y + \tau_{yz} n_z \,, \\
s_z &= \tau_{zx} n_x + \tau_{zy} n_y + \sigma_z n_z \,.
\end{aligned} \tag{18.4}$$

The system (18.4) could be extended to a group of transformations giving the stress components in a new system of coordinates as functions of the components in (18.1). Because of the special form of these transformations, the array (18.1) is called a *tensor*. It follows directly from (18.2) that it is symmetric, and because of its physical application it is known as the *stress tensor*.

The transformations mentioned will not be formulated here. However, we will at least calculate the normal stress on the oblique element. It is

$$s_n = sn = s_x n_x + s_y n_y + s_z n_z \,, \tag{18.5}$$

and evaluation by means of (18.4) leads to

$$s_n = \sigma_x n_x^2 + \sigma_y n_y^2 + \sigma_z n_z^2 + 2\tau_{yz} n_y n_z + 2\tau_{zx} n_z n_x + 2\tau_{xy} n_x n_y \,, \tag{18.6}$$

where use has been made of (18.2).

Now the question is posed whether there are normal vectors n such that the corresponding surface element dA is free of shear stress. If there is such a normal vector, it satisfies the requirement

$$s = \sigma n \,, \tag{18.7}$$

where σ denotes the corresponding normal stress. If (18.7) is used to express (18.7) in terms of its components, it is seen that n_x, n_y, n_z must satisfy the system of linear equations

$$\begin{aligned}
(\sigma_x - \sigma) n_x + \tau_{xy} n_y + \tau_{xz} n_z &= 0 \,, \\
\tau_{yx} n_x + (\sigma_y - \sigma) n_y + \tau_{yz} n_z &= 0 \,, \\
\tau_{zx} n_x + \tau_{zy} n_y + (\sigma_z - \sigma) n_z &= 0 \,.
\end{aligned} \tag{18.8}$$

This system can be obtained in yet another way. In fact, if we ask for those elements of area in which the normal stress is extremal, it is necessary to find the extrema of (18.6) subject to the side condition

$$p = n^2 = n_x^2 + n_y^2 + n_z^2 = 1 \,. \tag{18.9}$$

Using the Lagrange multiplier σ, we obtain the following conditions for an extremum:

$$\frac{\partial}{\partial n_x}(s_n - \sigma p) = 0, \qquad \frac{\partial}{\partial n_y}(s_n - \sigma p) = 0, \qquad \frac{\partial}{\partial n_z}(s_n - \sigma p) = 0. \quad (18.10)$$

Further treatment of these conditions with (18.6) and (18.9) again leads to equations (18.8). Thus, when there are surface elements which are free of shear stress, the normal stresses on them are extremal.

The system of linear homogeneous equations (18.8) always has the trivial solution $n_x = n_y = n_z = 0$, which, however, is not applicable because of condition (18.9). Nontrivial solutions exist if and only if the determinant of the coefficients vanishes; i.e., if

$$\begin{vmatrix} \sigma_x - \sigma & \tau_{xy} & \tau_{xz} \\ \tau_{yx} & \sigma_y - \sigma & \tau_{yz} \\ \tau_{zx} & \tau_{zy} & \sigma_z - \sigma \end{vmatrix} = 0. \quad (18.11)$$

The expanded form of condition (18.11) is

$$\sigma^3 - I_1\sigma^2 + I_2\sigma - I_3 = 0, \quad (18.12)$$

when the notation

$$
\begin{aligned}
I_1 &= \sigma_x + \sigma_y + \sigma_z, \\
I_2 &= \sigma_y\sigma_z + \sigma_z\sigma_x + \sigma_x\sigma_y - \tau_{yz}^2 - \tau_{zx}^2 - \tau_{xy}^2, \\
I_3 &= \sigma_x\sigma_y\sigma_z - \sigma_x\tau_{yz}^2 - \sigma_y\tau_{zx}^2 - \sigma_z\tau_{xy}^2 + 2\tau_{yz}\tau_{zx}\tau_{xy}
\end{aligned}
\quad (18.13)
$$

is used. Relation (18.12) is a cubic equation for σ. It has three roots $\sigma_1, \sigma_2, \sigma_3$. On the one hand, they are independent of the choice of the system of coordinates, and on the other, they are completely determined by the coefficients (18.13). Consequently, these coefficients I_1, I_2, I_3 are independent of the coordinates; they are called the *fundamental invariants* of the state of stress.

Of the three roots of a cubic equation with real coefficients, at least one is real and may be denoted by σ_3. If it is substituted into (18.8), at least one normal vector n_3 is obtained, such that the surface to which it is normal is free of shearing stress and has the further property that its normal stress σ_3 is extremal compared with that on neighboring surface elements. The line 3 defined by n_3 is called a *principal axis* of the state of stress, the surface element 3' defined by this normal is called a *principal surface element*, and the corresponding normal stress σ_3 is called a *principal stress*.

If it is now supposed that the system of axes x, y, z has been chosen so that the z-axis has the direction 3, then $\tau_{yz} = \tau_{zx} = 0$, and the state of stress (Fig. 18.4) is given by the components

$$
\begin{matrix}
\sigma_x & \tau_{xy} & 0 \\
\tau_{yx} & \sigma_y & 0 \\
0 & 0 & \sigma_3
\end{matrix}
\quad (18.14)
$$

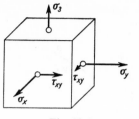
Fig. 18.4

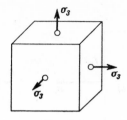
Fig. 18.5

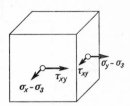
Fig. 18.6

It can be thought of as the sum of two states of stress with the components

$$\begin{matrix} \sigma_3 & 0 & 0 \\ 0 & \sigma_3 & 0 \\ 0 & 0 & \sigma_3 \end{matrix} \qquad (18.15)$$

and

$$\begin{matrix} \sigma_x - \sigma_3 & \tau_{xy} & 0 \\ \tau_{yx} & \sigma_y - \sigma_3 & 0 \\ 0 & 0 & 0. \end{matrix} \qquad (18.16)$$

The first (18.15) is illustrated in Fig. 18.5 and has the property, common with the state of stress in a fluid at rest (see Section 14), that no shearing stresses arise, no matter how the axes are oriented, and that the normal stresses are all equal; it is therefore called a *state of hydrostatic stress*. The second state, given by (18.16), is shown in Fig. 18.6 and is characterized by the fact that on the elementary cube only the stress components parallel to the x, y-plane are nonzero. For this reason it is called a *plane state of stress*. In the following it will be studied more closely with the aim of later returning to the *three-dimensional state of stress* by superposition of (18.16) and (18.15).

The state of stress at a point P is called *plane* when there is a surface element through P that is free of stress. The plane E of this element is called the *stress-free plane*.

Fig. 18.7

In a flat lamina (Fig. 18.7) which is loaded only on the edge, it is at least approximately true that there is a plane state of stress at each point, since each elementary cuboid cut from the full thickness of the lamina has two stress-free faces. Moreover, the stress-free plane is similarly oriented at every point, so that it is usual to speak of a *state of plane stress throughout the body*.

If a system of axes is used, the x, y-plane of which corresponds with E, then only the stress components σ_x, σ_y, $\tau_{xy} = \tau_{yx}$ (shown in Fig. 18.8) will be non-

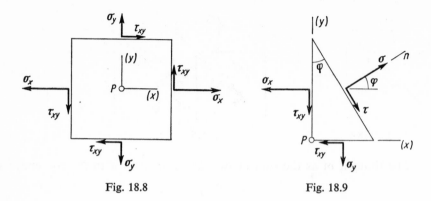

Fig. 18.8 Fig. 18.9

zero. This remains true even when the axes are rotated about the z-axis; therefore the stress vector on every plane normal to the stress-free plane will be parallel to the latter.

Let the values of σ_x, σ_y, τ_{xy} be known. Then, in order to find the components of stress on an element of surface that is perpendicular to E and has a normal inclined at an angle φ to the x-axis, we will consider the wedge-shaped element of volume in Fig. 18.9. It can be regarded as the limiting case of the tetrahedron in Fig. 18.3 with

$$n_x = \cos \varphi, \qquad n_y = \sin \varphi, \qquad n_z = 0. \tag{18.17}$$

The components of the stress vector on the sloping surface are found, by substitution of (18.17) into (18.4), to be

$$s_x = \sigma_x \cos \varphi + \tau_{xy} \sin \varphi, \qquad s_y = \tau_{xy} \cos \varphi + \sigma_y \sin \varphi, \qquad s_z = 0. \tag{18.18}$$

The stress components σ and τ in Fig. 18.9 are

$$\sigma = s_x \cos \varphi + s_y \sin \varphi, \qquad \tau = s_x \sin \varphi - s_y \cos \varphi. \tag{18.19}$$

By (18.18), these can also be written as

$$\sigma = \sigma_x \cos^2 \varphi + \sigma_y \sin^2 \varphi + 2\tau_{xy} \cos \varphi \sin \varphi,$$
$$\tau = (\sigma_x - \sigma_y) \cos \varphi \sin \varphi + \tau_{xy}(\sin^2 \varphi - \cos^2 \varphi), \tag{18.20}$$

or

$$\sigma = \tfrac{1}{2}(\sigma_x + \sigma_y) + \tfrac{1}{2}(\sigma_x - \sigma_y) \cos 2\varphi + \tau_{xy} \sin 2\varphi,$$
$$\tau = \tfrac{1}{2}(\sigma_x - \sigma_y) \sin 2\varphi - \tau_{xy} \cos 2\varphi. \tag{18.21}$$

It is obvious that the normal stress σ on the sloping element should be considered positive when the stress is tensile, and, by Fig. 18.9, the shear stress τ positive when the interior of the body lies to the right for an observer looking

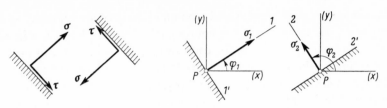

Fig. 18.10   Fig. 18.11

in the direction of τ. According to this new convention, which is particularly suitable for a discussion of the plane state of stress and which here replaces the former one, the stress components (Fig. 18.10) on both faces of a section again have the same sign in spite of the opposite directions.

The transformations (18.21) have a similar structure to those in (15.15) for the moments of inertia of area. For this reason, similar results are to be expected here. Thus, the requirement that $\tau = 0$, by the second equation (18.21), leads to the relation

$$\tan 2\varphi = \frac{2\tau_{xy}}{\sigma_x - \sigma_y},\qquad(18.22)$$

which, subject to the condition that $\sigma_x - \sigma_y$ and τ_{xy} do not vanish simultaneously, has a solution φ_1, $\varphi_1 \pm \pi/2$, ... in each quadrant. In every point P, therefore, there are two *principal axes* 1 and 2 (Fig. 18.11) such that the *principal elements* 1' and 2' which are perpendicular to these will be free of shear stress. By differentiation of the first relation (18.21) it can also be verified that the normal stresses on the surface elements 1' and 2', namely the *principal stresses* σ_1 and σ_2, are extremal. One is the minimum and the other the maximum value of σ for the surface elements under consideration. In the special case $\sigma_x = \sigma_y, \tau_{xy} = 0$, every axis in E through P is a principal axis, and the normal stress is the same for every one of these axes.

The principal axes at point P define a preferred system of coordinates (see Fig. 18.12). If these are used, the transformations (18.21) reduce to

$$\sigma = \tfrac{1}{2}(\sigma_1 + \sigma_2) + \tfrac{1}{2}(\sigma_1 - \sigma_2)\cos 2\varphi,$$
$$\tau = \tfrac{1}{2}(\sigma_1 - \sigma_2)\sin 2\varphi.\qquad(18.23)$$

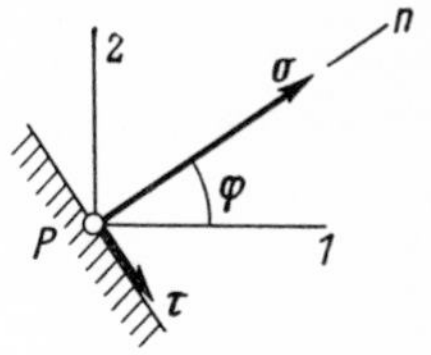

Fig. 18.12

By virtue of the analogy with (15.19), these transformations could be interpreted graphically in a manner similar to those of the moments of inertia. However, since the normal stress, in contrast to the axial moment of inertia, can assume negative values, another interpretation is more suitable. It is based on the *stress diagram* introduced by Mohr (1882).

If the components of stress σ and τ on an element of area normal to E and passing through P are marked off as coordinates in the σ, τ-plane (see Fig. 18.13), we obtain an image point (σ, τ) for each surface element. Thus, in particular, corresponding to the principal elements $1'$ and $2'$, we have the image points 1 and 2 with the coordinates $(\sigma_1, 0)$ and $(\sigma_2, 0)$, respectively. The circle on the diameter 1–2 has a radius $|\sigma_1 - \sigma_2|/2$ and its center lies on the σ-axis at a distance $(\sigma_1 + \sigma_2)/2$ from the origin. If N is the point on the circle such that the arc from 1 to N subtends an angle 2φ at the center, then its coordinates are equal to the right-hand sides of (18.23). The image points of all surface elements in Fig. 18.12 thus lie on this stress circle. Moreover, each element whose normal subtends an angle φ with the first principal axis has an image point that with the point 1 subtends an angle 2φ (with agreeing sign) at the center of the stress diagram.

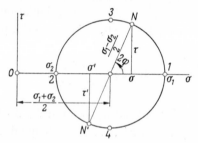

Fig. 18.13

The two opposite faces of a section correspond to the same point in the stress diagram, and the image points of two mutually perpendicular elements are diametrically opposite, like N and N'. The fact that $\sigma + \sigma' = \sigma_1 + \sigma_2$ verifies the invariance of the sum of the normal stresses on two mutually perpendicular sections, which indeed follows from the first relation (18.13). The relation $\tau' = -\tau$ is a symbolic statement of the theorem of the reciprocity of the components of shearing stress. Figure 18.13 confirms that the principal stresses are extremal and shows that the greatest absolute shear stress is

$$|\tau|_{\max} = \tfrac{1}{2}|\sigma_1 - \sigma_2|. \tag{18.24}$$

It acts on the elements with the image points 3 or 4, i.e., on surface elements that bisect the angle between the principal elements.

From the relation between the angles in Figs. 18.12 and 18.13, it follows that two surface elements with an angle φ between them correspond to image points that subtend an angle 2φ at the center of the stress circle. The sense of rotation from one element to the other is preserved. This furnishes a simple graphical interpretation of the transformations (18.21). If the state of stress at P is given by the stress components $\sigma_x, \sigma_y, \tau_{xy}$ on the surface elements normal to the axes,

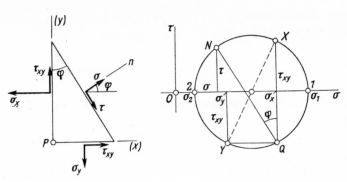

Fig. 18.14

(Fig. 18.14), then, by adhering to the sign convention in the σ, τ-plane, we obtain the image points X and Y and the stress circle with XY as diameter. If now lines are drawn through X and Y parallel to the corresponding surface elements, they intersect on the stress circle at a point Q called the *pole*. Through the pole Q we draw a line parallel to the sloping surface element (the normal of which is inclined at an angle φ to the x-axis) and the intersection with the circle is denoted N. Since by construction arc XN subtends an angle φ at the circumference and thus the corresponding angle at the center is 2φ, point N is the image point of the sloping side and the appropriate components of stress σ, τ acting on it can be read off as the coordinates of N. Thus, as soon as the pole is given, we have a quite simple construction for the components of stress on an arbitrary surface element normal to E. The construction can also be used to determine the principal surface elements which are parallel to the joins Q–1 and Q–2.

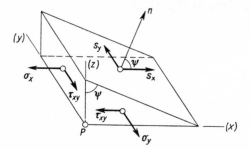

Fig. 18.15

In connection with questions of strength, it is not sufficient to limit consideration to surface elements normal to the stress-free surface E, as has so far been done. In order to obtain the stress on a plane skew to E, let us consider the wedge-shaped element in Fig. 18.15 whose base is a rectangle in E with sides parallel to the x- and y-axes. Let the normal n to the sloping face make an angle ψ with E. Thus, n and the x-axis also subtend the angle ψ.

Since the state of stress is still plane, the only components of stress on the nonsloping faces are σ_x, σ_y, and τ_{xy}. Moreover we have

$$n_x = \cos\psi, \qquad n_y = 0, \qquad n_z = \sin\psi, \tag{18.25}$$

so that, by (18.4), the components of the stress vector on the sloping face are given by

$$s_x = \sigma_x \cos\psi, \qquad s_y = \tau_{xy} \cos\psi, \qquad s_z = 0. \tag{18.26}$$

Whence it follows that the stress vector on the sloping face is also parallel to the stress-free plane. By Fig. 18.15, the components of stress on the sloping face are

$$\sigma = s_x \cos\psi, \qquad \tau = \sqrt{s_x^2 \sin^2\psi + s_y^2}, \tag{18.27}$$

where, here and henceforth, τ indicates only the magnitude of the shearing stress; there is no point in introducing yet another sign convention. Substitution of (18.26) into (18.27) finally leads to

$$\sigma = \sigma_x \cos^2\psi, \qquad \tau = \cos\psi \sqrt{\sigma_x^2 \sin^2\psi + \tau_{xy}^2}. \tag{18.28}$$

This shows that in contrast to the normal stress, the shearing stress on a sloping element can be greater than on the elements normal to E.

Figure 18.16 shows once more the stress circle, determined by σ_1 and σ_2, for surface elements normal to E through P. Since now $\tau \geq 0$, only one half of the circle has been drawn. Let the point X correspond to the surface element parallel to the y, z-plane in Fig. 18.15. By adding the squares of the relations (18.28), we obtain

$$\sigma^2 + \tau^2 = (\sigma_x^2 + \tau_{xy}^2)\cos^2\psi = (\sigma_x^2 + \tau_{xy}^2)\frac{\sigma}{\sigma_x}$$

or

$$\sigma^2 - \frac{\sigma_x^2 + \tau_{xy}^2}{\sigma_x}\sigma + \tau^2 = 0. \tag{18.29}$$

The image points of all sloping elements that correspond to various values of ψ thus lie on a circle having center on the σ-axis and passing through the points O and X, since (18.29) is satisfied by both $\sigma = \tau = 0$ and $\sigma = \sigma_x$, $\tau^2 = \tau_{xy}^2$. The circle is tangential to the τ-axis at the origin. Because of the fact that $\tau \geq 0$, only the upper half of the circle is considered, and, since by (18.28) $|\sigma| \leq |\sigma_x|$, only the arc OX. On this arc are situated the image points of the whole family of planes that contain the lines (y) parallel to the y-axis through P.

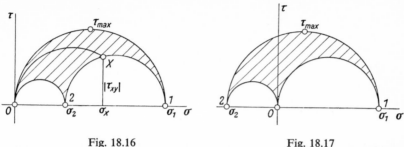

Fig. 18.16   Fig. 18.17

If now a similar consideration is applied to other surface elements at P normal to E, i.e., to systems of coordinates obtained from that in Fig. 18.15 by rotation about the z-axis, we simply obtain other points X on the circle 1–2 in Fig. 18.16. The image points of all surface elements through P thus lie in the hatched region between the semicircles given by the points 0, 1, and 2. Moreover, this region lies outside the semicircle 1–2 when, as in Fig. 18.16, σ_1 and σ_2 have the same sign. When they have opposite signs (Fig. 18.17), however, it lies inside the semicircle. It is concluded from this that the greatest absolute normal stress is given by the magnitude of one of the two principal stresses. Thus, according to the numbering of the principal axes, the greatest absolute normal stress is

$$|\sigma|_{\max} = \max\left(|\sigma_1|, |\sigma_2|\right), \tag{18.30}$$

and it acts on a surface element normal to E. It also follows that the greatest shearing stress is given by

$$\tau_{\max} = \tfrac{1}{2}\max\left(|\sigma_1 - \sigma_2|, |\sigma_1|, |\sigma_2|\right). \tag{18.31}$$

When the normal stresses have the same sign, it occurs on a surface element skew to E.

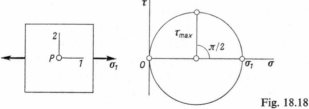

Fig. 18.18

If one of the two principal stresses, for example σ_2, is zero, we speak of a *uniaxial state* of stress. Then every plane E through P that contains the first principal axis is stress free. The stress diagram for such a plane is shown in Fig. 18.18. The image region for all skew planes reduces to the upper half of the circle. The greatest absolute normal stress $|\sigma|_{\max}=|\sigma_1|$ acts on the first principal element, the greatest shearing stress $\tau_{\max}=|\sigma_1|/2$ on all surface elements inclined at an angle $\pi/4$ to the first principal axis.

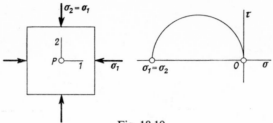

Fig. 18.19

If the principal stresses σ_1 and σ_2 are equal, the circle degenerates to a point on the σ-axis, as shown in Fig. 18.19. Thus, on every element through P normal to E we have the stress components $\sigma = \sigma_1$ and $\tau = 0$. The image region for the skew elements reduces to a semicircle, and again we have $|\sigma|_{max} = |\sigma_1|$ and $\tau_{max} = |\sigma_1|/2$.

If the principal stresses σ_1 and σ_2 are equal and opposite, the center of the stress circle is at the origin (Fig. 18.20) and the image region of the elements skew to E lies inside the circle. The greatest absolute normal stress is $|\sigma|_{max} = |\sigma_1|$ and occurs on both principal elements. The greatest absolute shearing stress $\tau_{max} = |\sigma_1|$ acts on those surface elements which bisect the angle between the principal elements.

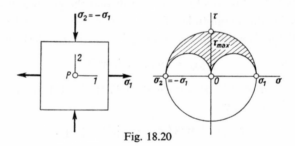

Fig. 18.20

From the three-dimensional point of view, a plane state of stress with, say, the principal axes 1 and 2 and the principal stresses σ_1' and σ_2' has a third principal axis with the principal stress $\sigma_3' = 0$ in the normal 3 to the stress-free plane E. If a hydrostatic state of stress σ_3 is superposed on this, we obtain a *three-dimensional* (or spatial) *state of stress*. This differs from the plane state in that all normal stresses are increased by σ_3, while the shearing stresses remain unaltered. The principal axes are thus still the axes 1, 2, 3, and the principal stresses are

$$\sigma_1 = \sigma_1' + \sigma_3, \qquad \sigma_2 = \sigma_2' + \sigma_3, \qquad \sigma_3. \qquad (18.32)$$

In the stress diagram, this superposition of the hydrostatic state of stress σ_3 merely means that the τ-axis is displaced a distance σ_3 to the left, thus transforming Fig. 18.16 into Fig. 18.21. The hatched image region of all surface elements through P is now bounded by three equally significant semicircles, pefined by the points 1, 2, 3 with the abscissae σ_1, σ_2, σ_3. A symmetry thus

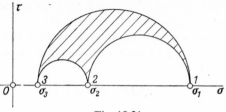

Fig. 18.21

arises that was not evident in the plane state of stress. According to the numbering of the axes, the magnitude of one or other of the principal stresses is the
greatest absolute normal stress, and half the modulus of the difference of two
principal stresses is the greatest absolute shearing stress. Thus we have

$$|\sigma|_{max} = \max\left(|\sigma_1|, |\sigma_2|, |\sigma_3|\right) \tag{18.33}$$

and

$$\tau_{max} = \tfrac{1}{2}\max\left(|\sigma_2 - \sigma_3|, |\sigma_3 - \sigma_1|, |\sigma_1 - \sigma_2|\right). \tag{18.34}$$

These relations, symmetric with respect to the three principal axes, represent
a generalization of (18.30) and (18.31) to the three-dimensional state of stress.

Exercises

1. The plane state of stress at the point P of a solid body is given by the components
of stress shown in Fig. 18.22: $\sigma_x = -800$ lb*/in², $\sigma_y = 300$ lb*/in², $\tau_{xy} = 400$ lb*/in².
Use the stress diagram to determine the principal elements 1', 2', the principal axes
1, 2, and the principal stresses σ_1, σ_2. Also find the elements 3', 4' that are free of
normal stress and the corresponding shearing stress τ. Show these values on the diagram.

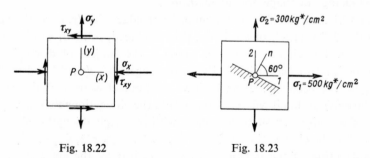

Fig. 18.22   Fig. 18.23

2. A plane state of stress is given at a point P in a solid by the principal axes 1, 2
and the principal stresses σ_1, σ_2 (see Fig. 18.23). Construct the corresponding stress
diagram and show (a) the stress components acting on a surface element inclined
at $\pi/3$, and (b) the element normal to E on which the greatest shearing stress acts,
together with the corresponding stress components. Are there surface elements skew

to E with even larger shearing stresses? How large is the greatest shearing stress and what is the orientation of the corresponding element?

3. To which surface elements through P correspond the three boundary circles of the hatched region in Fig. 18.21? Thus, on which surface elements does the greatest shearing stress always occur?

19. State of Strain

In the first chapter we have limited ourselves to rigid bodies. This is an idealization which will be dropped in the following. In fact, a solid that is loaded and supported in some way will deform, and this change of shape cannot always be neglected, even when it is small, as is the case with building and machine parts made of concrete or steel.

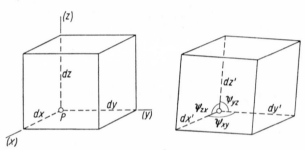

Fig. 19.1

The deformation of a body can be described in several ways. For instance, by subdividing the body into elementary cuboids and describing the change of state of each of these elements. The quantities that thus give information about the local change of shape are called *strains*.

Figure 19.1 shows an elementary cuboid with edges dx, dy, dz at the point P. During the deformation of the body, it is displaced, rotated, and its shape is also altered. The change of shape, which is the subject of discussion here, transforms it into a parallelepiped with the edges dx', dy', dz' and the angles $\psi_{yz}, \psi_{zx}, \psi_{xy}$, respectively. Henceforth we limit ourselves to small deformations (and rotations) so that it will be assumed that the elongations $dx' - dx$, $dy' - dy$, $dz' - dz$ of the edges are small compared with the original lengths of the edges, and also that the changes in the angles $\psi_{yz} - \pi/2$, $\psi_{zx} - \pi/2$, $\psi_{xy} - \pi/2$ are small. The deformation of the cuboid is then described by the six *components of strain*, namely by the three *normal strains*

$$\varepsilon_x = \frac{dx' - dx}{dx}, \qquad \varepsilon_y = \frac{dy' - dy}{dy}, \qquad \varepsilon_z = \frac{dz' - dz}{dz}, \qquad (19.1)$$

i.e., by the specific changes in the lengths of the edges referred to the original lengths, and by the three *shears*

$$\gamma_{yz} = \frac{\pi}{2} - \psi_{yz}, \qquad \gamma_{zx} = \frac{\pi}{2} - \psi_{zx}, \qquad \gamma_{xy} = \frac{\pi}{2} - \psi_{xy}, \qquad (19.2)$$

i.e., by the decrease of the angles between the edges. All the six components of strain are small compared with unity, and the whole of the following treatment will be linearized in the sense that products and powers of these quantities will be neglected.

It can be shown that the normal strains (19.1) and half the shears (19.2) at a point P form a symmetric tensor

$$\begin{matrix} \varepsilon_x & \tfrac{1}{2}\gamma_{xy} & \tfrac{1}{2}\gamma_{xz} \\ \tfrac{1}{2}\gamma_{yx} & \varepsilon_y & \tfrac{1}{2}\gamma_{yz} \\ \tfrac{1}{2}\gamma_{zx} & \tfrac{1}{2}\gamma_{zy} & \varepsilon_z \end{matrix} \qquad (19.3)$$

i.e., that they transform in the same way as the stress components (Section 18) when the system of coordinates is rotated. In particular, at each point P there is at least one *system of principal axes* 1, 2, 3 in which the shears vanish and the normal strains ε_1, ε_2, ε_3, called the *principal strains*, are extremal. It is not necessary to go into the details here; however, it may be noted that corresponding to the hydrostatic state of stress we have a state of strain $\varepsilon_1 = \varepsilon_2 = \varepsilon_3$, which is called a *dilatation* and consists in an equal strain of the material in all directions. Moreover, the case $\varepsilon_z = \gamma_{yz} = \gamma_{zx} = 0$ is referred to as a *plane state of strain* and can be treated with the aid of a *strain diagram* similar to the stress circle used for plane states of stress.

To the order of accuracy used here, the volume $dV = dx\,dy\,dz$ is independent of the shearing and is transformed into

$$dV' = dx'\,dy'\,dz' = (1 + \varepsilon_x)(1 + \varepsilon_y)(1 + \varepsilon_z)\,dx\,dy\,dz.$$

Thus, to this order, we have

$$dV' = (1 + \varepsilon_x + \varepsilon_y + \varepsilon_z)\,dV,$$

and hence the specific change of volume, i.e., the change per unit of original volume is

$$\varepsilon = \frac{dV' - dV}{dV} = \varepsilon_x + \varepsilon_y + \varepsilon_z. \qquad (19.4)$$

This is also called the *volumetric dilatation*, and, just as with the quantity $\sigma_x + \sigma_y + \sigma_z$ in (18.13), it is invariant under rotation of the system of coordinates.

It is obvious that the state of strain (19.3) at a point P in a body is a function of the state of stress (18.1) at that point. The nature of this function depends on the material and must be determined by experiments. For the discussion of this dependence we limit ourselves in the following to *homogeneous* and *isotropic bodies*, i.e., to materials with properties which are the same at all points as well as for all directions at each point.

The most important engineering material, namely steel, has a crystalline structure, and is thus neither homogeneous nor isotropic. However, by virtue of the small dimensions of the individual crystals and the irregular arrangement in the structure, volume elements that are not too small behave practically as though homogeneous and isotropic. In this case, one speaks of a *quasi-homogeneous* and *quasi-isotropic material*, and when the dimensions of the body to be studied are not too small, it can be treated as a homogeneous isotropic material.

The simplest experiment for clarifying the relation between the stresses and the strains is the tensile test, in which a cylindrical rod of length l, diameter b, and cross-sectional area A is subjected to an axial tensile force N. If it is possible to distribute the tensile force uniformly over the faces of the rod, we will expect that the interior is subjected to a uniform, uniaxial state of stress with the one nonzero stress component $\sigma_1 = N/A$. The experiment shows that the rod extends by an amount Δl and the diameter decreases uniformly by an amount $-\Delta b$ for not too large values of the tensile force N. One concludes that there is a uniform state of strain with the principal strain $\varepsilon_1 = \Delta l/l$ in the axial direction and $\varepsilon_2 = \varepsilon_3 = \Delta b/b$ in the transverse direction.

The quantitative evaluation of the experiment next shows the relation between ε_1 and σ_1 in the so-called *stress-strain diagram*. For *brittle metals* like cast iron, this has the form shown in Fig. 19.2; for *ductile materials* like steel, the form in Fig. 19.3.

The graph in Fig. 19.2 consists of a slightly curved arc that is traversed upward during loading and downward during unloading. The stress σ_b corresponds to rupture of the rod and is thus called the *rupture limit* or *ultimate stress*. If the bar is unloaded before it is reached, it will resume its original shape. Thus, according to the definition in the Introduction, it behaves *elastically* right up to the ultimate stress.

The graph in Fig. 19.3 has a practically straight branch on which the material again behaves elastically. At the stress σ_f there follows an approximately horizontal section. At this stage the bar yields, that is, the bar extends without any further increase in stress; the value σ_f is called the *yield stress*. When unloading (and reloading) follows yielding, the image point no longer follows the full line but moves down the (dashed) line parallel to the straight-line branch. Thus, a certain strain remains even after complete unloading; this means that

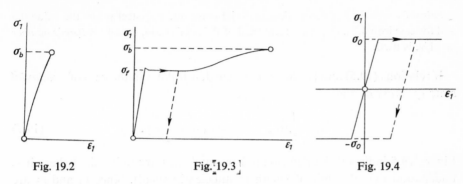

Fig. 19.2   Fig. 19.3   Fig. 19.4

the material behaves *plastically* after the yield stress has been attained. A further rise in the heavy curve up to the ultimate stress σ_b indicates the *work-hardening* due to the plastic deformations.

The complex behavior of the materials characterized by the graphs in Figs. 19.2 and 19.3 can be idealized by the stress-strain diagram in Fig. 19.4 consisting entirely of straight lines (even for compression). In a brittle material, this idealization consists in replacing the arc in Fig. 19.2 by a straight-line segment; σ_0 denotes the fracture stress, and the rest of the graph is not of importance. For a ductile material, σ_0 is to be interpreted as the yield stress, and the essential idealization here is the neglect of the work-hardening in Fig. 19.3, which will be regarded as a latent reserve of strength. It is obvious that the graph in Fig. 19.4 can be considered only as a rough approximation, all the more so since it has been assumed that the ultimate stresses for tension and compression are equal. Without some idealization, there would be no hope of making a transition to more complicated states of stress.

According to the approximation of Fig. 19.4, the stress σ_1 in the *elastic range* is proportional to the strain ε_1. We have Hooke's law (1678)

$$\sigma_1 = E\varepsilon_1, \tag{19.5}$$

where the constant of proportionality E is called the *elastic modulus*.

The elastic modulus, which can be interpreted as the initial slope of the graph in Fig. 19.4, is a material constant with the dimensions of a stress. It can be regarded as that stress which would double the length of a specimen if Hooke's law were to remain valid for such a large strain. In fact, the law remains valid only for strains less than a few parts in a thousand. For iron we have $E = 3 \times 10^7$ lb*/in².

In the elastic region, the so-called *cross contraction* $|\varepsilon_2|$ or $|\varepsilon_3|$ is also proportional to the stress σ_1. This can be expressed by the relation

$$\varepsilon_2 = \varepsilon_3 = -\nu\varepsilon_1, \tag{19.6}$$

where the constant of proportionality ν is named after Poisson (1781–1840).

Poisson's ratio is a dimensionless material constant. For steel it has the value 0.3 and for cast iron 0.25. Often the reciprocal of Poisson's ratio, namely *Poisson's number* $m = 1/v$, is used.

If relations (19.5) and (19.6) are combined, it follows in the case of a *uniaxial state of stress* σ_1 that the strains are

$$\varepsilon_1 = \frac{1}{E}\sigma_1, \qquad \varepsilon_2 = \varepsilon_3 = -\frac{v}{E}\sigma_1. \qquad (19.7)$$

Figure 19.5 indicates the deformation of an elementary unit cube (where it is understood that the unit of length is sufficiently small). Since ε_2 and ε_3 are nonzero, the state of strain is not uniaxial. However, as always occurs in isotropic bodies, the principal axes of the states of stress and strain coincide, since there is clearly no shearing. By (19.7), the volumetric dilatation (19.4) will be

$$\varepsilon = \frac{1}{E}(1 - 2v)\sigma_1, \qquad (19.8)$$

and since it is certainly never negative when σ_1 is positive, it follows for an arbitrary elastic material that

$$v \leq \tfrac{1}{2}, \qquad (19.9)$$

where the limiting case $v = \tfrac{1}{2}$ corresponds to an incompressible material.

In the *plastic region*, Hooke's law (19.5) is not valid. In fact, if no unloading occurs, we have $\sigma_1 = \sigma_0$ while ε_1 increases. At the same time ε_2 and ε_3 decrease, so that the volumetric dilatation (19.4) remains constant.

In extending these results to more complicated states of stress, we will limit ourselves to the *elastic domain*. In this case, as will be shown in the next section, the state of strain associated with a given state of stress depends only on this and not on the way in which it was produced. Therefore, the deformations resulting from a state of stress with several nonzero stress components can be obtained by imagining the individual stress components to be applied one after the other to the elementary cube and then superposing the corresponding deformations. Within the scope of our linearized theory we can even directly superpose the strain components.

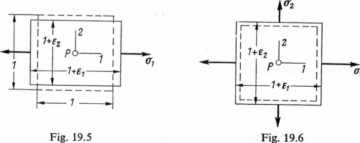

Fig. 19.5   Fig. 19.6

If a *state of plane stress* (Fig. 19.6) is given by the principal axes 1 and 2 and the principal stresses σ_1 and σ_2, then the parts of the principal strains arising from σ_1 will be given by (19.7). The other principal stress σ_2 produces the strains

$$\varepsilon_2 = \frac{1}{E}\sigma_2, \qquad \varepsilon_3 = \varepsilon_1 = -\frac{v}{E}\sigma_2, \tag{19.10}$$

and superposition of (19.7) and (19.10) leads to the resultant strain components

$$\varepsilon_1 = \frac{1}{E}(\sigma_1 - v\sigma_2), \qquad \varepsilon_2 = \frac{1}{E}(\sigma_2 - v\sigma_1), \qquad \varepsilon_3 = -\frac{v}{E}(\sigma_1 + \sigma_2). \tag{19.11}$$

It is seen that even here, in general, the state of strain will not be plane.

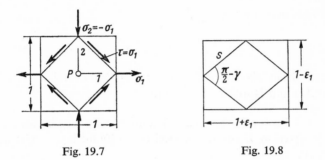

Fig. 19.7   Fig. 19.8

If we set $\sigma_2 = -\sigma_1$, we obtain the state of stress illustrated in Fig. 18.20. Since only a shear stress $\tau = \sigma_1$ acts on the surface element bisecting the angle between the principal elements 1' and 2', it is possible to cut an inscribing cuboid out of the unit cube shown in Fig. 19.7 such that all faces are free of normal stress. This state of stress is thus called one of *pure shear*. Figure 19.8 shows both volume elements after the deformation. By (19.11), the principal strains

$$\varepsilon_1 = -\varepsilon_2 = \frac{1+v}{E}\sigma_1 = \frac{1+v}{E}\tau, \qquad \varepsilon_3 = 0 \tag{19.12}$$

describe the deformation of the unit cube. Thus, the edge normal to the plane of the diagram retains its length 1, whereas the other edges with the original length $1/\sqrt{2}$ are transformed to

$$s = \frac{1}{2}\sqrt{(1 + \varepsilon_1)^2 + (1 - \varepsilon_1)^2} = \frac{1}{\sqrt{2}}(1 + \varepsilon^2)^{1/2} = \frac{1}{\sqrt{2}}\left(1 + \frac{1}{2}\varepsilon_1^2 + \dots\right),$$

which means that they also, to the present degree of accuracy, remain unextended. On the other hand, the originally right angles are altered by the deformation. Indeed, it is seen from Fig. 19.8, by using a well-known trigonometric identity, that

$$\tan\left(\frac{\pi}{4} - \frac{\gamma}{2}\right) = \frac{1 - \tan\gamma/2}{1 + \tan\gamma/2} = \frac{1 - \varepsilon_1}{1 + \varepsilon_1}.$$

By (19.12), it then follows that

$$\tan\frac{\gamma}{2} = \frac{\gamma}{2} = \varepsilon_1 = \frac{1 + v}{E}\tau. \qquad (19.13)$$

The strain accompanying a state of pure shear is thus limited to a pure shear deformation

$$\gamma = \frac{1}{G}\tau, \qquad (19.14)$$

where the constant of proportionality

$$G = \frac{E}{2(1 + v)} \qquad (19.15)$$

is called the *shear modulus*. Note the analogy between the relation $\tau = G\gamma$ following from (19.14) and Hooke's law (19.5).

The shear modulus is a further material constant with the dimensions of a stress. It is, however, given by E and v. For steel ($E = 3.10^7$ lb*/in², $v = 1/3$) we have $G = 1.125\ 10^7$ lb*/in².

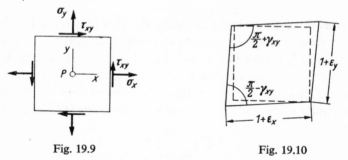

Fig. 19.9   Fig. 19.10

Superposition of the plane state of stress σ_x, σ_y in Fig. 19.6 on the state of pure shear τ_{xy} leads to a state of plane stress in an arbitrary system of axes as indicated in Fig. 19.9. The associated state of strain (Fig. 19.10), by (19.11) and (19.14), is found to be

$$\varepsilon_x = \frac{1}{E}(\sigma_x - v\sigma_y), \qquad \varepsilon_y = \frac{1}{E}(\sigma_y - v\sigma_x),$$

$$\varepsilon_z = -\frac{v}{E}(\sigma_x + \sigma_y), \qquad \gamma_{xy} = \frac{1}{G}\tau_{xy} \qquad (19.16)$$

where ε_x and ε_y are no longer principal strains.

Finally, it can be seen without further effort that when the *state of stress* is *three-dimensional*, the accompanying components of strain in an arbitrary system of axes are given by

$$\varepsilon_x = \frac{1}{E}\left[\sigma_x - v(\sigma_y + \sigma_z)\right], \qquad \gamma_{yz} = \frac{1}{G}\tau_{yz},$$

$$\varepsilon_y = \frac{1}{E}\left[\sigma_y - v(\sigma_z + \sigma_x)\right], \qquad \gamma_{zx} = \frac{1}{G}\tau_{zx}, \qquad (19.17)$$

$$\varepsilon_z = \frac{1}{E}\left[\sigma_z - v(\sigma_x + \sigma_y)\right], \qquad \gamma_{xy} = \frac{1}{G}\tau_{xy},$$

i.e., by three normal strains and three shears. As is to be expected, these most general stress-strain relations for a linear elastic body again have a symmetric structure.

Exercises

1. Determine the principal strains for the state of stress given in Exercise 2 of Section 18 when the material is cast iron.

2. From (19.13) it follows that $\gamma/2 = \varepsilon_1$ in the state of pure shear. Verify this result by means of the strain diagram.

20. Strain Energy

Let the body in Fig. 20.1 be loaded and held in position in some arbitrary fashion. The deformation can be described not only by the strains, but also by the displacements Δr of the points P throughout the body. Since, in particular, the points of application of the external forces are displaced, each of these forces performs an amount of work during the loading process. We now imagine that the external forces, either simultaneously or in some sequence, are slowly increased from zero to their final values, so that no perceptible motion occurs. The work thereby performed by these forces is called the *work of deformation W*.

Each individual element of the body is subjected to forces that can be classified as either internal or external (relative to the whole body). Since there is no perceptible motion, such forces on each element are in equilibrium during the whole loading process. Whence it follows that the total work of the internal forces during the application of the loads is $-W$.

Provided that the internal forces are *conservative*, it follows from Section 13 that they have

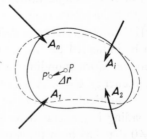

Fig. 20.1

a total potential U that can be normalized to be zero in the unloaded state. It is called the *deformation energy*, and can be regarded as the work of the internal forces during a (gradual) unloading of the body and thus also as the work of the external forces during a (gradual) loading of the body. In this case, therefore, we have $W = U$, which means that the deformation work is dependent only on the final state and not on the way this is reached.

If the internal forces are *not conservative*, as is the case when internal friction is present, there is no deformation energy U. When the body is deformed from a given state and then returned again by some loading process, the work of the external forces is not zero. The external forces will perform a positive amount of work and the internal ones a negative amount, and heat will be produced. Hence the work of deformation depends not only on the final state but also on the deformation or loading history.

This can be elucidated by considering an element in the form of a unit cube (Fig. 20.2), in which the state of stress is uniaxial and the principal axis 1 is parallel to one of the edges. The deformation work per unit volume will be called the *specific deformation work* or the *strain work* $\bar{W}$, and the *specific strain energy* will be denoted by $\bar{U}$. If σ_1 is the final stress and ε_1 the corresponding strain, the stress corresponding to an intermediate strain ε can be denoted by $\sigma(\varepsilon)$. In order to calculate the work, it can be imagined that the left-hand face, say, is fixed. Since the change in cross section due to cross contraction can be neglected in the linear theory, the work corresponding to a change $d\varepsilon$ in the strain will be

$$d\bar{W} = \sigma(s)\, d\varepsilon, \tag{20.1}$$

and therefore the total work of deformation will be

$$\bar{W} = \int_0^{\varepsilon_1} \sigma(\varepsilon)\, d\varepsilon. \tag{20.2}$$

Now $\bar{W}$ is a single-valued function of ε_1 if and only if $\sigma(\varepsilon)$ is single-valued, as occurs in the elastic region of the stress-strain diagram (Fig. 20.3), namely when $\sigma(\varepsilon)$ is below σ_0. Here, the deformation work $\bar{W}$ is equal to the strain energy $\bar{U}$. It can be indicated by the area between the curve $\sigma(\varepsilon)$, the ε-axis, and the end ordinate. Corresponding to the stress $\sigma = 0$ we have the strain $\varepsilon = 0$ and the strain energy $\bar{U} = 0$. After reaching the yield stress σ_0, the function $\sigma(\varepsilon)$ becomes multivalued and there is no longer a strain energy. The stress $\sigma = 0$ after unloading is associated with a residual strain $\varepsilon \neq 0$ and a deformation work $\bar{W} \neq 0$ that has been transformed into heat and can again be illustrated by an area in Fig. 20.3.

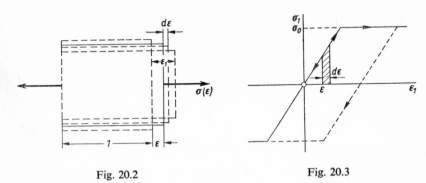

Fig. 20.2   Fig. 20.3

These results can now be used to make the definition of elasticity given in the Introduction more precise: by an *elastic* (solid) *body* will henceforth be understood one in which the internal forces are conservative. In the following we will restrict ourselves to elastic bodies or the elastic region. Then it can be assumed that the state of stress is uniquely determined by the state of strain. Because of the linear relations represented by Hooke's law, the inverse is also true: the state of strain is uniquely given by the state of stress.

With Hooke's law (19.5), the strain energy (20.2) in a *uniaxial state of stress* assumes the form

$$\bar{U} = E \int_0^{\varepsilon_1} \varepsilon \, d\varepsilon = \tfrac{1}{2} E \varepsilon_1^2, \tag{20.3}$$

and, by a further application of (19.5), we can also write

$$\bar{U} = \tfrac{1}{2}\sigma_1\varepsilon_1 \quad \text{or} \quad \bar{U} = \frac{\sigma_1^2}{2E}. \tag{20.4}$$

The first form (20.4) is especially instructive; the numerical factor $\tfrac{1}{2}$ can be explained by the fact that the stress in the course of the extension increases from zero up to its final value.

For the *state of plane stress* given by the principal stresses, these can be thought of as simultaneously increasing up to their end values. By analogy to the first relation (20.4) we have

$$\bar{U} = \tfrac{1}{2}(\sigma_1\varepsilon_1 + \sigma_2\varepsilon_2), \tag{20.5}$$

and, when (19.11) is used to eliminate the principal strains, this yields

$$\bar{U} = \frac{1}{2E}(\sigma_1^2 + \sigma_2^2 - 2\nu\sigma_1\sigma_2). \tag{20.6}$$

With $\sigma_1 = -\sigma_2 = \tau$, it follows from (20.6) for the *state of pure shear* that

$$\bar{U} = \frac{1}{2E}(2\tau^2 + 2v\tau^2) = \frac{1 + v}{E}\tau^2,$$

or, written with the shear modulus (19.15),

$$\bar{U} = \frac{\tau^2}{2G} = \tfrac{1}{2}\tau\gamma, \tag{20.7}$$

where the analogy to (20.4) should be observed.

By superposing (20.5) or (20.6) on (20.7) one could now also write the strain energy for a plane state of stress referred to arbitrary coordinates. Instead let it be observed that for a *three-dimensional state of stress*

$$\bar{U} = \tfrac{1}{2}(\sigma_x\varepsilon_x + \sigma_y\varepsilon_y + \sigma_z\varepsilon_z + \tau_{yz}\gamma_{yz} + \tau_{zx}\gamma_{zx} + \tau_{xy}\gamma_{xy}), \tag{20.8}$$

where this expression also can be written in terms of the stresses alone by means of (19.17).

In Section 18, the three-dimensional state of stress was represented as the sum of a hydrostatic and a plane state of stress. However, it can also be resolved in another way. Let the *mean normal stress* be defined as

$$s = \tfrac{1}{3}(\sigma_x + \sigma_y + \sigma_z), \tag{20.9}$$

which, by (18.13), is equal to $I_1/3$ and is thus invariant. Now the state of stress can be subdivided into the hydrostatic state

$$\begin{matrix} s & 0 & 0 \\ 0 & s & 0 \\ 0 & 0 & s \end{matrix} \tag{20.10}$$

and the state

$$\begin{matrix} s_x = \sigma_x - s & \tau_{xy} & \tau_{xz} \\ \tau_{yx} & s_y = \sigma_y - s & \tau_{yz} \\ \tau_{zx} & \tau_{zy} & s_z = \sigma_z - s \end{matrix} \tag{20.11}$$

Of the above two tensors, the first one is called an *isotropic tensor*. Its components are the same in any system of coordinates. By (20.9), the second tensor (20.11) has the property that its *trace*, i.e., the sum of the elements in the leading diagonal, vanishes. Such a tensor is called a *deviator*.

Similarly, when a third of the volumetric dilatation,

$$e = \tfrac{1}{3}\varepsilon = \tfrac{1}{3}(\varepsilon_x + \varepsilon_y + \varepsilon_z), \tag{20.12}$$

is defined as the *mean normal strain*, the state of strain can be decomposed into an isotropic tensor

$$\begin{array}{ccc} e & 0 & 0 \\ 0 & e & 0 \\ 0 & 0 & e \end{array} \tag{20.13}$$

and a deviator

$$\begin{array}{ccc} e_x = \varepsilon_x - e & \tfrac{1}{2}\gamma_{xy} & \tfrac{1}{2}\gamma_{xz} \\ \tfrac{1}{2}\gamma_{yx} & e_y = \varepsilon_y - e & \tfrac{1}{2}\gamma_{yz} \\ \tfrac{1}{2}\gamma_{zx} & \tfrac{1}{2}\gamma_{zy} & e_z = \varepsilon_z - e . \end{array} \tag{20.14}$$

Here, the isotropic tensor describes a pure dilatation, i.e., a change of volume without change of shape of the element, and the deviator a change of shape without dilatation.

By (20.12), we have

$$e_x = \varepsilon_x - e = \tfrac{2}{3}\varepsilon_x - \tfrac{1}{3}(\varepsilon_y + \varepsilon_z),$$

and, by (19.17), this can also be written as

$$e_x = \frac{2}{3E}[\sigma_x - \nu(\sigma_y + \sigma_z)] - \frac{1}{3E}[\sigma_y + \sigma_z - \nu(2\sigma_x + \sigma_y + \sigma_z)],$$

or more briefly as

$$e_x = \frac{1+\nu}{3E}(2\sigma_x - \sigma_y - \sigma_z). \tag{20.15}$$

Similar results hold for e_y and e_z. Introducing the shear modulus (19.15), we have

$$e_x = \frac{1}{6G}(2\sigma_x - \sigma_y - \sigma_z), \dots, \tag{20.16}$$

where the dots here and in the following indicate cyclic permutation. Moreover, by (20.12) and (19.17),

$$e = \frac{1-2\nu}{3E}(\sigma_x + \sigma_y + \sigma_z)$$

or, by (20.9),

$$e = \frac{1-2\nu}{E}s. \tag{20.17}$$

Using (20.14) and (20.12), the strain energy (20.8) takes the form

$$\bar{U} = \tfrac{1}{2}(\sigma_x e_x + \dots + \tau_{yz}\gamma_{yz} + \dots) + \tfrac{1}{2}(\sigma_x + \dots)e. \tag{20.18}$$

The first term clearly stems from the change of shape; the second from the change of volume. The strain energy can thus be decomposed into a *distortional energy* $\bar{U}_g$ and a *dilatational energy* $\bar{U}_v$, where, by (20.18) and (20.16),

$$\bar{U}_g = \frac{1}{6G}\left[\sigma_x^2 + \ldots - \tfrac{1}{2}\sigma_x(\sigma_y + \sigma_z) - \ldots + 3\tau_{yz}^2 + \ldots\right]$$

or

$$\bar{U}_g = \frac{1}{6G}(\sigma_x^2 + \sigma_y^2 + \sigma_z^2 - \sigma_y\sigma_z - \sigma_z\sigma_x - \sigma_x\sigma_y + 3\tau_{yz}^2 + 3\tau_{zx}^2 + 3\tau_{xy}^2), \qquad (20.19)$$

and, by (20.18), (20.9), and (20.17),

$$\bar{U}_v = \frac{3}{2}se = \frac{3}{2}\frac{1-2v}{E}s^2 = \frac{1-2v}{6E}(\sigma_x + \sigma_y + \sigma_z)^2. \qquad (20.20)$$

This decomposition is of importance in judging the strength of a material.

Exercises

1. Write the strain energy for the state of plane stress σ_x, σ_y, τ_{xy} and split it up into distortional and dilatational energy, expressing both in terms of the given stress components.

2. In a similar manner, discuss the uniaxial state of stress σ_1, the state of pure shear τ, and the hydrostatic state of stress s.

21. Yield and Fracture Conditions

If a body is supported and loaded in an arbitrary manner, the state of stress in the interior will vary from point to point. If for the sake of simplicity it is assumed that the state is uniaxial at every point, the only nonzero principal stress increases at each point with increase of loading. The point where the yield or ultimate stress σ_0 is first attained is called the *endangered point* of the body.

In a *brittle material* a fracture can be avoided by ensuring that $|\sigma_1|$ remains less than σ_0 at the endangered point and thus in the whole body. If often occurs, however, that at certain parts of the body, the actual stresses are larger than those calculated by the simplifying methods used in strength of materials; this can be due to pre-stressing, or stress concentrations near points of application of concentrated forces, holes, or notches. For this reason one defines an *allowable normal stress*

$$\sigma_{al} = \frac{\sigma_0}{n} \qquad (21.1)$$

formed with a *safety factor n*, and requires that at the endangered point

$$|\sigma_1| \le \sigma_{al}. \tag{21.2}$$

Here the factor n represents safety against fracture.

In setting the safety factor n, it should be observed that the stresses in the body when the *loading is suddenly applied* can be twice as large as in the static case, i.e., when the loading is gradual. Moreover, if the *load* is *varying* or *oscillating*, account must be taken of *fatigue*. This term refers to the fact that after many variations of the loading, fracture can occur under stresses that lie considerably below the statical ultimate limit. Finally there are other factors that play a role in setting the safety factor, such as danger to human beings, the required life of the structure, its weight, and economic considerations.

In a *ductile material*, a similar procedure may be based on the yield stress σ_0 if plastic deformation is to be completely avoided. The factor n represents the safety against yielding. In many cases, however, local yielding can be allowed; very often it is even desired in order to remove dangerous stress concentrations. In any case, this yielding must be considered when estimating the safety against fracture in a ductile material. The fracture will occur when the plastic region has extended sufficiently. Thus, for an estimate of the safety against fracture, it is also necessary to bring the plastic behavior of the body into consideration, even when it is not intended to increase the loading so far that considerable yielding would occur.

The *design* of a body, i.e., the determination of the dimensions that it must have in order to be able to carry a given loading without endangerment according to the above-mentioned points of view, will be discussed in detail in the next section. Before this, however, we must consider how to determine the yield and fracture stresses when the states of stress are more complex than the uniaxial one.

Let it be assumed that the state of stress at an arbitrary point P of a body (for example, at the endangered point) is three-dimensional and that the stresses increase from zero in an arbitrary manner. Then the (ductile or brittle) material will begin to yield or fracture under definite values of the stress components. The states of stress under which this occurs are given by the *yield condition* and the *fracture condition*, respectively. At present there are two such conditions, which for practical purposes differ so little from each other that experiments have not clearly confirmed one or the other. These conditions will be described in the following. In practice it is usual to choose the one that makes the mathematical treatment of the problem at hand more tractable.

The *Tresca condition*, formulated by Tresca (1868), makes the greatest shear stress responsible for the appearance of plastic flow or fracture. According to it, yielding or fracture takes place when the greatest shear stress at the point P

has reached a certain value τ_0. Therefore we have

$$\tau_{\max} = \tau_0.\tag{21.3}$$

Since we have $\tau_{\max} = |\sigma_1|/2$ in a uniaxial state of stress, τ_0 can be derived from the yield stress σ_0 for uniaxial tension by

$$\tau_0 = \frac{\sigma_0}{2},\tag{21.4}$$

and therefore condition (21.3) becomes

$$\tau_{\max} = \frac{\sigma_0}{2}.\tag{21.5}$$

If the *three-dimensional state of stress* is given by the principal stresses σ_1, σ_2, σ_3, the greatest shear stress follows from (18.34). Thus the Tresca condition can also be written in the form

$$\max\left(|\sigma_2 - \sigma_3|, |\sigma_3 - \sigma_1|, |\sigma_1 - \sigma_2|\right) = \sigma_0.\tag{21.6}$$

For a *state of plane stress* ($\sigma_3 = 0$), the condition (21.6) reduces to

$$\max\left(|\sigma_1|, |\sigma_2|, |\sigma_1 - \sigma_2|\right) = \sigma_0.\tag{21.7}$$

This condition can be represented in the σ_1, σ_2-plane by the hexagon illustrated in Fig. 21.1. Each state of stress for which the material still behaves elastically is represented by an interior point Q. With increasing loading, yielding or fracture of the material occurs when the image point Q reaches the boundary, namely, at the so-called *yield* or *fracture locus*.

For a *uniaxial state of stress* ($\sigma_2 = \sigma_3 = 0$), the condition (21.6) reduces to $|\sigma_1| = \sigma_0$, as is to be expected.

The *condition of von Mises* (1913) considers the distortional energy responsible for the inception of plastic flow or fracture. According to this condition, yielding or fracture begins when the distortional energy (20.19) at the point P

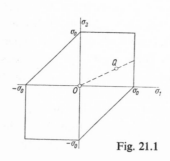

Fig. 21.1

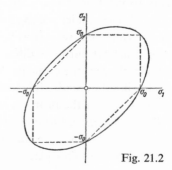

Fig. 21.2

reaches a definite value $\bar{U}_0$. Therefore, we have

$$\sigma_x^2 + \sigma_y^2 + \sigma_z^2 - \sigma_y\sigma_z - \sigma_z\sigma_x - \sigma_x\sigma_y + 3\tau_{yz}^2 + 3\tau_{zx}^2 + 3\tau_{xy}^2 = 6G\bar{U}_0. \tag{21.8}$$

Since the left-hand side reduces to σ_1^2 for a linear state of stress σ_1, the right-hand side can, with

$$6G\bar{U}_0 = \sigma_0^2, \tag{21.9}$$

be expressed in terms of σ_0. Therefore, condition (21.8), for the *three-dimensional state of stress*, becomes

$$\sigma_x^2 + \sigma_y^2 + \sigma_z^2 - \sigma_y\sigma_z - \sigma_z\sigma_x - \sigma_x\sigma_y + 3\tau_{zy}^2 + 3\tau_{zx}^2 + 3\tau_{xy}^2 = \sigma_0^2. \tag{21.10}$$

When the state of stress is given in principal axes, this becomes

$$\sigma_1^2 + \sigma_2^2 + \sigma_3^2 - \sigma_2\sigma_3 - \sigma_3\sigma_1 - \sigma_1\sigma_2 = \sigma_0^2. \tag{21.11}$$

For the *state of plane stress*, (21.10) reduces to

$$\sigma_x^2 + \sigma_y^2 - \sigma_x\sigma_y + 3\tau_{xy}^2 = \sigma_0^2, \tag{21.12}$$

while (21.11) becomes

$$\sigma_1^2 + \sigma_2^2 - \sigma_1\sigma_2 = \sigma_0^2. \tag{21.13}$$

In the σ_1, σ_2-plane (Fig. 21.2), the last condition can be represented by an ellipse as yield or fracture diagram, which circumscribes the hexagon in Fig. 21.1.

As is to be expected, condition (21.11) reduces to $|\sigma_1| = \sigma_0$ for a *uniaxial state of stress*. In this case, the conditions of Tresca and von Mises coincide. In the following sections we will mainly encounter uniaxial states of stress, and then we will have the same simple condition valid for both theories.

In applying these yield or fracture conditions, a certain caution is called for. There are brittle materials, such as concrete, which have different ultimate limits for uniaxial tension and compression. These differences are represented by neither the Tresca nor the von Mises condition. Moreover, with ductile materials, especially at high temperatures, one observes *creep*, i.e., a deformation that increases with time while the stresses remain constant. Of course, this phenomenon also will not be described by the combination of stress-strain relations like (19.17) with yield conditions of the type considered here.

Exercises

1. There is a state of plane stress σ_x, $\sigma_y = 0$, τ_{xy} at the endangered point P of a ductile body. Formulate the yield conditions of Tresca and of von Mises in terms of the prescribed stress components and discuss the yield curves in the σ_x, τ_{xy}-plane.

2. For a three-dimensional state of stress given by the principal stresses σ_1, σ_2, σ_3, the yield condition is represented by a so-called yield surface in the $\sigma_1, \sigma_2, \sigma_3$-space. Describe these surfaces for the conditions of Tresca and von Mises.

22. Concentric Tension and Compression

We now turn attention to problems arising in strength of materials and concerned with bars and beams that are loaded in various ways. Now that the tensile test has already been discussed in Section 19, tensile and compressive loading can easily be disposed of. In the meantime we wish to prepare the ground for the next section, in which other types of loading will be discussed.

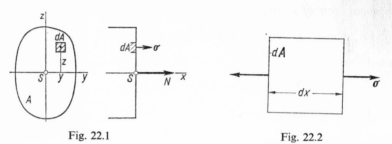

Fig. 22.1   Fig. 22.2

The notion of a bar or beam was defined at the beginning of Section 17. Figure 22.1 shows an arbitrary section through a bar. Let the cross-sectional area be A and the centroid be at S. We will confine attention to *untwisted bars*, i.e., to those for which the principal axes at S in all sections have the same direction. Then the coordinate system can be chosen so that the x-axis coincides with the axis of the undeformed bar, and the y- and z-axes with the principal axes of an arbitrary section. By Section 15, the principal moments of inertia of the section in Fig. 22.1 are

$$I_y = \int_A z^2 \, dA, \qquad I_z = \int_A y^2 \, dA, \qquad (22.1)$$

and the product moment C_{yz} vanishes.

If s is the stress vector at an element dA of the cross section, then $s \, dA$ are the forces transmitted by the section. They are unknown in detail but the stress resultants can be obtained by the methods discussed in Section 17. In the case of a slender bar subjected to tension, compression, or bending, a good approximation for the stresses s is obtained by making the *simplifying assumptions* that (1) the longitudinal fibers do not affect each other, and (2) the cross sections remain plane during the deformation.

On the basis of the first assumption, four of the six longitudinal faces of the elementary cuboid abutting the surface element dA (Fig. 22.2) are free of stress. By the reciprocity of the stress components (Section 18), only normal stresses act on the remaining faces. The state of stress is thus uniaxial with σ as the only nonzero principal stress. For the time being we will limit ourselves to the *elastic response*, so that Hooke's law (19.5) is still valid. The axial extension of the cuboid will now be given by

$$\Delta\,dx = \varepsilon\,dx = \frac{\sigma}{E}dx\,. \tag{22.2}$$

The tranverse contraction leads to a transverse displacement of the element. To the first order of accuracy, this can be neglected, and then the second assumption demands that $\Delta\,dx$ be a linear function of the tranverse coordinates y and z. Thus, by (22.2), we have

$$\sigma = a + by + cz\,, \tag{22.3}$$

where a, b, and c are as yet undetermined constants. Consequently, the normal stress is distributed linearly over the cross section.

If the section forces $\sigma\,dA$ in a cross section are reduced at the centroid S, a normal force N and two bending moments M_y, M_z are obtained, given by

$$N = \int_A \sigma\,dA = a \int_A dA + b \int_A y\,dA + c \int_A z\,dA\,,$$

$$M_y = \int_A \sigma z\,dA = a \int_A z\,dA + b \int_A yz\,dA + c \int_A z^2\,dA\,, \tag{22.4}$$

$$-M_z = \int_A \sigma y\,dA = a \int_A y\,dA + b \int_A y^2\,dA + c \int_A yz\,dA\,.$$

Since S lies on the x-axis, it follows from Section 10 that, for instance, the second and third integrals in the expression for N must vanish. The first one represents the area A of the cross section. Since the remaining integrals, by (22.1), represent the principal moments of inertia of the cross section at S, we have

$$N = aA\,, \qquad M_y = cI_y\,, \qquad M_z = -bI_z\,,$$

or

$$a = \frac{N}{A}\,, \qquad b = -\frac{M_z}{I_z}\,, \qquad c = \frac{M_y}{I_y}\,. \tag{22.5}$$

In this way the distribution of stress (22.3) is given in terms of the stress resultants.

In the case of concentric tension or compression, the stress resultant by Fig. 22.1, consists of only a normal force N. Then it follows from (22.5) that $b=c=0$, and the distribution of normal stress in the section is given by

$$\sigma = \frac{N}{A}\,. \tag{22.6}$$

Being expressed by N and A, it is dependent only on x, i.e., the position of the section, and is distributed uniformly over each section. According to the sign of N, we have either compressive or tensile stress.

By (22.2) and (22.6), the slice lying between x and $x+dx$ extends (or contracts) by an amount

$$\Delta\,dx = \frac{N}{EA}\,dx.\qquad(22.7)$$

The axis of the bar remains straight and the change in length of the whole bar is given by

$$\Delta l = \int_0^l \frac{N(x)}{EA(x)}\,dx.\qquad(22.8)$$

By (22.7), the normal strain in a section is inversely proportional to the quantity EA, which is called the *tensile rigidity*.

When only two equal and opposite axial forces are applied to the ends of a cylindrical or prismatic bar (Fig. 22.3), both N and A are constant. The stress distribution is thus the same in all sections, and the elongation (22.8) is now given by

$$\Delta l = \frac{Nl}{EA}.\qquad(22.9)$$

Since the state of stress is uniaxial, both yield or fracture conditions discussed in Section 21 coincide. In order to avoid yielding or fracture, it is necessary that

$$|\sigma| \le \sigma_{al}, \quad \text{where} \quad \sigma_{al} = \frac{\sigma_0}{n},\qquad(22.10)$$

in all sections. For the design of a structure, it is necessary that the inequality

$$\left|\frac{N}{A}\right|_{max} \le \sigma_{al}\qquad(22.11)$$

is satisfied for all cross sections. The section in which N/A is maximal is called the *endangered cross section*.

Fig. 22.3

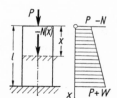

Fig. 22.4

When the bar is cylindrical or prismatic, (22.11) can be written in the form

$$A \geq \frac{|N|_{\max}}{\sigma_{al}}. \tag{22.12}$$

The endangered section can here by found directly from the normal-force diagram.

When a bar is subjected to compression, there is often a danger of *buckling* even before σ_{al} has been reached. Design according to (22.11) or (22.12) is then not sufficient, and it must, as will be shown in Section 27, be supplemented by design against buckling.

If the cylindrical bar in Fig. 22.3, consisting of steel with the data $l=20$ ft, $P=26,000$ lb*, $\sigma_{al}=20,000$ lb*/in², $E=3.10^7$ lb*/in², is to be designed, it follows, by (22.12) since $N=P$ everywhere, that the required cross section must satisfy

$$A \geq \frac{P}{\sigma_{al}} = 1.3 \text{ in}^2.$$

If we choose $A=1.3$ in², in order to make full use of the bar, the extension, by (22.9), will be

$$\Delta l = \frac{\sigma_{al}\, l}{E} = 0.16 \text{ in},$$

i.e., just over 0.05 % of the length.

Fig. 22.4 shows a vertical cylindrical column that is loaded by the force P and its own weight W. The normal force in the section x has the magnitude

$$N(x) = -P - \frac{W}{l}x.$$

The normal-force diagram is indicated in Fig. 22.4. The section $x=l$ is endangered and the greatest absolute normal force is $|N|_{\max}=P+W$. We have to require that

$$|\sigma|_{\max} = \frac{P+W}{A} \leq \sigma_{al},$$

and the elongation of the column is furnished by

$$\Delta l = -\frac{1}{EA} \int_0^l \left(P + \frac{W}{l}x \right) dx = -\frac{1}{EA}\left(P + \frac{W}{2} \right) l.$$

It represents a shortening of the column.

We are now in the position to solve *statically indeterminate problems* insofar as they are connected with tension or compression of bars. Such bars have more supports than would be necessary for maintaining equilibrium. The additional supports, however, limit the range of possible deformations, and the equations for determining the reactions are obtained by augmenting the equations of equilibrium by those that express what is known about the deformations.

The fixed-end uniform beam in Fig. 22.5 is not pre-stressed and is loaded by the axial force P. If the weight of the beam can be neglected, then only the axial reactions B and C arise. The only nontrivial equilibrium condition is

Fig. 22.5

$$B + C = P ; \qquad (22.13)$$

the problem is thus simply statically indeterminate. A second equation for B and C is obtained by expressing the fact that the elongation Δl of the whole bar must vanish by virtue of the type of support. The section on which P acts divides the bar into two fields 1 and 2 with the lengths b and c, and, of course, we have

$$b + c = l. \qquad (22.14)$$

In field 1 the normal force is B, but in field 2 it is $-C$. The elongation of each field, by (22.9), will be

$$\Delta b = \frac{Bb}{EA}, \qquad \Delta c = -\frac{Cc}{EA}. \qquad (22.15)$$

Thus, the condition $\Delta l = \Delta b + \Delta c = 0$ furnishes the second equation

$$Bb = Cc \qquad (22.16)$$

for the reactions. Then, with (22.16), (22.13), and (22.14), the reactions are found to be

$$B = \frac{c}{l} P , \qquad C = \frac{b}{l} P . \qquad (22.17)$$

If it is assumed that $b < c$, then $B > C$ so that the design must be based on the inequality

$$P \le \frac{l}{c} A \sigma_{\mathrm{al}} .$$

or, if a safety factor of one is adopted,

$$P < \frac{l}{c} A \sigma_0 . \qquad (22.18)$$

If the loading of a ductile bar is gradually increased, the whole endangered cross section will become *plastic* as soon as $|\sigma| = \sigma_0$ there. The material in this section will begin to yield, and the distribution of stress given by relation (22.6) will remain valid. However, relations (22.7) to (22.9), which are based on Hooke's law, will cease to hold. When the structure is statically determinate, the loading P cannot increase above that value P_0 for which the endangered cross section becomes plastic and the change of length $|\Delta l|$ increases with yielding without any further increase of P. If it is required to prevent *collapse*, i.e., destruction by unlimited yielding, then P must be kept below P_0. This is achieved by design according to (22.11) or (22.12). If, however, the structure is statically indeterminate, then the onset of plastic yielding does not lead to collapse of the bar, since there will still be elastic fields that are able to carry the loads. In this case P can be increased above P_0 until it reaches the value $P = P^*$ for which so many sections yield that collapse occurs. The load P^* is called the *limit load*, and in such cases the design is based on the condition

$$P \leq \frac{P^*}{n}, \tag{22.19}$$

where n is the safety factor against collapse (or rupture).

For the bar in Fig. 22.5 we have, when $b < c$, that $B > C$ in the whole elastic domain. The whole of field 1 will become plastic when the stress in it reaches

$$\sigma = \frac{B}{A} = \frac{c}{l}\frac{P}{A} = \sigma_0,$$

and thus when the load reaches

$$P = P_0 = \frac{l}{c} A\sigma_0. \tag{22.20}$$

Since field 2 is still elastic under this loading, the bar does not collapse under P_0. The loading can be further increased till field 2 also becomes plastic. During this stage (22.16) does not hold any longer. Instead, we know that B remains constant:

$$B = A\sigma_0. \tag{22.21}$$

By (22.13), we therefore have

$$C = P - A\sigma_0, \tag{22.22}$$

and collapse occurs when C becomes equal to $A\sigma_0$. The limit load is thus given by

$$P^* = 2A\sigma_0. \tag{22.23}$$

Since $b < c$ implies that $c > l/2$, this limit load is greater than the load (22.20) at *incipient plastic flow*. This estimate of the limit load is based on the assumption that there is no danger of buckling.

In this section we have determined the reactions, the stress resultants, the stresses, and the deformations on the basis of forces applied to the undeformed bar. Of course, in general, objection can be raised against such a procedure, since the body is in equilibrium only in the deformed configuration. With concentric tension or compression, however, the loads are displaced along their lines of action, so that the simplified treatment is admissible.

On the other hand, it is clear that the assumptions about the independence of the longitudinal fibers and about the sections remaining plane are simplifications that cannot always be justified even when they are exactly fulfilled in simpler cases. For example, the external forces (such as P in Fig. 22.5) are usually not distributed uniformly over the section to which they are applied, and this results in a deviation from the distribution of stress given by the idealization (22.6). Also abrupt changes in the cross section along the x-axis disturb the stress distribution. However, experiments show that such disturbances on account of the interaction of the longitudinal fibers gradually die out with distance from the region concerned; above all when the cross sections are compact. Therefore, the results of this section can be regarded as at least useful approximations for slender bars with compact and only slowly varying cross sections. The same applies to the following sections.

Exercises

1. Figure 22.6 shows a weight $W=1000$ lb* suspended by three elastic wires with elastic modulus $E=3.10^7$ psi and allowable stress $\sigma_{a1}=24,000$ psi. Calculate the required cross-sectional areas of the wires. Then, making use of the fact that the fractional elongations of the wires are small, determine the amount z by which the weight descends vertically as a result of the deformation of the wires.

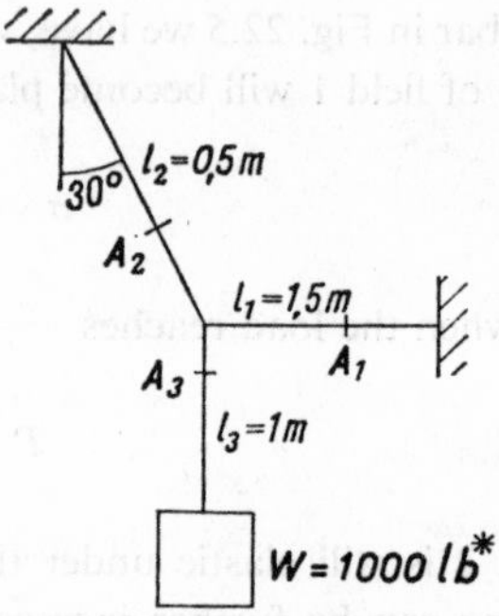

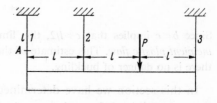

Fig. 22.6

2. A vertical column is fixed at the lower end. It is loaded both by the axial force P acting downward at the uppermost cross section and by its own weight. The specific weight of the material is γ, and the allowable stress σ_{a1}. How must the cross section A increase with depth if the column is to be fully exploited, i.e., if the stress in all sections should be σ_{a1}?

3. A rigid beam (Fig. 22.7), the weight of which may be neglected, is suspended on three wires of length $l=1$ m, cross-sectional area $A=1$ mm², elastic modulus 2×10^6 kg*/cm² and yield stress $\sigma_0=1500$ kg*/cm². Which wire begins to yield first when the load P is gradually increased from zero? What is the corresponding load P_0? Which wire begins to yield next? How large is the limit load P^*?

Fig. 22.7

23. Simple Bending

According to Section 17, a beam is subjected to bending if the external forces intersect its axis normally. *We speak of simple bending* if in addition (1) these forces all lie in one plane (the so-called *loading-plane*), and (2) the *loading line b* (Fig. 23.1), i.e., the intersection of the loading plane with an arbitrary cross section, is one of the principal axes passing through S, for instance, the z-axis.

The loading of a section then consists of a bending moment M_b in the y-axis and a shearing force Q in the z-axis.

Here again we make the simplifying assumptions that the longitudinal fibers are independent and that the sections remain plane, so that the state of stress is again uniaxial as in Fig. 22.2 and the distribution of the axial stress over the cross section is once more given by (22.3), provided that the response is purely *elastic*. With $N=0$, $M_y=M_b$, $M_z=0$, the coefficients (22.5) turn out to be $a=b=0$ and $c=M_b/I_y$. Thus, the distribution of normal stress will have the form

$$\sigma = \frac{M_b}{I_y}z. \tag{23.1}$$

Of course, the reduction of the stresses $\sigma\,dA$ at S does not yield a shearing force Q, which means that the assumptions used are too restrictive in this case. Nevertheless, it can be shown (Section 25) that the error for rather slender beams is negligibly small, so that the shearing force may be neglected for the time being.

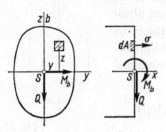

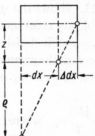

Fig. 23.1   Fig. 23.2

By (23.1), the normal stress depends on x through M_b and I_y, and in each section it is proportional to the distance from the principal axis through S perpendicular to the loading line. This axis on which $\sigma=0$ is called the *neutral axis n* of the cross section and the corresponding layer of fibers in the plane of x and n is called the *neutral plane*. The bending moment can be denoted simply by M, and the moment of inertia by I. Then, (23.1) reads

$$\sigma = \frac{M}{I}z. \tag{23.2}$$

Since not only the stresses but also the strains are proportional to z, the axis of the beam will bend during the deformation. The curved axis will be called the *deflection curve*. In order to calculate its curvature, consider a volume element in the form of a cuboid as shown in Fig. 23.2. Its elongation is

$$\Delta\,dx = \varepsilon\,dx = \frac{\sigma}{E}\,dx = \frac{Mz}{EI}\,dx. \tag{23.3}$$

Let it be supposed that section x is fixed. Then the centroids of the surface elements in section $x + dx$ will be coplanar also after the deformation. By (23.2) and consideration of similar triangles in Fig. 23.2, the radius of curvature ϱ is furnished by the relation

$$\frac{z}{\varrho} = \frac{\Delta\,dx}{dx} = \frac{Mz}{EI}.$$

The curvature is thus given by

$$\frac{1}{\varrho} = \frac{M}{EI}. \tag{23.4}$$

Hence it is inversely proportional to the so-called *flexural rigidity EI*, which, like M, can be a function of x.

Figure 23.3 shows the stress distribution (23.2) over an arbitrary cross section. The greatest absolute stress, which is decisive in choosing the cross section, occurs at the greatest distance from the neutral axis, that is, for $z = e_1$, or $z = -e_2$. It is obtained from

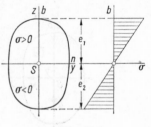

Fig. 23.3

$$|\sigma|_{\max} = \frac{|M|}{I}\,e, \quad \text{where} \quad e = \max\left(|e_1|, |e_2|\right). \tag{23.5}$$

The two quantities I and e, depending only on the shape of the cross section, can be combined into the *axial section modulus Z* defined by the formula

$$Z = \frac{I}{e}. \tag{23.6}$$

Then we write relation (23.5) in the form

$$|\sigma|_{\max} = \frac{|M|}{Z}. \tag{23.7}$$

The section modulus has the dimensions $[L^3]$ and is given in in³.

For a rectangle of sides b and h, we have $I = bh^3/12$, by Section 15. Moreover, $e = h/2$ so that

$$Z = \frac{bh^2}{6}. \tag{23.8}$$

For a circle of radius r we have $I=\pi r^4/4$ and $e=r$, so that

$$Z=\frac{\pi}{4}r^3,$$ (23.9)

and in the case of an annulus of radii R and r, the section modulus is

$$Z=\frac{\pi}{4}\frac{R^4-r^4}{R}.$$ (23.10)

For the standard rolled steel sections, all necessary data, including Z, are to be found in the handbooks.

When a beam is subjected to bending, a cross section of given area A is particularly economical if its shape is chosen so as to have a large section modulus Z. Of the three cross sections represented in Fig. 23.4, the second is more favorable than the first, and the third, the so-called I-section, is more favorable than the second. Carried to the extreme, this tendency to increase Z leads to the use of a truss, in which all fibers are fully exploited.

It has already been emphasized that certain materials, such as concrete, have a lower strength in tension than in compression. In such cases, the strength is increased by reinforment of the tension side.

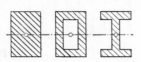

Fig. 23.4

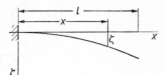

Fig. 23.5

Since the state of stress in a beam is uniaxial, yielding or rupture can be avoided by ensuring that $|\sigma|_{max}\leq\sigma_{al}$ in every cross section. Thus, by (23.7), the condition

$$\left|\frac{M}{Z}\right|_{max}\leq\sigma_{al}$$ (23.11)

must be complied with in every cross section. The section in which M/Z attains its maximum value is called the endangered cross section.

With prismatic beams, condition (23.11) can be written in the form

$$Z\geq\frac{|M|_{max}}{\sigma_{al}}.$$ (23.12)

In this case, the endangered cross section can be obtained directly from the bending-moment diagram.

The deflection curve of a beam can be represented by a function $\zeta(x)$ as in Fig. 23.5. In many cases its slope is everywhere small, so that consideration can be restricted to linear terms in $\zeta' = d\zeta/dx$. To this accuracy, the element of arc is

$$ds = \sqrt{1 + \zeta'^2}\,dx = (1 + \tfrac{1}{2}\zeta'^2 + \cdots)\,dx = dx,$$

which means that the axial displacements of the centroids of the cross sections can be neglected. Thus, the displacements are normal to the axis and are given by ζ. To the same accuracy, the curvature of the deflection curve is given by

$$\varrho = \pm\,\frac{(1 + \zeta'^2)^{3/2}}{\zeta''} = \pm\,\frac{1}{\zeta''}(1 + \tfrac{3}{2}\zeta'^2 + \cdots) = \pm\,\frac{1}{\zeta''},$$

and substitution into (23.4) yields the differential equation

$$\zeta'' = \pm\,\frac{M}{EI} \qquad\qquad (23.13)$$

for the deflection curve. The sign on the right-hand side depends on the conventions for M and ζ; it is best determined in each individual case. Integration of (23.13) gives rise to two arbitrary constants that are fixed by the boundary conditions.

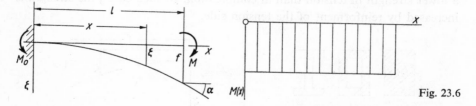

Fig. 23.6

When the cantilever beam (Fig. 23.6) is subjected to a couple M at the free end, the only reaction at the fixed end is the moment $M_0 = M$. The bending moment at section x is M, and the shearing force vanishes. The bending-moment diagram is thus a rectangle, and all sections are equally endangered. The design is carried out according to (23.12). If the data are $M = 3000$ lb* ft and $\sigma_{al} = 20,000$ psi, this yields

$$Z \geq \frac{36,000}{20,000} = 1.8\ \text{in}^3. \qquad\qquad (23.14)$$

Now, if an American Standard I-beam (Fig. 23.7) is to be used, it can be seen from the American Institute of Steel Construction Handbook that the 3 I 5.7 with section modulus 1.7 in³ is too small, whereas the 3 I 7.5 with section modulus 1.9 in³ and $I = 2.9$ in⁴ would be large enough to ensure a working stress less than 20,000 psi.

By (23.4), the deflection curve has a constant curvature and is therefore a circular arc, whose radius is given by

$$\varrho = \frac{EI}{M} = \frac{3 \times 10^7 \cdot 2.9}{36,000} = 2417\ \text{in} = 201\ \text{ft}$$

when the modulus of elasticity is $E = 3 \times 10^7$ psi.

Fig. 23.7

If we proceed from the differential equation (23.13), it is first seen from Fig. 23.6 that the positive sign is to be chosen. Then, since the right-hand side is a constant, two integrations lead to

$$\zeta = \frac{M}{EI}\left(\frac{x^2}{2} + c_1 x + c_2\right).$$

The boundary conditions $\zeta(0)=0$, $\zeta'(0)=0$ yield $c_1=c_2=0$ and therefore, to this accuracy, a parabola

$$\zeta = \frac{M}{2EI} x^2.$$

The greatest displacement f occurs at the free end, and it is

$$f = \zeta(l) = \frac{Ml^2}{2EI}, \tag{23.15}$$

or with $l=10$ ft and the above values,

$$f = \frac{36{,}000 \cdot 120^2}{2 \cdot 3 \times 10^7 \cdot 2.9} = 2.98 \,\text{in.}$$

The greatest slope of the deflection curve also occurs at the free end. According to the present theory it amounts to

$$\alpha = \zeta'(l) = \frac{Ml}{EI}. \tag{23.16}$$

Substituting the numerical values, we obtain

$$\alpha = \frac{36{,}000 \cdot 120}{3 \times 10^7 \cdot 2.9} = 0.050 \,\text{radians}$$

or in degree measure

$$\alpha° = \frac{180}{\pi}\alpha = 2.8°.$$

The cantilever beam in Fig. 23.8 carries a uniformly distributed load P. The reactions consist of a force P and a moment $Pl/2$. The bending moment in section x is

$$M(x) = \frac{P}{2l} x^2.$$

The bending-moment diagram is therefore bounded by a parabola. If the beam is

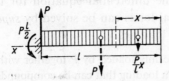
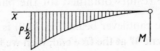

Fig. 23.8

prismatic, the root section, with

$$|M|_{max} = P\frac{l}{2} \tag{23.17}$$

will be the endangered region. The differential equation of the deflection curve is

$$\zeta'' = \frac{P}{2lEI}x^2 .$$

Its first integral is

$$\zeta' = \frac{P}{2lEI}\left(\frac{x^3}{3} + c_1\right),$$

or, since the boundary condition $\zeta'(l)=0$ leads to $c_1 = -l^3/3$,

$$\zeta' = \frac{P}{6lEI}(x^3 - l^3) .$$

Another integration gives

$$\zeta = \frac{P}{6lEI}\left(\frac{x^4}{4} - l^3x + c_2\right),$$

or, since the second boundary condition $\zeta(l)=0$ leads to $c_2 = 3l^4/4$,

$$\zeta = \frac{P}{24lEI}(x^4 - 4l^3x + 3l^4) .$$

The greatest deflection f is

$$f = \zeta(0) = \frac{Pl^3}{8EI}, \tag{23.18}$$

and the steepest slope is

$$\alpha = |\zeta'(0)| = \frac{Pl^2}{6EI} . \tag{23.19}$$

When a problem is statically determinate, there are just as many boundary conditions at our disposal as are needed for the determination of the constants of integration. In the preceding examples, the position of the greatest deflection or steepest slope could be given at the outset. In more complicated cases, however, it is necessary to discuss the function $\zeta(x)$, whereby use can be made of the fact that, by (23.13), the inflections in the deflection curve correspond with the zeros of the bending moment.

Since in the approximation used here the loads move along their lines of application, it is permissible, as in Section 22, to base all the calculations on the conditions related to the undeformed beam. Since all the relations used are linearly dependent on the loads, and since the differential equation for the deflection curve is linear, problems with several loads can be solved by *superposition* of the results obtained for the partial loadings.

If a prismatic cantilever beam (Fig. 23.9) is uniformly loaded by P together with a couple of moment M at the free end, then we have a loading that can be compounded

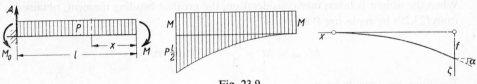

Fig. 23.9

from those in Figs. 23.6 and 23.8. The reactions are

$$A = P, \qquad M_0 = M + P\frac{l}{2},$$

and could have been gained by superposing the reactions from Figs. 23.6 and 23.8. This applies also to the bending moment

$$M(x) = M + \frac{P}{2l}x^2 \ ;$$

in particular, the bending-moment diagram can be obtained by compounding the diagrams for the two simpler cases. The endangered area is the root section with the greatest absolute moment:

$$|M|_{max} = M + P\frac{l}{2}, \tag{23.20}$$

which also follows by superposition. The stresses (23.2) and the curvatures (23.13) of the deflection curve can also be superposed. Here, the differential equation is

$$\zeta'' = \frac{1}{EI}\left(M + \frac{P}{2l}x^2\right).$$

Since it is linear and the greatest deflection f and steepest slope α for each partial loading occur at the same position, f and α can also be obtained by superposition.

The possibility of using superposition is above all of importance when the weight of the beam, which is unknown at the start of the design procedure, gives rise to an additional flexural loading that cannot be overlooked.

The design of the case in Fig. 23.6 with $M = 3000$ lb* ft gave the standard section 3 I 7.5 with section modulus 1.9 in^3 when the weight was neglected. Thus, the greatest absolute stress, apart from the effect of the weight, will, by (23.7), be

$$|\sigma|_{max} = \frac{36,000}{1.9} = 19,000 \text{ psi},$$

which is less than the working stress of $\sigma_{al} = 20,000$ psi. The weight of the beam, however, represents an additional continuously distributed load, as represented in Fig. 23.8. For the rolled section chosen, the specific loading 7.5 lb*/ft for $l = 10$ ft means a total weight of

$$W = 75 \text{ lb*}.$$

When the weight is taken into consideration, the greatest bending moment, obtained from (23.20) by replacing P by W, is

$$M_{\max} = M + \frac{Wl}{2} = 3375 \text{ lb* ft.}$$

Therefore, we actually have

$$|\sigma|_{\max} = \frac{|M|_{\max}}{Z} = \frac{3375 \times 12}{1.9} = 21,300 \text{ psi.}$$

Since this value is higher than the admissible stress σ_{al}, it is necessary to choose at least the next stronger section, namely the 4 I 7.7 standard section. However, since not only the section modulus but also W increases, the design can be regarded as complete only if a repetition of the calculations for this section leads to $|\sigma|_{\max} < \sigma_{al}$.

The design described above is based on the requirement that the yield or ultimate limit should not be attained at any point in the beam. With ductile materials, however, *local plastic flow* does not necessarily lead to failure. What actually happens is that first of all only the outermost fibers yield when the yield stress σ_0 is attained in the endangered section. With increasing loading, the plastic region also extends to the inner fibers and the neighboring sections. For the partially plastic cross sections also, it is usual to retain the simplifying assumptions about the independence of the longitudinal fibers and that sections remain plane. Then, the equation on the extreme left of (23.3) remains valid; the distribution of normal stress, however, is no longer given by (23.2), and the curvature of the deflection curve no longer follows from (23.4). More specifically, the normal stress in those fibers lying in the plastic region will have the constant value σ_0. When a cross section is symmetric about the y-axis, this will remain the neutral axis, and, as long as an elastic core remains, the stress distribution will be represented by a broken curve as in Fig. 23.10. As the loading further increases, the elastic core progressively shrinks. Its disappearance in the endangered cross section (Fig. 23.11) leads to failure in a statically determinate beam.

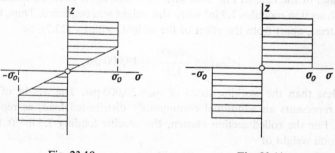

Fig. 23.10   Fig. 23.11

Let M_0 be the bending moment under which the yield stress first appears in the outer fibers of a section, and M^* that under which the whole cross section becomes plastic. A bending moment greater than M^* cannot be carried by the section; under M^* it becomes a so-called *plastic hinge*. The ratio $k = M^*/M_0$ represents the reserve of strength which, by virtue of the plastic behavior, remains in a cross section designed with the condition $|\sigma|_{max} \leq \sigma_0$. It depends on the shape of the cross section and is therefore called the *shape factor k*. Since in statically determinate problems the bending moment in an arbitrary section is proportional to the loading, the factor k here represents the ratio of the limit load to that loading under which yielding first occurs.

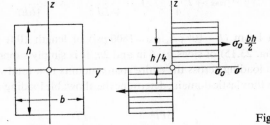

Fig. 23.12

For the rectangle in Fig. 23.12, we have $Z = bh^2/6$, and therefore, by (23.7), in the elastic region

$$|\sigma|_{max} = \frac{6|M|}{bh^2}.$$

Whence is obtained the moment M_0 for incipient yielding:

$$M_0 = \frac{bh^2}{6} \sigma_0.$$

When the cross section has yielded completely, the stress distribution is equivalent to a couple of moment

$$M^* = \sigma_0 \frac{bh}{2} \cdot \frac{h}{2} = \frac{bh^2}{4} \sigma_0.$$

The shape factor thus turns out to be

$$k = \frac{M^*}{M_0} = 1.5.$$

For cross sections that are particularly favorable for flexural loading, i.e., when the area is concentrated at a large distance from the neutral axis, the shape factor has a markedly smaller value than in the last example. Thus, for the standard I-sections, the shape factor k is about 1.15.

Exercises

1. A prismatic cantilever beam (Fig. 23.13) of length l and flexural rigidity EI is loaded at the free end by the force P, which is not large enough to cause plastic yielding. Draw the bending-moment diagram and show that

$$|M|_{\max} = Pl, \qquad f = \frac{Pl^3}{3EI}, \qquad \alpha = \frac{Pl^2}{2EI}.$$

2. Figure 23.14 shows a simple prismatic beam loaded at the center by the concentrated force P. Show that

$$|M|_{\max} = P\frac{l}{4}, \qquad f = \frac{Pl^3}{48EI}, \qquad \alpha = \frac{Pl^2}{16EI}.$$

3. A wooden beam ($E=10^6$ psi, $\sigma_{al}=1800$ psi) of length 10 ft has a rectangular cross section (Fig. 23.15) of sides $a=6$ in and $2a$. It is simply supported at both ends and the uniform loading across the entire span amounts to a total weight P. Limiting consideration to the elastic domain, determine the allowable loading P_{al} and verify that

$$f = \frac{5Pl^3}{384EI}, \qquad \alpha = \frac{Pl^2}{24EI}.$$

Which is the smallest American Standard Beam of steel ($E=3.10^7$ psi, $\sigma_{al}=20,000$ psi) that can carry the same load?

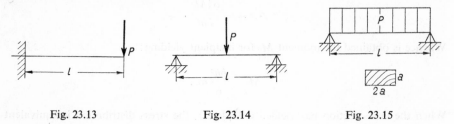

Fig. 23.13   Fig. 23.14   Fig. 23.15

4. Determine the shape factor k for a circular cross section.

24. Statically Indeterminate Flexure Problems

A problem is statically indeterminate when there are more supports present than are necessary to maintain equilibrium. Then the equilibrium conditions (as well as any possible symmetry conditions) are not sufficient for the determination of the reactions. Nevertheless, the expression for the bending moment and, in the *elastic region*, the differential equation for the elastic curve can be formulated. Both these relations will, of course, contain unknown reactions, and these will also occur, along with the constants of integration, in the equation for the deflection curve. The redundant supports, however, represent additional conditions for the elastic curve, and the boundary conditions yield the further equations which are necessary for the determination of the constants of integration and the reactions.

For the fixed-end beam with the uniformly distributed load P (Fig. 24.1), the equilibrium and symmetry conditions furnish the vertical reactions $P/2$ and the fact that the moments M_e are equal; in the present approximation there is no horizontal reaction. Since the magnitude of M_e remains free, the problem is simply statically indeterminate. The bending moment in section x is

$$M(x) = M_e - \frac{P}{2}x + \frac{P}{2l}x^2 . \tag{24.1}$$

The differential equation of the deflection curve therefore reads

$$\zeta'' = \frac{1}{2lEI}(Px^2 - Plx + 2M_el) .$$

Two integrations lead to

$$\zeta = \frac{1}{24lEI}(Px^4 - 2Plx^3 + 12M_elx^2 + c_1x + c_2) .$$

For the determination of the integration constants c_1, c_2, and the moment M_e, we have at our disposal the boundary conditions

$$\zeta(0) = 0 , \qquad \zeta'(0) = 0 , \qquad \zeta(l) = 0 , \qquad \zeta'(l) = 0 ,$$

as well as the symmetry condition

$$\zeta'\left(\frac{l}{2}\right) = 0 .$$

The first two boundary conditions yield $c_1 = c_2 = 0$, so that

$$\zeta = \frac{1}{24lEI}(Px^4 - 2Plx^3 + 12M_elx^2);$$

each of the three remaining conditions leads to

$$M_e = P\frac{l}{12} . \tag{24.2}$$

Thus, the bending moment finally is

$$M(x) = P\left(\frac{l}{12} - \frac{x}{2} + \frac{x^2}{2l}\right), \tag{24.3}$$

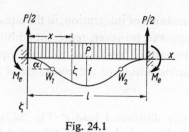

Fig. 24.1　　　　　　　　　　　　　　　　Fig. 24.2

and is represented by the parabola in Fig. 24.2. The greatest absolute bending moment is

$$|M|_{\max} = M_e = P\frac{l}{12}.$$

Then, at last, the equation of the deflection curve is found to be

$$\zeta = \frac{P}{24lEI}(x^4 - 2lx^3 + l^2x^2).$$

From this can be found the greatest deflection f and also the steepest slope α, which occurs at the inflection points W_1 and W_2 of the deflection curve.

Statically indeterminate problems can often also be solved by *superposition*.

Let the beam in Fig. 24.1 be cut through at the center, and let us confine our attention to the left-hand half; see Fig. 24.3. On symmetry grounds, it is seen that there will be no shearing force in the section $l/2$, but the bending moment M', which was present before the cut was made, must be introduced. Now we have a cantilever beam of length $l/2$ that carries the uniformly distributed load $P/2$ and is loaded by the moment M' at the free end. The statically indeterminate problem has thereby been reduced to a statically determinate one. Of course the moment M' is unknown, but it can be determined by the condition that the slope of this auxiliary beam should vanish at the free end. The fixing moment is clearly given by

Fig. 24.3

$$M_e = P\frac{l}{8} - M'. \tag{24.4}$$

For loading by M' alone, the slope of the deflection curve at the free end would, by (23.16), be

$$\alpha' = -\frac{M'(l/2)}{EI},$$

and for the uniform loading alone, by (23.19), it would be

$$\alpha'' = \frac{(P/2)(l/2)^2}{6EI}.$$

Thus we have

$$\alpha = \alpha' + \alpha'' = -\frac{M'l}{2EI} + \frac{Pl^2}{48EI} = 0 ,$$

from which it follows that

$$M' = P\frac{l}{24} ,$$

which, by (24.4), again leads to the fixing moment (24.2).

The methods so far discussed are based on the differential equation for the deflection curve and are thus invalidated as soon as the beam becomes partially *plastic*, i.e., when the moment in the endangered section exceeds that moment denoted by M_0 in Section 23. With a further rise in loading, the bending moment here increases until the section becomes a plastic hinge under the moment M^*. When the support is statically indeterminate there is no consequent failure, because there is still a sufficient number of supports remaining. The loading can indeed be raised further, and the bending moment in the plastic hinge will remain constant, namely equal to M^*. Since M^* is known with σ_0 and the dimensions of the cross section, the degree of indeterminacy decreases with the appearance of each plastic hinge. It is thus necessary to pursue only the distribution of bending moments with further increases of loading. The limit load is finally obtained as that loading for which the last plastic hinge necessary for failure is developed.

Let us consider the beam in Fig. 24.1. In the elastic region, the magnitude of the bending moment is greatest in the root section; it is given by (24.2). Plastic flow begins in this section when

$$M_e = P\frac{l}{12} = M_0 = Z\sigma_0 ,$$

i.e., under the loading

$$P_0 = \frac{12M_0}{l} . \tag{24.5}$$

With a further increase of loading, (24.1) remains valid; however, all other relations become inapplicable. Since the distribution of stress in the root section assumes the form shown in Fig. 23.10, the fixing moment, although increasing, remains below the value (24.2). If the shape factor of the cross section is denoted by k, the root sections will become plasic hinges as soon as the fixing moment reaches the value

$$M_e = M^* = kM_0 . \tag{24.6}$$

From now on they remain constant, and the beam behaves as though it were simple and loaded at both ends by the additional moments M^*. If P increases, yielding finally appears at the center section. In this phase, the bending moment, by (24.1) and (24.6), will be

$$M\left(\frac{l}{2}\right) = kM_0 - P\frac{l}{4} + P\frac{l}{8} = kM_0 - P\frac{l}{8} < 0.$$

As soon as the magnitude of the bending moment here also attains the value M^*, that is,

$$\left| M\left(\frac{l}{2}\right) \right| = P\frac{l}{8} - kM_0 = kM_0, \tag{24.7}$$

another plastic hinge develops and allows the beam to collapse. By (24.7) and (24.5), the limit load is given by

$$P^* = 16k\frac{M_0}{l} = \frac{4}{3}kP_0.$$

Consequently, failure occurs under a load that is $k'=4k/3$ times as large as the loading at the beginning of flow.

If the cross section of the beam is rectangular, then according to Section 22, the form factor is $k=1.5$; the reserve of strength in the plastic region will thus be represented by the factor $k'=2$.

We are now in a position to also treat statically indeterminate systems consisting of bars under tension or compression together with bending.

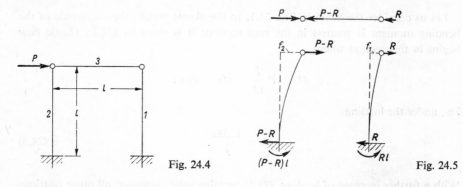

Fig. 24.4   Fig. 24.5

Figure 24.4 shows a frame consisting of three prismatic bars of identical lengths l and equal values of A, Z, I, E, and σ_0. The vertical bars are built in at the lower ends. The horizontal one is connected to them by frictionless hinges and loaded at the left-hand extremity by the force P. Figure 24.5 shows the individual bars of the frame separately in their deformed shapes. The equilibrium conditions have been used to express all the forces shown acting on each bar in terms of P and a single reaction R

that remains unknown. Since there is no further equilibrium condition at our disposal, the problem is simply statically indeterminate. So long as the whole frame behaves elastically, the elongation of the horizontal member will be

$$\Delta l = -\frac{Rl}{EA},$$

and the displacements of the ends of the vertical members, by the results of Exercise 1, Section 23, will be

$$f_1 = \frac{Rl^3}{3EI}, \qquad f_2 = \frac{(P-R)\,l^3}{3EI}.$$

Since the connection in the hinges is also maintained during the deformation, we must have $f_2 - f_1 = -\Delta l$; the further condition necessary for the determination of R thus is

$$\frac{(P-2R)\,l^3}{3EI} = \frac{R\,l}{EA}. \tag{24.8}$$

Denoting the radius of gyration of the cross section of the vertical bars by i, we can write relation (24.8) in the form

$$\frac{Pl^2}{3i^2} = \left(\frac{2}{3}\frac{l^2}{i^2} + 1\right) R.$$

Then, with the notation

$$\mu = \frac{3}{2}\frac{i^2}{l^2} > 0,$$

the forces acting on the vertical bars are found to be

$$R = \frac{1}{1+\mu}\frac{P}{2} < \frac{P}{2}, \qquad P-R = \frac{1+2\mu}{1+\mu}\frac{P}{2} > \frac{P}{2}.$$

The left-hand bar is thus more endangered than the right-hand one; for $i \ll 1$, however, the difference is not large.

We will now assume that the horizontal bar is not endangered and that in particular, there is also no danger of its buckling. Then, the left-hand vertical bar will begin to yield in the root section, when $M=M_0$ there, i.e., when

$$(P-R)\,l = \frac{1+2\mu}{2\,(1+\mu)}\,Pl = M_0$$

or

$$P_0 = \frac{2\,(1+\mu)}{1+2\mu}\frac{M_0}{l}. \tag{24.9}$$

With increasing loading, a plastic hinge will develop here and the limit load is attained when one develops in the right-hand bar also. Then we have

$$Rl = (P-R)\,l = M^* = kM_0;$$

the limit load is thus given by

$$P^* = 2R = 2k \frac{M_0}{l}. \tag{24.10}$$

The reserve inherent in the plastic region is furnished by comparison of (24.9) with (24.10) and is found to be

$$k' = \frac{P^*}{P_0} = \frac{1 + 2\mu}{1 + \mu} k.$$

These examples show that when a problem is statically indeterminate, the calculation of the limit load is simpler than that of the allowable loading with a purely elastic treatment. The reason for this is the fact that with problems such as those treated here, the limit load is independent of the deformations.

Exercises

1. The prismatic elastic cantilever in Fig. 24.6 is simply supported at the tip and loaded at the center. Taking the material constants to be E and σ_0, determine the reactions, the bending-moment diagram, the endangered cross section, and the magnitude of the greatest bending moment. Also find the position and magnitude of the greatest deflection, the inflection point of the deflection curve, position and magnitude of the steepest slope, and the allowable loading for the case in which the cross section is a square of sides a.

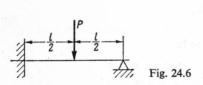

Fig. 24.6

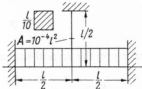

Fig. 24.7

2. A prismatic beam of ductile material with σ_0 is built in at both ends and is supported at the center by a wire of the same material (Fig. 24.7). Determine all reactions for elastic behavior, and also the endangered cross sections of beam and wire together with the corresponding stress resultants. Then calculate the smallest load P_0 under which a cross section begins to yield, the limit load P^*, and the reserve k' inherent in the plastic region.

25. Refinements to Flexure Theory

It was noted at the beginning of Section 23 that the flexure of a beam is, in general, accompanied by a *shearing force*. However, since it is incompatible with the simplifying assumptions that the longitudinal fibers are independent and that the sections remain plane, the shearing force has until now been neglected. As a matter of fact, in the cross section in Fig. 25.1, the shearing force must at least give rise to shear stresses τ parallel to the loading line z. Then, by the theorem on the reciprocity of the shearing stresses (Section 18), the longitudinal fibers cannot be independent. By this same theorem, it is also necessary that τ vanish on those surface elements of the section furthest from the neutral axis. The distribution of shear stress is therefore not uniform, and volume elements adjacent to the section will be subjected to varying amounts of shear, which warp the cross section.

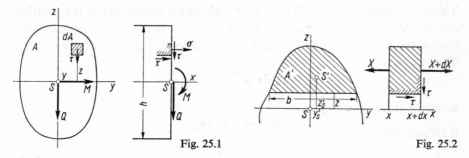

Fig. 25.1   Fig. 25.2

If the depth of the cross section is denoted by h and its area by A, then the orders of magnitude of Q and M will be

$$Q \sim \tau A, \qquad M \sim \sigma A h \, .$$

Since, in addition, with the length l of the beam, we have

$$M \sim Q l,$$

it follows that

$$\sigma h \sim \tau l \quad \text{or} \quad \tau \sim \frac{h}{l} \sigma \, .$$

For slender bars we can thus expect shear stresses that are small compared with the normal stresses. This justifies the procedure in Sections 23 and 24 for such bars.

For shorter beams, it is possible that six different components of stress will act on individual volume elements. For moderate degrees of slenderness, however, τ can be estimated by admitting the distribution of normal stress (23.2) as a first approximation and then deducing in a second step what the shear stress will be. Besides, since we are only making an estimate, the dependence of the stress τ on y may be neglected, or, equivalently, only the mean value over the breadth of the section will be used in the calculations. Moreover, we shall consider only prismatic beams.

Figure 25.2 shows an element of beam bounded by the sections x, $x+dx$, and z. Let its face have the centroid $S'(y'_s, z'_s)$. The integral

$$S = \int_{A'} z \, dA = A' z'_s \tag{25.1}$$

may be called the *static moment* of the area A' about the y-axis. Since the element of the beam is at rest, the forces acting on it must, in particular, satisfy the component condition for the x-axis. By (23.2) and (25.1), the magnitude of the contribution from section x will be

$$X = \int_{A'} \sigma \, dA = \frac{M}{I} \int_{A'} z \, dA = \frac{M}{I} S.$$

That from section $x+dx$ will be $X+dX$ and, by the reciprocity of the shearing stress, that from section z will be $\tau b \, dx$, where b is the width of the cross section at a distance z from the neutral axis and τ the shear stress there. Thus we have

$$\tau b \, dx + \frac{S}{I} dM = 0.$$

Since, by (17.6) and Fig. 25.2,

it follows that
$$dM = - Q \, dx,$$

$$\tau = \frac{Q}{I} \frac{S}{b}. \tag{25.2}$$

Thus τ depends on the value of Q at the section, and within it we have a dependence on b and S; in particular, τ vanishes with S at the points of the cross section furthest removed from the y-axis.

For a rectangular cross section (Fig. 25.3), b is constant, $I=bh^3/12$, and

$$S = A'z'_s = b\left(\frac{h}{2} - z\right) \cdot \frac{1}{2}\left(\frac{h}{2} + z\right) = \frac{b}{2}\left(\frac{h^2}{4} - z^2\right).$$

The shearing stress is thus distributed over the cross section according to the parabolic law

$$\tau = \frac{6Q}{bh^3}\left(\frac{h^2}{4} - z^2\right). \tag{25.3}$$

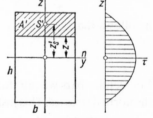

Fig. 25.3

If its mean value $\tau_m = Q/hb$ is introduced, (25.3) can also be written in the form

$$\tau = \frac{3}{2} \tau_m \left(1 - 4\frac{z^2}{h^2}\right). \tag{25.4}$$

Then it follows that

$$\tau_{max} = \tau(0) = \frac{3}{2} \tau_m. \tag{25.5}$$

Another reason now becomes obvious why no danger is presented by the shearing stresses in relatively slender beams, for which the above estimate gives a fairly reliable picture of the state of stress. Namely, τ vanishes at those points

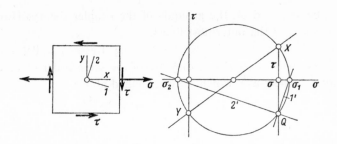

Fig. 25.4

of the cross section where $|\sigma|$ is maximal, and, conversely, τ is maximal where $|\sigma|$ either vanishes or is at least small.

If, in spite of this, it is required to take the shearing stresses into account, let it be imagined that a stress diagram (Fig. 25.4) has been constructed for every element of area in the cross section. From these, we can read off (1) the principal elements 1' and 2' and the principal axes 1 and 2 of the plane state of stress, (2) the principal stresses

$$\sigma_{1,2} = \frac{\sigma}{2} \pm \sqrt{\frac{\sigma^2}{4} + \tau^2},\tag{25.6}$$

and (3) the greatest shearing stress

$$\tau_{\max} = \frac{|\sigma_1 - \sigma_2|}{2} = \sqrt{\frac{\sigma^2}{4} + \tau^2}.\tag{25.7}$$

The Tresca yield or fracture condition (21.7), by (25.7), now is

$$\sigma^2 + 4\tau^2 = \sigma_0^2.\tag{25.8}$$

The corresponding von Mises' condition has the form

$$\sigma_1^2 + \sigma_2^2 - \sigma_1\sigma_2 = (\sigma_1 - \sigma_2)^2 + \sigma_1\sigma_2 = \sigma_0^2.\tag{25.9}$$

The values (25.6) now lead to the relation

$$\sigma^2 + 3\tau^2 = \sigma_0^2,\tag{25.10}$$

which also follows directly from (21.12). In order to avoid yielding or fracture, respectively, it is necessary to guarantee that the left-hand side of either (25.8) or (25.10) remains less than σ_0^2 at every point in the cross section.

The *principal stress trajectories* are defined as those curves in the longitudinal section of the beam which at every point have the direction of one or other of the two principal axes. A certain amount of reflection based on Fig. 25.4 shows that these curves, in a length free of external forces, will have the shape sketched in Fig. 25.5. These curves can be made visible by photoelastic methods. On the whole, the picture deviates considerably from the parallel grid that would be expected on the grounds of the simpler theory. However, the deviation is small in the outermost fibers.

Hitherto, we have not considered the shearing stresses parallel to the y-axis. In many cross sections, however, they are of the same order of magnitude as those parallel to the z-axis which were estimated above.

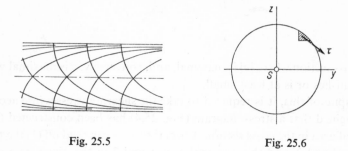

Fig. 25.5   Fig. 25.6

For a circular cross section (Fig. 25.6), it follows from the theorem of the reciprocity of the shear stresses that τ must be directed tangentially at the boundary. It then follows immediately that both components are of the same order of magnitude.

When a cross section is symmetric with respect to the z-axis, all the shearing stresses parallel to the y-axis cancel each other. If this symmetry is not present, the reduction of the shearing forces at the centroid of the section yields a moment M_x; the sections are then also subjected to torsion.

For a channel section (Fig. 25.7), the shearing stresses that are mainly parallel to the sides of the channel can be reduced at the centroid into not only a shearing force Q but also a torsion moment M_x. If the beam is not to twist, it is necessary that the loading line b be shifted from the centroid to the left. The point T where it must intersect the y-axis in order that $M_x = 0$, is called the *shear center*.

Simple bending was defined at the beginning of Section 23 by the conditions that (1) the external forces lie in a loading plane, and (2) the loading line, formed by the intersection of this plane with a cross section, should correspond with a principal axis. If the second condition is omitted, we have a loading line b that is inclined at an angle α to the z-axis (Fig. 25.8). The same angle is included between the vector M of the bending moment and the y-axis. In this case, referred to as *oblique bending*, the angle α is the same in all cross sections. If the first condition is not satisfied, there is no longer a loading line. Then the inclination α of the bending moment varies in general from section to section. Such cases are referred to as *general bending*.

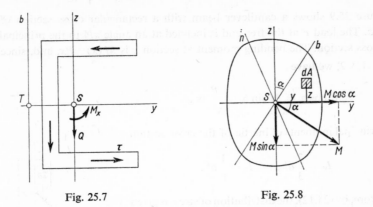

Fig. 25.7   Fig. 25.8

If consideration is limited to slender beams, the shearing force can again be neglected. The bending moment can be resolved along the principal axes into the components

$$M_y = M \cos \alpha, \qquad M_z = - M \sin \alpha. \tag{25.11}$$

The simplifying assumptions about the independence of the longitudinal fibers and that sections remain plane again lead to a uniaxial state of stress, as in Fig. 22.2. In the *elastic regime*, the distribution of the normal stresses over the cross section is again given by (22.3). With $N=0$ and the values in (25.11), the coefficients (22.5) turn out to be $a=0$, $b= M \sin \alpha/Iz$, and $c = M \cos \alpha/I_y$. Thus we have

$$\sigma = \frac{M \sin \alpha}{I_z} y + \frac{M \cos \alpha}{I_y} z. \tag{25.12}$$

When $\alpha=0$, this relation becomes identical with (23.1), as is to be expected. It is also clear that this distribution of stress can be obtained by the superposition of two simple bendings with moments $M \cos \alpha$ and $M \sin \alpha$.

By (25.12), the neutral axis n has the equation

$$\frac{\sin \alpha}{I_z} y + \frac{\cos \alpha}{I_y} z = 0. \tag{25.13}$$

It still passes through the centroid S of the cross section but no longer corresponds with a principal axis. The normal stress σ is proportional to the distance from the neutral axis; so also is the normal strain. With oblique bending, the neutral axes of all cross sections lie in a plane and the deflection curve in a normal plane along the x-axis. In the case of general bending, however, the deflection curve is three dimensional.

Figure 25.9 shows a cantilever beam with a rectangular cross section of sides a and $2a$. The load P at the free end is inclined at an angle $\pi/4$ to the principal axes of the cross section. The bending moment at section x is $M(x)=Px$, and, since $\cos\alpha = \sin\alpha = 1/\sqrt{2}$, we have

$$M\cos\alpha = M\sin\alpha = \frac{P}{\sqrt{2}}x.$$

The principal moments of inertia of the cross section are

$$I_y = \frac{2}{3}a^4, \qquad I_z = \frac{1}{6}a^4.$$

Therefore, by (25.12), the distribution of stress is given by

$$\sigma = \frac{Px}{\sqrt{2}a^4}\left(6y + \frac{3}{2}z\right).$$

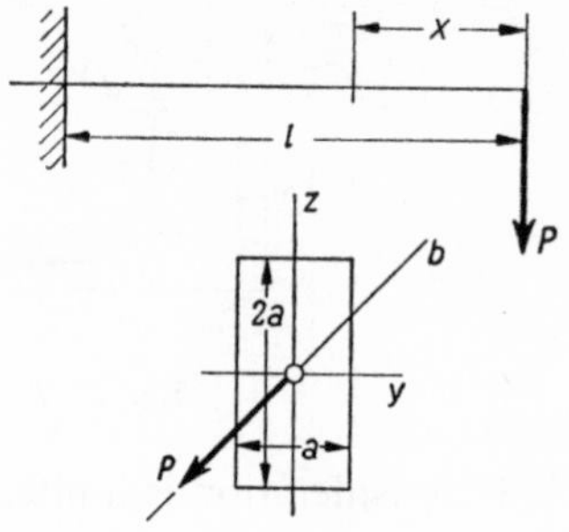

The neutral axis n has the equation

$$z = -4y,$$

and the greatest absolute stress arises in the corners of the root cross section marked in Fig. 25.10. Here we have

$$|\sigma|_{max} = \frac{9Pl}{2\sqrt{2}a^3}.$$

The deflection curve lies in the plane

$$z = \frac{1}{4}y,$$

which is spanned by the normal e to n and the x-axis.

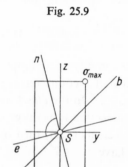

Fig. 25.9

Fig. 25.10

Since, with oblique bending, the neutral axis n is no longer normal to the loading plane b, the loads no longer move along their lines of action during the deformation. Thus it is not completely correct to carry out the design without giving consideration to the deformations. The lateral displacements of the loads involve a certain amount of torsion in addition to the flexural moments acting in each cross section.

Exercises

1. An elastic prismatic beam (Fig. 25.11) has a square cross section, is simply supported at both ends, and is loaded in the center. Determine the distribution of normal and shear stress at section $x=a$. Then construct the stress circles for the points P_1, P_2, and P_3 of this cross section.

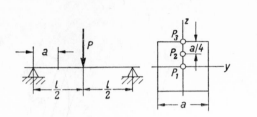

Fig. 25.11 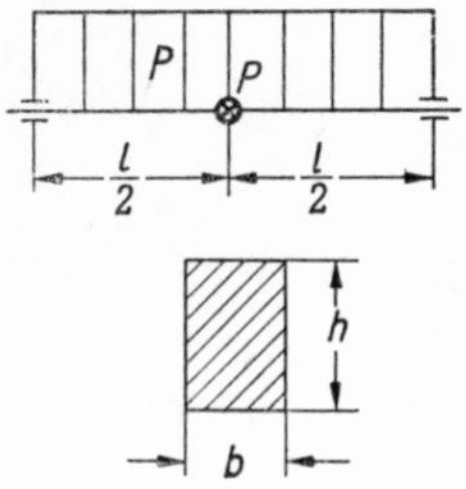   Fig. 25.12

2. An elastic beam (Fig. 25.12) of length $l=4$ ft and rectangular cross section of sides $b=1$ in and $h=1\frac{1}{2}$ in is built in at both ends. It carries a uniformly distributed load P and a horizontal concentrated force P is applied at the center. The allowable stress is $\sigma_{al}=18,000$ psi. Determine the reactions and draw the bending moment diagrams for the two loadings. Locate the endangered section and then in it determine (a) the loading line, (b) the neutral axis, and (c) the greatest absolute stress. How large is the allowable loading P_{al}?

26. Eccentric Tension and Compression

By Section 17, a column or bar is subjected to eccentric tension or compression when the lines of action of the external forces are either skew to the axis or parallel to it. Apart from a possible shearing force, which will be neglected, in a section (Fig. 26.1) we have a normal force N along the axis (shown in Fig. 26.1 as a vector pointing outward) and a bending moment M. These stress resultants are equivalent to an eccentric normal force N. If the coordinates of the point of application B of the eccentric normal force are denoted by η, ζ, the components of the bending moment are

$$M_y = N\zeta, \qquad M_z = -N\eta. \qquad (26.1)$$

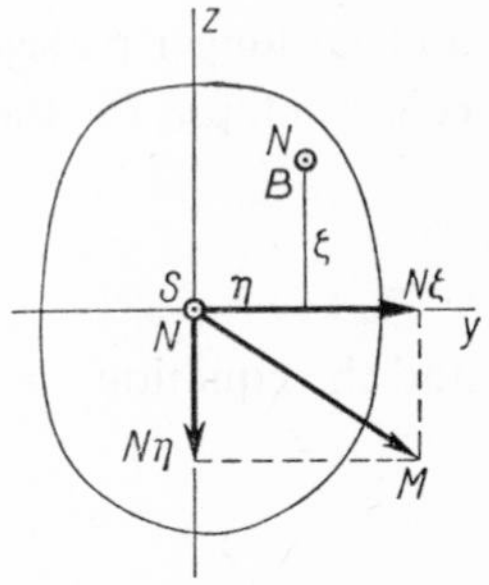

Fig. 26.1

We make use once more of the simplifying assumptions formulated at the beginning of Section 22. Then, in the elastic regime we again have the uniaxial state of stress with the distribution of normal stress given by (22.3). By (26.1) and (15.21), the coefficients (22.5) are

$$a = \frac{N}{A}, \qquad b = -\frac{M_z}{I_z} = \frac{N\eta}{Ai_z^2}, \qquad c = \frac{M_y}{I_y} = \frac{N\zeta}{Ai_y^2},$$

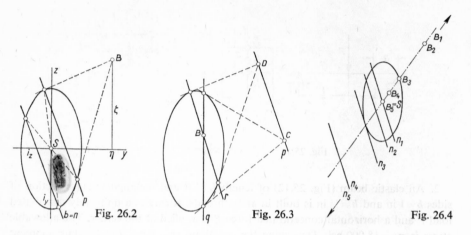

Fig. 26.2   Fig. 26.3   Fig. 26.4

so that the normal stress is given by

$$\sigma = \frac{N}{A}\left(1 + \frac{\eta}{i_z^2}y + \frac{\zeta}{i_y^2}z\right). \tag{26.2}$$

It can obviously be gained by the superposition of two simple bendings on a centric tension or compression.

The neutral axis n has the equation

$$\frac{\eta}{i_z^2}y + \frac{\zeta}{i_y^2}z + 1 = 0 \tag{26.3}$$

and no longer passes through the centroid of the cross section. By (15.25), the central ellipse for the cross section is given by

$$\frac{y^2}{i_z^2} + \frac{z^2}{i_y^2} - 1 = 0, \tag{26.4}$$

and the equation

$$\frac{\eta}{i_z^2}y + \frac{\zeta}{i_y^2}z - 1 = 0 \tag{26.5}$$

represents the polar line p of the point $B(\eta, \zeta)$ with respect to this ellipse. When B lies outside the ellipse (Fig. 26.2), this is obtained geometrically by constructing the two tangents to the ellipse through B and joining the points of contact. Comparison of (26.3) with (26.5) shows that the neutral axis n for the eccentric point of application B can be constructed as the *antipolar* b of B with respect to the central ellipse, whereby the antipolar is defined as the reflection of the polar p in the centroid.

Equation (26.5) for the polar is symmetric in the coordinates y, z and η, ζ. Therefore, if C is a point on the polar p of B, then its polar q passes through B. Whence we obtain a simple construction (Fig. 26.3) for the polar p of a point of application B lying inside the ellipse: we draw two lines q and r through B and determine their poles C and D; the line through C and D is the required polar p of B.

If the point of application B of the force is now allowed to move along a diameter of the ellipse, it follows from the above theorem that its antipolar pivots round the antipole of this diameter. Since this is at infinity, the various neutral axes n corresponding to these locations of B will form a family of parallels. Figure 26.4 shows a few such points of application together with the corresponding neutral axes. The neutral axis n_1 through the centroid S corresponds to the infinitely remote point of application B_1, i.e., to the limiting case of pure bending. At the other extreme, the point of application B_5 at the centroid corresponds to a neutral axis n_5 at infinity, i.e., to the limiting case of concentric tension or compression.

The tensile strength of concrete and masonry is small compared with that in compression. Thus, when a column of such material is subjected to eccentric pressure, the point of application of the force is chosen so close to the centroid that the neutral axis does not intersect the cross section, thereby guaranteeing that only compressive stresses arise in the whole section. The region in the cross section that satisfies these conditions is called the *kern*. The boundary of the kern (Fig. 26.5) is obtained as the locus of all points B_1, B_2, ..., whose antipolars n_1, n_2, ... relative to the central ellipse are tangential to the boundary of the cross section. Thus, it is the locus of the antipoles of all tangents on the smallest convex envelope of the cross section.

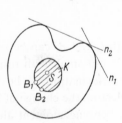

Fig. 26.5

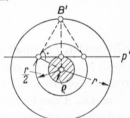

Fig. 26.6

When the cross section is a circle of radius r (Fig. 26.6), the central ellipse, by Section 15, is a circle of radius $r/2$. If we construct the polar p' of a point B' on the boundary of the cross section and let the distance of p' from the center be ϱ, then the similarity of the right triangles in Fig. 26.6 yields the relation $\varrho r = r^2/4$. Thus $\varrho = r/4$, and hence the antipoles of all tangents to the cross section are at a distance $r/4$ from S; the kern is a circle of radius $r/4$.

When the cross section is a rectangle (Fig. 26.7), by Section 15, we have $i_y{}^2 = h^2/12$ and $i_z{}^2 = b^2/12$. Equation (26.3) for the neutral axis is thus

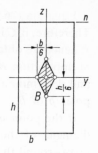

$$\frac{12\eta}{b^2} y + \frac{12\zeta}{h^2} z + 1 = 0 . \qquad (26.6)$$

The upper edge of the rectangle has the equation

$$z = \frac{h}{2} \quad \text{or} \quad -\frac{2}{h} z + 1 = 0 . \qquad (26.7)$$

Fig. 26.7

The coordinates η, ζ of the point of application B having this edge as its neutral axis n are obtained by identifying equations (26.6) and (26.7). The result is

$$\eta = 0 , \qquad \zeta = -\frac{h}{6} .$$

Similarly the points of application are obtained for the case that one of the other sides should be a neutral axis. Since B traverses a straight line as the neutral axis n pivots around a corner, the kern is a rhombus with the diagonals $b/3$ and $h/3$.

The deformation of the bar consists in a change of length and a curvature of the axis. By Sections 22 and 23, we have in the elastic domain the approximations

$$\Delta l \sim \frac{Nl}{EA}, \qquad f \sim \frac{Ml^2}{EI} = \frac{Nel^2}{EI},$$

where e denotes the eccentricity of the point of application. Whence it further follows that

$$\frac{\Delta l}{f} \sim \frac{J}{Ael} = \frac{i}{l} \cdot \frac{i}{e} .$$

When a bar is slender, i is small compared with l, and Δl can be neglected in comparison with f, insofar as the eccentricity is not small with respect to the size of the cross section. In such cases, then, the deformation can be determined by pure bending, i.e., it can be obtained by neglecting the change of length and finding the *deflection curve* on the basis of the bending moment alone.

Figure 26.8 shows a cantilever beam of square cross section loaded by the eccentric tensile force P acting at the mid-point of the upper side of the free end. The stress resultants of an arbitrary section consist, insofar as they can be determined without taking account of the deformation, in the normal force $N = P$ and the bending moment $M = Pa/2$, whose vector lies along the y-axis. The stress distribution (26.2) is therefore given in all sections by

$$\sigma = \frac{P}{a^2} + \frac{Pa/2}{a^4/12} z = \frac{P}{a^2}\left(1 + 6\frac{z}{a}\right),$$

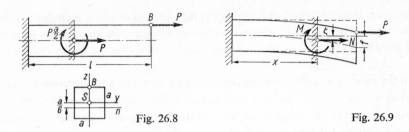

Fig. 26.8   Fig. 26.9

and the neutral axis has the equation $z = -a/6$. The greatest absolute normal stress occurs at the upper boundary of the section and has the value

$$|\sigma|_{\max} = \sigma\left(z = \frac{a}{2}\right) = 4\frac{P}{a^2},$$

i.e., it is four times as great as the value when the force is axial. The deflection curve (Fig. 26.9) satisfies the differential equation

$$\zeta'' = \frac{M}{EI}$$

with a constant right-hand side. The greatest displacement, which appears at the free end and has already been calculated in Section 23, amounts to

$$f = \frac{Ml^2}{2EI} = \frac{P(a/2)\,l^2}{2E(a^4/12)} = \frac{3Pl^2}{Ea^3}.$$

For the numerical values $a=2$ in, $l=3$ ft, $\sigma_{\mathrm{al}}=20{,}000$ psi, and $E=3\times10^7$ psi, the allowable loading will be

$$P_{\mathrm{al}} = \frac{a^2}{4}\sigma_{\mathrm{al}} = \frac{4}{4}\,20{,}000 = 20{,}000\ \mathrm{lb}^*.$$

Thus, the greatest displacement will be

$$f = \frac{3\times20{,}000\times(36)^2}{3\times10^7\times(2)^3} = 0.324\ \mathrm{in.}$$

With eccentric tension or compression, the loads do not move along their lines of action during the deformation. The results obtained in this section are thus applicable only when the displacement of the deflection curve is small in comparison with the dimensions of the cross section. In the preceding example this is clearly not the case. Therefore, in such cases, it is necessary to take the deformations into consideration right from the start.

If the deformation of the beam in Fig. 26.8 is taken into account, it is seen from Fig. 26.9 that at section x the normal force P is accompanied by the bending moment

$$M(x) = P\left(\frac{a}{2} - f + \zeta\right).$$

It is smaller than $Pa/2$ everywhere except at the end section, where it attains this maximum value. Therefore, the above calculations overestimate the stresses in general and likewise the deformations, even though $|\sigma|_{max}$ and thus the design remain valid.

In the case of eccentric tension, the bending moment and therefore the deformation will be overestimated if the loading is determined without regard to the deformation. On the other hand, this method will lead to an underestimate of the moment and deformation in the case of eccentric compression. Since this can be dangerous, it is necessary to confirm at the conclusion of the calculations that the deformation actually remains small or, better still, to take it into account from the beginning.

Figure 26.10 shows the deflection curve of a prismatic cantilever beam compressed at the free end by the force P with eccentricity e. If the deformation is considered, the bending moment is

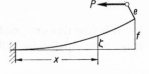

Fig. 26.10

$$M(x) = P(e + f - \zeta). \tag{26.8}$$

Thus, the deflection curve has the differential equation $\zeta'' = (P/EI)(e + f + \zeta)$. With the notation

$$\kappa^2 = \frac{P}{EI}, \tag{26.9}$$

this can also be written as

$$\zeta'' + \kappa^2\zeta = \kappa^2(e + f).$$

The general solution is

$$\zeta = A\cos\kappa x + B\sin\kappa x + e + f,$$

and the boundary conditions $\zeta(0)=0$, $\zeta'(0)=0$ yield

$$A = -(e + f), \qquad B = 0,$$

so that

$$\zeta = (e + f)(1 - \cos\kappa x).$$

The additional condition $\zeta(l)=f$ furnishes

$$f = \frac{1 - \cos\kappa l}{\cos\kappa l}e \quad \text{or} \quad e + f = \frac{e}{\cos\kappa l}, \tag{26.10}$$

so that we finally obtain

$$\zeta(x) = \frac{1 - \cos\kappa x}{\cos\kappa l}e. \tag{26.11}$$

The final expression for the bending moment would now be obtained by substitution of (26.10) and (26.11) into (26.8). However, it is immediately obvious that the greatest absolute bending moment occurs at the root cross section and, by (26.10), it will have the value

$$|M|_{max} = P(e + f) = \frac{Pe}{\cos \kappa l}.$$

Now the beam can be designed. Figure 26.11 shows the graphs of the functions

$$\cos \kappa l, \qquad \frac{|M|_{max}}{Pe} = \frac{1}{\cos \kappa l},$$

$$\frac{f}{e} = \frac{1}{\cos \kappa l} - 1.$$

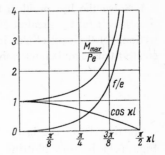

Fig. 26.11

The last two have a vertical asymptote at $\kappa l = \pi/2$. Thus, by (26.9), there is a *critical load*

$$P_c = \frac{\pi^2 EI}{4l^2} \tag{26.12}$$

under which $|M|_{max}$ and f increase above all bounds, no matter what value the eccentricity e may have.

The results obtained in this example are also typical for other cases of eccentric compression. There is always a critical loading P_c under which $|\sigma|_{max}$ and f theoretically become infinite. Long before reaching such a state, namely for relatively small values of f, the greatest absolute stress attains the value σ_0. Thus, the beam either yields or fractures under a load smaller than P_c. In fact, the larger the eccentricity e, the smaller this load will be. Figure 26.11 also shows that designing without regard to the deformation is permissible only if $P \ll P_c$.

Here also, as in the last section, we could investigate the behavior in the *plastic regime*. This, however, is very much dependent on the shape of the stress-strain diagram. Since the diagram in Fig. 19.4 used up to now is only a rough approximation, the results would be quite unreliable.

Exercises

1. Construct the kern for the cross section consisting of four squares, as shown in Fig. 26.12.

2. The elastic column in Fig. 26.13 is fixed at the base, has the cross section of Fig. 26.12, and is loaded at the free end by the force P applied to the point B. Neglecting the deformation, determine the distribution of stresses, the neutral axis, and also the location and magnitude of the greatest tensile and compressive stress. The data are: $a = 2$ cm, $l = 5$ m, $P = 100$ kg*, and $E = 2.1 \times 10^6$ kg*/cm².

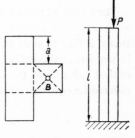

Fig. 26.12   Fig. 26.13

3. Solve the last problem taking the deformation into consideration. Determine successively (a) the greatest displacement of the deflection curve, (b) the endangered section, (c) the neutral axis in this section, and (d) location and magnitude of the greatest tensile and compressive stress.

27. Buckling

Starting from the last example in Section 26 and redrawing the graph in Fig. 26.11 by now plotting f/i against κl for different values of the parameter e/i, we obtain the family of curves in Fig. 27.1, which all have a common asymptote at $\kappa l = \pi/2$. From this it follows that as the load P approaches the critical load (26.12), the column loaded as shown in Fig. 26.10 will be endangered, no matter how small the eccentricity e of the load. Since it is practically impossible to achieve an exactly concentric loading, *buckling* of the member is always to be expected immediately before reaching the *buckling load* (26.12). Even when the loading is exactly concentric, there is danger of buckling under P_c, since in this case f/i is represented by the limiting curve consisting of the segment $0 < \kappa l < \pi/2$ of the horizontal axis together with the vertical asymptote, and when $\kappa l = \pi/2$, the deflection f/i can assume an arbitrary value.

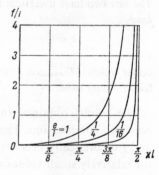

Fig. 27.1

The danger of buckling is also present when the end conditions are different from those considered here. Of course, the buckling load is not, in general, given by (26.12). But P_c can still be obtained by a limit process $e \to 0$. However, the buckling load can also be defined as the smallest load under which the concentrically compressed bar is in equilibrium with a deflected axis. It can be demonstrated by a dynamic investigation that the undeflected configuration is stable when $P < P_c$, neutral when $P = P_c$, and labile, or completely unstable, when $P > P_c$.

The left-hand end of the prismatic bar of length l shown in Fig. 27.2 is hinged to a wall, while the other end, to which the load P is applied, is hinged in such a way that it is free to slide in the axial direction. Then, the only reaction that arises (also in the deflected configuration) is the axial force P at the stationary hinge. Under the critical value of P, the axis is bent. Since the bending moment is then $M = P\zeta$, the differential equation of the deflection curve is $\zeta'' = -(P/EI)\zeta$ or

$$\zeta'' + \kappa^2 \zeta = 0, \quad \text{where} \quad \kappa^2 = \frac{P}{EI}. \tag{27.1}$$

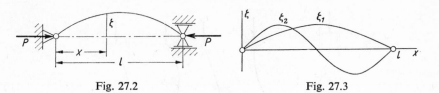

Fig. 27.2   Fig. 27.3

The most general solution contains two constants of integration A and B, and is given by

$$\zeta = A \cos \kappa x + B \sin \kappa x \,.$$

The first boundary condition $\zeta(0)=0$ yields $A=0$, and therefore

$$\zeta = B \sin \kappa x \,. \tag{27.2}$$

The second boundary condition $\zeta(l)=0$ can be satisfied by either

$$B = 0 \quad \text{or} \quad \sin \kappa l = 0 \,. \tag{27.3}$$

For arbitrarily prescribed values of P and hence of κ, the second condition (27.3) is not satisfied in general. Thus, the problem has only the trivial solution $\zeta \equiv 0$, which corresponds to the unbent state of the bar. If, however,

$$\kappa l = n\pi \,,$$

where n is an integer, then apart from the trivial solution $\zeta \equiv 0$, we also have non-trivial ones,

$$\zeta = B \sin \frac{n\pi x}{l} \,,$$

i.e., equilibrium configurations with a bent axis. The solution with $n=0$ is to be rejected by virtue of the second condition (27.1), and the negative values of n can be omitted, since they only change the sign of $\zeta(x)$. Consequently, there are nontrivial solutions for

$$\kappa_n = \frac{n\pi}{l} \qquad (n = 1, 2, \ldots) \,. \tag{27.4}$$

They are

$$\zeta_n(x) = B_n \sin \frac{n\pi x}{l} \qquad (n = 1, 2, \ldots) \,, \tag{27.5}$$

and each of them contains a free amplitude B_n. The corresponding loads, by (27.1), are

$$P_n = \frac{n^2 \pi^2 EI}{l^2} \qquad (n = 1, 2, \ldots) \,. \tag{27.6}$$

Figure 27.3 shows the solutions (eigenfunctions) (27.5) of this typical *eigenvalue problem* for $n=1$ and $n=2$. The corresponding loads (eigenvalues), by (27.6), are

$$P_1 = \frac{\pi^2 EI}{l^2} \,, \qquad P_2 = \frac{4\pi^2 EI}{l^2} \,, \ldots \,.$$

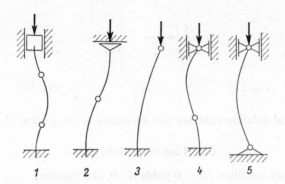

1   2   3   4   5   Fig. 27.4

Since, however, the buckling load was defined as the smallest load under which the bar is in equilibrium in a deflected configuration, the cases $n = 2, 3, \ldots$ are of no significance, and the buckling load is

$$P_c = P_1 = \frac{\pi^2 EI}{l^2}. \tag{27.7}$$

If it is observed that the sine curves (27.5) have the half wavelengths $\lambda_1 = l$, $\lambda_2 = l/2, \ldots$, the buckling load can be written in the form

$$P_c = \frac{\pi^2 EI}{\lambda_{\max}^2}.$$

Figure 27.4 shows the five most important cases of buckling of a bar supported only at its ends. Moreover, only those deflection curves that have a minimum number of inflection points have been drawn in; these are marked by small circles. Let us suppose that a length between two inflection points is cut out and the line joining them is used as reference axis. We have the following considerations concerning the reactions to be introduced at the cuts:

(1) The bending moments vanish in accordance with Section 23.
(2) By equilibrium considerations, the shearing forces must also vanish.
(3) Therefore, only normal forces are possible.

Thus, this section between two inflections behaves exactly as the whole bar in Fig. 27.2, and it deflects into the form of half a sine wave. Consequently, in each of these cases in the *elastic regime* we have

$$P_c = \frac{\pi^2 EI}{\lambda_{\max}^2}, \tag{27.8}$$

if $\lambda_{\max}$ is the greatest distance between two consecutive points of inflection. Relation (27.8) was derived by Euler (1707–1783), and $\lambda_{\max}$ is called the *free buckling length* of the bar. Its respective values in the cases in Fig. 27.4 are:

Buckling case	1	2	3	4	5
λ_{max}	$\frac{1}{2}l$	l	$2l$	$0.7l$	l

This verifies in particular the earlier results (26.12) and (27.7) for the buckling cases 3 and 5, respectively.

In the preceding considerations it was assumed that the plane in which the bar buckles is known. Since, however, it was assumed that $e=0$, this is not in general the case, and then the possibility of buckling in the direction of either of the two principal directions of the cross section must be considered. In this case, not only the moments of inertia but also the boundary conditions may be different.

If a prismatic bar is supported by a long cylindrical hinge (Fig. 27.5), buckling in the x, ζ-plane involves buckling case 5 with the buckling load

$$P_c' = \frac{\pi^2 E I_y}{\lambda_{max}'^2},$$

and $\lambda'_{max}=l$. For buckling in the x, η-plane we have case 1 with

$$P_c'' = \frac{\pi^2 E I_z}{\lambda_{max}''^2}$$

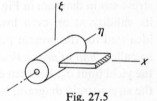

Fig. 27.5

and $\lambda''_{max}=l/2$. It is then a question of whether I_y/λ'^2_{max} or I_z/λ''^2_{max} is the smaller; accordingly, the bar buckles in the x, ζ- or the x, η-plane.

Euler's buckling formula in such cases is best applied in the form

$$P_c = \pi^2 E \left(\frac{I}{\lambda^2}\right)_{min}, \tag{27.9}$$

where the minimum refers first to a comparison of both principal axes and secondly, in each buckling plane, to the comparison of the various deflection curves.

When the boundary conditions for both buckling directions are identical, I_{min} determines the buckling load; buckling thus occurs in the direction of the smallest resistance. For this reason, it is advantageous to use a cross section with $I_y=I_z$, and above all a circular annulus which has an especially large moment of inertia for a given cross-sectional area A.

Using the radius of gyration i of the cross section, we obtain, instead of (27.9),

$$P_c = \pi^2 E A \left(\frac{i}{\lambda}\right)^2_{min}. \tag{27.10}$$

If it is observed that the compressive stress (here taken to be positive) just before buckling is $\sigma_c = P_c/A$, and if we introduce the so-called *slenderness ratio s* of the bar, being defined by

$$s = \left(\frac{\lambda}{i}\right)_{max},$$ (27.11)

then (27.10) can also be written in the form

$$\sigma_c = \frac{\pi^2 E}{s^2}.$$ (27.12)

In the process of design, it is necessary to guarantee that the actual load remains below the buckling load. Thus, with a safety factor n, we set

$$P \leq \frac{P_c}{n} \quad \text{or} \quad \sigma \leq \frac{\sigma_c}{n}.$$ (27.13)

The Euler buckling formula in all its forms is based on the differential equation of the elastic line and thus on Hooke's law. For a material with the stress-strain diagram in Fig. 19.4, it is valid in the region $\sigma_c < \sigma_0$. In fact, it loses its validity at an even lower compressive stress, since the diagram is over-idealized for the present purpose. Hooke's law is actually only valid up to the so-called *limit of proportionality* σ_p (Fig. 27.6), which can lie significantly below the yield limit σ_0. Between σ_p and σ_0, the usual materials still behave elastically; the stress-strain diagram, however, is curved and this curvature has a considerable effect on the buckling stress.

The Euler formula is therefore admissible only for the compressive stresses

$$\sigma_c = \frac{\pi^2 E}{s^2} \leq \sigma_p,$$

i.e., for slenderness ratios s that lie above the so-called *limit slenderness*

$$s^* = \pi \sqrt{\frac{E}{\sigma_p}}.$$ (27.14)

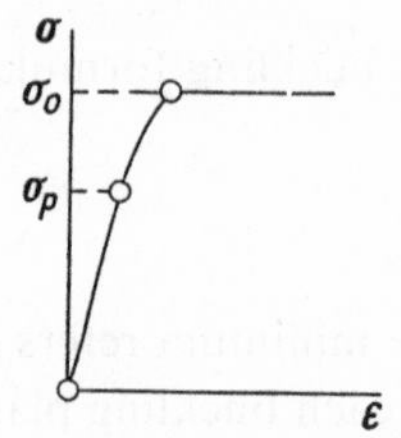

Fig. 27.6

For mild steel with $\sigma_p = 20{,}600$ psi and $E = 3 \times 10^7$ psi, the limit slenderness has the value

$$s^* = \pi \sqrt{\frac{3 \times 10^7}{20{,}600}} = 120.$$ (27.15)

It can be shown that in the range $\sigma_p \leq \sigma_c \leq \sigma_0$ the Euler formula can be used in a modified form, namely by replacing the modulus of elasticity E by the so-called *tangent modulus*, i.e., by the slope of the stress-strain diagram at the point σ_c. Where a reliable diagram is not available, use can be made of an approximate formula due to von Tetmajer (1850–1905).

Figure 27.7 shows the Euler buckling stress (27.12) as a function of the slenderness s. This hyperbolic curve is, however, valid only for $s \geq s^*$, where the ordinate at the point s^* has the value σ_p. When $s \leq s^*$, the Euler curve must be replaced by another. This curve must, indeed, reach the value σ_0 when $s=0$, since a column with very small slenderness must yield under σ_0. In order to replace the Euler formula in the interval $0 \leq s \leq s^*$, we can, as a first approximation, draw a straight line through the points (s^*, σ_p) and $(0, \sigma_0)$. Thus, in the region of small slenderness, we obtain the buckling formula

$$\sigma_c = \sigma_0 - (\sigma_0 - \sigma_p)\frac{s}{s^*}. \tag{27.16}$$

For the mild steel in the last example with $\sigma_0 = 36{,}000$ psi, (27.16) assumes the form

$$\sigma_c = 36{,}000 - \frac{15{,}400}{120}s = 36000 - 128\,s, \tag{27.17}$$

which is expressed in pounds per square inch.

Formula (27.16) has been verified experimentally for many materials by von Tetmajer; the numerical values can be found in the technical handbooks.*

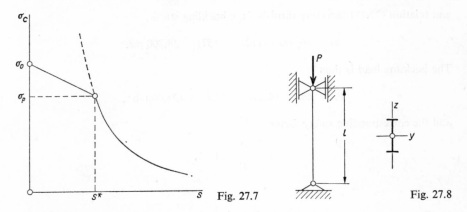

Fig. 27.7　　　　　　　　　　　　　　　Fig. 27.8

Figure 27.8 shows a compression member which is hinged at both ends and is to be a U.S. standard beam. It is so oriented that buckling takes place in the direction of the y-axis. Its length is 3 ft, the loading $P=10{,}000$ lb*, and the safety factor against buckling should be $n=10$. The material is mild steel with numerical data as in preceding examples. Thus, the Tetmajer formula is given by (27.17).

Since we have case 5, $\lambda_{max} = l$ and, by (27.8), $I_{min} = I_z$. By way of trial we first use the Euler Formula (27.8). We have

$$P \leq \frac{P_k}{n} = \frac{\pi^2 E I_z}{n l^2}$$

---

* Additional design data for compression members can be found in the Manual of the American Institute of Steel Construction, *Allowable Loads on Columns*, p. 209.

and therefore

$$I_z \geq \frac{nl^2 P}{\pi^2 E} = \frac{10\,(36)^2\,10^4}{\pi^2\,3 \times 10^7} = 0.438 \text{ in}^4.$$

The smallest U.S. standard beam with a moment of inertia satisfying this inequality is the 3 I 5.7 with $I_z = 0.46$ in^4 and $A = 1.64$ in^2. For this cross section the slenderness is

$$s = \frac{l}{i_z} = \frac{36}{0.53} = 68.$$

Since it is smaller than the limit slenderness (27.15) for the material used, the design based on Euler's formula is invalid. We must therefore apply the formula of Tetmajer (27.17). It is to be expected, that this section, which is just large enough according to the Euler formula, is too weak. In fact, the next section 4 I 9.5 proves to be too small also. We now try the 5 I 14.75 with $I_z = 1.70$ in^4, $i_z = 0.63$ in, and $A = 4.29$ in^2. The slenderness ratio in this case is

$$s = \frac{36}{0.63} = 57,$$

and relation (27.17) therefore furnishes the buckling stress

$$\sigma_c = 36{,}000 - (128) \times (57) = 28{,}700 \text{ psi.}$$

The buckling load is thus

$$P_c = A\sigma_c = (4.29) \times (28.7) = 123{,}000 \text{ lb*},$$

and the corresponding safety factor

$$n = \frac{P_c}{P} = 12.3.$$

Exercises

1. A bar (Fig. 27.9) of length 12 ft, which consists of four unequal-leg angles L 2 $\times$ 1½ $\times$ ¼ welded together as shown, is built-in at both ends without pre-stressing. The modulus of elasticity is to be taken as 3×10^7 psi and assumed independent of temperature. Determine its slenderness ratio s and the plane in which it will buckle. How great can the temperature increase Δt be (with a safety factor $n = 10$ against buckling), if

$$\Delta l = \alpha l \Delta t, \qquad \alpha = 12 \times 10^{-6}\ ^\circ\text{C}^{-1}$$

is the law by which it would elongate when not constrained at the ends?

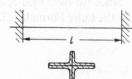

Fig. 27.9

2. Verify Euler's buckling formula in the buckling cases 1, 2, and 4 by setting up the differential equation of the deflection curve and solving the corresponding eigenvalue problem.

3. The column of length 4 ft built in as in Fig. 27.10 is composed of structural steel with $\sigma_p = 22{,}000$ psi, $\sigma_0 = 32{,}000$ psi, and $E = 3 \times 10^7$ psi, and has a circular cross section. A concentric compressive force $P = 30{,}000$ lb* is applied. Calculate (to the nearest quarter inch) the radius necessary in order that the safety factor against buckling be at least 5.

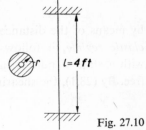

Fig. 27.10

28. Torsion

By Section 17, a shaft is subjected to torsion alone if the external forces appear in the form of couples in planes normal to the axis. Then, the stress resultant of a section consists (Fig. 28.1) in a torsion moment M_t. If polar coordinates r, φ are introduced in the cross section, the element of surface is given by $dA = r\,dr\,d\varphi$, and the stresses $s\,dA$ on these elements must yield a resultant couple equivalent to the torsion moment.

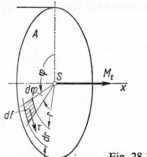

Fig. 28.1

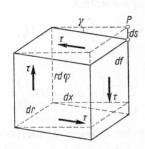

Fig. 28.2

The simplifying assumptions of Section 22 lead to normal stresses in the section and are untenable here. On the other hand, progress can be made by assuming that the cross sections rotate about their centroids S, without change of shape. The deformation is then described by the angle $\vartheta(x)$ of rotation. Since this rotation does not alter the loading in any way, the stresses can again be determined without regard to the deformation.

Figure 28.2 shows a volume element, with edges dx, dr, and $r\,d\varphi$, which is adjacent to the surface element dA. During the twisting of the cross section, it experiences a pure shear γ, which depends only on x and r. Since the displacement ds of the corner P can be represented in the forms

$$ds = r\,d\vartheta = \gamma\,dx,$$

the (algebraic) shearing strain can be expressed in the form

$$\gamma = r\frac{d\vartheta}{dx} \tag{28.1}$$

by means of the distance r from the axis and the *specific twist* $d\vartheta/dx$. In the *elastic regime*, it follows from Section 19 that this distortion is associated with a state of pure shear τ, in which planes normal to the radius are stress free. By (28.1), the shearing stress (now to be treated as algebraic) is given by

$$\tau = G\gamma = G\frac{d\vartheta}{dx}r, \tag{28.2}$$

and, on the section, it is directed azimuthally, i.e., perpendicularly to the radius. It depends on the section through $d\vartheta/dx$ and in each section on r.

By virtue of the reciprocity of the shear stresses, τ must be directed azimuthally at the edge of the cross section (Fig. 28.3). At the same time it must always be tangential. The simplifying assumption introduced above can thus be sustained only for *rotationally symmetric cross sections*, i.e., for circular and annular shapes. It is therefore necessary that we restrict ourselves to such sections for the present.

From the equivalence of the stresses on a section with the torsion moment, we obtain

$$\int\limits_A \tau r\, df = M_t,$$

and with (28.2)

$$G\frac{d\vartheta}{dx}\int\limits_A r^2\, df = GJ\frac{d\vartheta}{dx} = M,$$

Fig. 28.3

where J is the polar moment of inertia of the section about its centroid S and the torsion moment is simply denoted by M. The twist per length is thus given by

$$\frac{d\vartheta}{dx} = \frac{M}{GJ}. \tag{28.3}$$

It is inversely proportional to the *torsional stiffness* GJ. The total twist of the shaft furnished by (28.3) is

$$\vartheta = \int\limits_0^l \frac{M(x)}{GJ(x)}\, dx. \tag{28.4}$$

It should be noted that (28.4) gives the angle of twist in radian measure; the transition to $\vartheta°$ is effected by multiplying by $180/\pi$.

When two equal and opposite moments M are applied to the ends of a circular shaft, we have $M(x) = M$ and J constant. The total twist is thus

$$\vartheta = \frac{Ml}{GJ}. \tag{28.5}$$

Substituting (28.3) into (28.2), we obtain a linear distribution of shearing stress

$$\tau = \frac{M}{J} r \tag{28.6}$$

over the cross section. This is represented in Fig. 28.4 for an annulus with radii r_o and r_i. The greatest absolute shear stress occurs at the outer boundary, and it has the magnitude

$$|\tau|_{\max} = \frac{|M|}{J} r_o.$$

Introducing the *polar section modulus*

$$Z_p = \frac{J}{r_o}, \tag{28.7}$$

depending only on the cross section, we have

$$|\tau|_{\max} = \frac{|M|}{Z_p}. \tag{28.8}$$

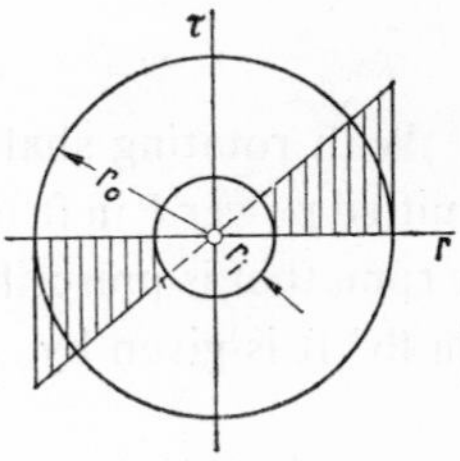

Fig. 28.4

The polar section modulus has the dimension $[L^3]$ and will be given in in³.

For a circle of radius R, it follows from Section 15 that $J = \pi R^4/2$ and further $r_o = R$, so that

$$Z_p = \frac{\pi}{2} R^3. \tag{28.9}$$

For an annulus with the radii r_o and r_i, the corresponding result is

$$Z_p = \frac{\pi}{2} \frac{r_o^4 - r_i^4}{r_o}. \tag{28.10}$$

In order to prevent yielding or fracture, we must see to it that in every section $|\tau|_{\max} \leq \tau_{\mathrm{al}}$. In view of (28.8), this condition can be recast in the form

$$\left| \frac{M}{Z_p} \right|_{\max} \leq \tau_{\mathrm{al}} \tag{28.11}$$

by comparing all cross sections. The section in which M/Z_p is maximal is the endangered cross section.

For a cylindrical shaft, (28.11) can be written as

$$Z \geq \frac{|M|_{\max}}{\tau_{\mathrm{al}}}. \tag{28.12}$$

In this case, the endangered section can be obtained directly from the torsion moment diagram.

The relations thus far obtained can easily be remembered by virtue of their similarity with those for concentric compression or tension and those for simple bending. They are valid not only for shafts at rest but also for uniformly rotating ones. Since the drive is not always exactly uniform and therefore torsional oscillations are to be expected, the design by (28.11) is often supplemented by the additional requirement that the twist per length should not exceed a prescribed limit. Thus it is quite usual to restrict the specific twist to be less than some value β of the order 5 to 10 minutes per foot and to supplement condition (28.11) by the requirement

$$\left| \frac{d\vartheta^0}{dx} \right| \leq \beta. \tag{28.13}$$

With rotating shafts it is very often not the torsion moment but the transmitted power P in ft lb*/min together with the number of revolutions per minute, ν rpm, that is prescribed. It is shown in dynamics that the transmitted moment in lb* ft is given by

$$M = \frac{P}{2\pi\nu}. \tag{28.14}$$

When the shaft is cylindrical and loaded only at the ends, (28.14) represents the greatest absolute torsion moment.

Let it be required to design the solid cylindrical shaft (Fig. 28.5) with the properties
$$G = 1.2 \times 10^7 \text{ psi} \qquad \text{and} \qquad \tau_{al} = 4000 \text{ psi},$$

if it is to transmit at $\nu = 700$ rpm a power of $P = 400$ horsepower (hp) $= 1.32 \times 10^7$ ft lb*/min.

By (28.14), the torsion moment is

$$M = \frac{P}{2\pi\nu} = \frac{1.32 \times 10^7}{2\pi \, (700)} = 3000 \text{ lb* ft} = 36,000 \text{ lb* in.}$$

With the radius of the cross section denoted by R, the design according to stress, by (28.8) and (28.9), requires that

$$\tau_{max} = \frac{2M}{\pi R^3} \leq \tau_{al} \,,$$

and hence

$$R^3 \geq \frac{2M}{\pi\tau_{al}} = \frac{2 \cdot 36,000}{\pi \cdot 4000} = 5.73 \text{ in}^3,$$

or $R \geq 1.79$ in. Taking $R = 1\frac{7}{8}$ in, we have

$$\tau_{max} = \frac{2 \cdot 36,000}{\pi \, (1\frac{7}{8})^3} = 3480 \text{ psi},$$

and by (28.3)

$$\frac{d\vartheta}{dx} = \frac{2M}{G\pi R^4} = \frac{2 \cdot 36,000}{1.2 \times 10^7 \pi \, (1\tfrac{3}{8})^4} = 1.55 \, 10^{-4} \, \text{in}^{-1}$$

or

$$\frac{d\vartheta^\circ}{dx} = 12\frac{180}{\pi}1.55 \times 10^{-4} \, (60) = 6.4 \, \text{min ft}^{-1}.$$

This specific twist constitutes a borderline case according to (28.13). Thus, whether the design satisfies the deformation criterion will depend on which design value is chosen for β.

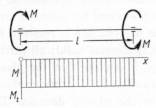

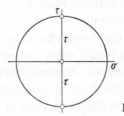

Fig. 28.5   Fig. 28.6

In order to have a definite safety factor n against yielding or fracture, we set

$$\tau_{al} = \frac{\tau_0}{n}, \tag{28.15}$$

where τ_0 is the yield or fracture limit for pure shear. Moreover, in order to express τ_0 in terms of the yield or fracture limit σ_0 for the uniaxial state of stress, we can use the stress diagram (Fig. 28.6), from which we read the principal stresses $\sigma_1 = \tau$ and $\sigma_2 = -\tau$. According to the Tresca condition (21.7), yielding or fracture sets in when $2\tau = \sigma_0$; we must therefore substitute

$$\tau_0 = \tfrac{1}{2}\sigma_0 \tag{28.16}$$

into (28.15). Condition (21.13) of von Mises, on the other hand, furnishes $3\tau^2 = \sigma_0^2$, and therefore instead of (28.16)

$$\tau_0 = \frac{1}{\sqrt{3}}\sigma_0 = 0.57\,\sigma_0, \tag{28.17}$$

i.e., a value for τ_0 about 15% greater.

The design according to (28.15) is based on the requirement that the yield or fracture limit should not be reached at any point in the shaft. With ductile materials, however, local *plastic yielding* does not lead to failure. In fact, when the yield stress τ_0 is reached with the torsion moment

$$M_0 = Z_p\tau_0, \tag{28.18}$$

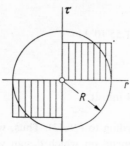

Fig. 28.7

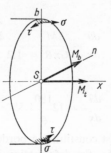

Fig. 28.8

it is first the extreme fibers that yield. Only when the loading increases do we have the plastic domain extending into the inner fibers and the adjacent cross sections. If the simplifying assumption about the deformation is retained for the partially plastic cross sections also, then (28.1) remains valid; all further relations, however, become invalid. Nevertheless, it is clear that the plastic domain has the shape of an annulus spreading inwardly with a shrinking elastic core, and that there is a state of pure shear τ_0 in the plastic domain. The torsion moment can be further increased to the value M^* under which the elastic core vanishes and the entire cross section becomes plastic. When the support is statically determinate, the ratio $k = M^*/M_0$ represents, just as with simple bending, the reserve of strength in the plastic region. Since this ratio depends on the shape of the cross section, it is again called the *shape factor*.

The torsional section modulus of a solid circular shaft of radius R is $Z_p = \pi R^3/2$. By (28.18), plastic yielding begins at the surface under the torsion moment

$$M_0 = \frac{\pi}{2} R^3 \tau_0 . \tag{28.19}$$

With increasing load, the plastic domain extends into the interior until complete plastic flow and thus collapse sets in under the distribution of shear stress shown in Fig. 28.7. The associated torsion moment is

$$M^* = \int_A \tau_0 r \, dA = \tau_0 \int_0^{2\pi} d\varphi \int_0^R r^2 \, dr = \frac{2}{3} \pi R^3 \tau_0 . \tag{28.20}$$

By (28.19) and (28.20), we thus have

$$M^* = \frac{4}{3} M_0 ,$$

and therefore a shape factor $k = \frac{4}{3}$.

A shaft is rarely subjected to torsion alone. When the axis is horizontal, gravity produces additional bending. This also occurs with cranks, as shown in

Fig. 17.16. Therefore, we will briefly discuss design with *torsion and bending*, once again limiting ourselves to rotationally symmetric cross sections and also to the elastic domain.

At the section shown in Fig. 28.8, let M_t be the torsion moment, M_b the bending moment with the loading line b, and n the neutral axis. By (23.7), we have at the extreme surface elements on the loading line b the greatest absolute normal stress

$$\sigma = \frac{|M_b|}{Z_a}, \tag{28.21}$$

and, by (28.8), at the external boundary the greatest absolute shearing stress

$$\tau = \frac{|M_t|}{Z_p}, \tag{28.22}$$

where Z_a is the axial and Z_p is the polar section modulus. In the section considered, the outermost elements of the loading line b are endangered. The state of stress is plane and is illustrated in the volume element in Fig. 28.9. Figure 28.10 shows the corresponding stress diagram. (It is similar to the one in Section 25 in connection with the consideration of shearing stresses accompanying simple bending). From the diagram we read off the principal stresses

$$\sigma_{1,2} = \frac{\sigma}{2} \pm \sqrt{\frac{\sigma^2}{4} + \tau^2}, \tag{28.23}$$

and the greatest shear stress

$$\tau_{\max} = \sqrt{\frac{\sigma^2}{4} + \tau^2}. \tag{28.24}$$

The yield or fracture condition of Tresca (21.5), in view of (28.24), now becomes

$$\sigma^2 + 4\tau^2 = \sigma_0^2; \tag{28.25}$$

that of von Mises (21.13), by (28.23), becomes

$$\sigma^2 + 3\tau^2 = \sigma_0^2. \tag{28.26}$$

Substitution of (28.21) and (28.22) into (28.25) or (28.26) leads to the conditions necessary for the design.

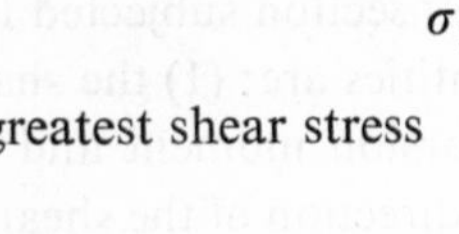

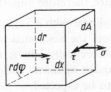

Fig. 28.9

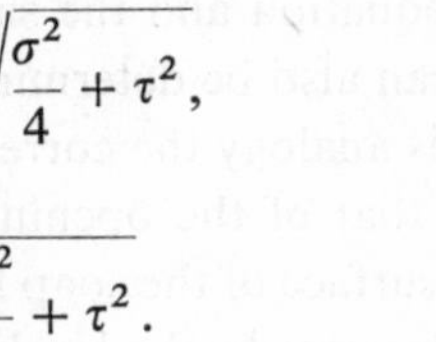

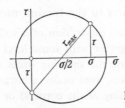

Fig. 28.10

It is clear that the present results are all the more exact, the more slender and the more nearly cylindrical the shaft is. Moreover, it was necessary to restrict ourselves to rotationally symmetric cross sections. *Cross sections without rotational symmetry* can be treated only by dropping the simplifying assumption regarding the deformation and making use of the exact methods of the theories of elasticity or plasticity. This exact treatment shows that between the torsion problem in the elastic region and the *membrane problem* there is an analogy, discovered by Prandtl (1875–1953).

Fig. 28.11

Fig. 28.12

If an opening is cut in a plane metal sheet (Fig. 28.11) and a soap film is stretched across the opening, then a small pressure difference between the lower and upper surfaces will cause the film to bulge into a curved surface. When the curvature of this surface is not too great, its shape can be determined by the same differential equation and the same boundary conditions from which the shearing stresses can also be determined in a cross section subjected to torsion (Fig. 28.12). In this analogy the corresponding entities are: (1) the shape of the cross section and that of the opening, (2) the torsion moment and twice the volume under the surface of the soap film, (3) the direction of the shearing stress τ and that of the tangent to the level contour, (4) the magnitude of τ and the slope of the soap film. On the basis of this analogy, the torsion problem for any simply connected cross section can be reduced to the membrane problem, which can be solved experimentally. In addition, since the membrane problem allows more appeal to intuition, it often makes qualitative statements possible.

The Prandtl analogy in the case of a rectangular cross section leads to a membrane as shown in Fig. 28.13 by a few level curves. The slope, and thus the shearing stress τ, vanishes at the center and at the corners. The greatest shearing stress occurs at the middle of the longer sides.

From this example it can be concluded that the projecting corners make only a small contribution to the torsion moment and are therefore superfluous.

Figure 28.14 shows the section of a solid circular cylinder with a keyway (of exaggerated size), together with some level contours from the associated membrane problem. In this case the shearing stress τ becomes theoretically infinite at the reentrant corners. Thus, even under arbitrarily small torsion moments, yielding (and a consequent rounding of the corners) or fracture is to be expected.

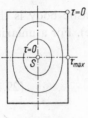

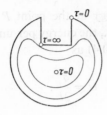

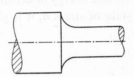

Fig. 28.13   Fig. 28.14   Fig. 28.15

Generalizing this result, we conclude that re-entrant corners are dangerous and must therefore be rounded off. Finally, it can be shown that also in the longitudinal section re-entrant corners severely diminish the strength, so that they also (Fig. 28.15) should be rounded off.

Exercises

1. A circular shaft (Fig. 28.16) of length $l = 15$ ft, radius $R = 2$ in, shear modulus $G = 1.1 \times 10^7$ psi, and yield stress $\sigma_0 = 30,000$ psi is supported by short radial bearings at each end and subjected to torsion by the two moments M. Neglecting the weight of the shaft, determine the moment M_0 under which yielding sets in, first according to the yield condition of Tresca, and secondly according to that of von Mises. Also calculate the corresponding angle of twist ϑ.

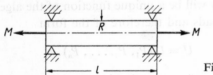

$M \longleftarrow$ R $\longrightarrow M$

l Fig. 28.16

2. Assume that the specific weight of the shaft is $\gamma = 0.28$ lb*/in³ and solve the preceding problem taking the weight into consideration.

3. Determine the shape factor k for a thin annular cross section of radius r.

29. Maxwell's Theorem

In this and the next section we will discuss a few theorems and methods based on the concept of strain energy. Since such an energy exists only when the internal forces are conservative, it is necessary to restrict attention to the *elastic body*. We will go even one step further and limit ourselves to bodies that are supported without friction and in which Hooke's law is valid. The relation between the components of stress and strain will thus be linear.

By Section 20, the *strain energy* at the point P of an elastic body is the specific energy of deformation (i.e., the energy per unit volume). For a uniaxial state of stress σ, it is given by (20.4) as

$$\bar{U} = \frac{\sigma^2}{2E},\tag{29.1}$$

and for a state of pure shear τ by (20.7) as

$$\bar{U} = \frac{\tau^2}{2G}.\tag{29.2}$$

With the aid of (20.8) and the stress-strain relations (19.17) it can be given, for the three-dimensional state of stress also, in terms of the components of stress. The total strain energy of the body is

$$U = \int_V \bar{U}\, dv,\tag{29.3}$$

and is thus a unique function of its state of stress.

If consideration is restricted to small loads, thus excluding such phenomena as buckling, the state of stress is then uniquely given by the loads and is, in particular, independent of the manner in which these are applied to the body. If it is supposed that the lines of action of the loads are prescribed once and for all, the strain energy will be a unique function of the algebraic magnitudes $P_1, P_2, \ldots, P_n$ of the loads and therefore of the form

$$U = U(P_1, P_2, \ldots, P_n).\tag{29.4}$$

With *concentric tension*, for example, the state of stress is uniaxial and, by (22.6), the only nonzero principal stress is

$$\sigma = \frac{N(x)}{A(x)}.\tag{29.5}$$

The strain energy corresponding to the volume element dv (Fig. 22.2) is, by (29.1), (29.3), and (29.5),

$$dU = \frac{\sigma^2}{2E}\, dv = \frac{N^2(x)}{2EA^2(x)}\, dA\, dx.$$

Integrating this expression first over the cross section, we obtain for the slice of thickness dx the strain energy

$$d'U = \frac{N^2(x)}{2EA(x)}\, dx.$$

Then, by integration over the length, the strain energy for the whole bar,

$$U = \int_0^l \frac{N^2(x)}{2EA(x)} dx,$$ (29.6)

is obtained. If it is supposed that $N(x)$ is expressed in terms of the loads, we thus have an actual representation of the form (29.4). Moreover, by (29.6), U is positive definite, i.e., the strain energy vanishes when all the loads are zero, and in all other cases it is positive. This is true in general, since the unloaded shape of the body is always stable.

When a cylindrical or prismatic bar is subjected to two equal and opposite axial forces acting at its ends, N and A are constant. Thus, by (29.6), we have

$$U = \frac{N^2 l}{2EA},$$ (29.7)

which can also be written in the form $U = N\Delta l/2$ by means of (22.9). The factor $\frac{1}{2}$ can be explained by the fact that as the bar is gradually loaded, the normal force increases proportionally to the elongation from zero up to the value N.

With the numerical values $N = 12,000$ lb*, $l = 10$ ft, $A = 1$ in², and $E = 3 \times 10^7$ psi, we obtain for example

$$U = \frac{(12,000)^2\, 120}{2 \times 3 \times 10^7} \times \frac{1}{12} = 24 \text{ ft lb *}.$$

With *simple bending*, by (23.2), we have instead of (29.5)

$$\sigma = \frac{M(x)}{I(x)} z.$$

The elementary strain energy is therefore

$$dU = \frac{\sigma^2}{2E} dv = \frac{M^2(x)}{2EI^2(x)} z^2\, dA\, dx,$$

that of a slice of thickness dx

$$d'U = \frac{M^2(x)}{2EI(x)} dx$$

and the total strain energy

$$U = \int_0^l \frac{M^2(x)}{2EI(x)} dx.$$ (29.8)

For the simply supported prismatic beam loaded at the center as shown in Fig. 29.1, the bending moment in the left-hand field is given by

$$M(x) = \frac{1}{2} Px \quad \left(0 \le x \le \frac{l}{2}\right).$$

The total strain energy is therefore

$$U = 2 \cdot \frac{P^2/4}{2EI} \int_0^{l/2} x^2 \, dx = \frac{P^2}{4EI} \frac{l^3}{24} = \frac{P^2 l^3}{96EI}. \tag{29.9}$$

In the case of the *torsion* of a shaft with a rotationally symmetric cross section, the state of stress is one of pure shear, where, by (28.6),

$$\tau = \frac{M(x)}{J(x)} r. \tag{29.10}$$

By (29.2) and (29.10), the elementary strain energy amounts to

$$dU = \frac{\tau^2}{2G} dv = \frac{M^2(x)}{2GI_p^2(x)} r^2 \, dA \, dx,$$

that of a slice of thickness dx is $d'U = [M^2(x)/2GJ(x)] \, dx$, and thus the total strain energy is

$$U = \int_0^l \frac{M^2(x)}{2GJ(x)} dx. \tag{29.11}$$

For a cylindrical shaft on the ends of which act two equal and opposite moments M we have $M(x) = M$ and J constant; thus

$$U = \frac{M^2 l}{2GJ} \tag{29.12}$$

or, by (28.5), $U = M \, \vartheta/2$.

Since in all these cases the strain energy is a quadratic function of the stress resultants and therefore also of the loads, it can not in general be gained by superposition.

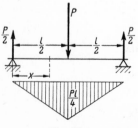

Fig. 29.1

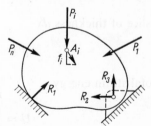

Fig. 29.2

Figure 29.2 shows an elastic body under the loads $P_1, P_2, \ldots, P_n$. Let the points of application be denoted by A_i and their *displacement components* in the direction of the loads by f_i. They are single-valued functions

$$f_i = f_i(P_1, P_2, \ldots, P_n) \tag{29.13}$$

of the loading. Under the assumption that the displacement components can be developed in power series of the loads, we have

$$f_i = \sum_{k=1}^{n} \alpha_{ik} P_k. \tag{29.14}$$

Since the displacements are measured from the natural configuration, no constant terms arise, and the terms of order higher than the first can be neglected within the compass of the linear theory.

If P_k is the only nonzero load, (29.14) reduces to $f_i = \alpha_{ik} P_k$. The coefficient α_{ik} therefore represents the displacement of the point of application A_i in the direction of P_i due to the load $P_k = 1$; it is called an *influence number*. Relation (29.14) expresses the possibility of determining the displacement components f_i by superposing the contributions originating from the individual loads.

Let all the loads P_i be applied to the body. If the load P_k subsequently increases further by an infinitesimal amount dP_k, the points of application A_i will undergo additional displacements df_i; the loads P_i therefore perform the additional amount of work

$$dW = \sum_{1}^{n} P_i \, df_i = \left(\sum_{i=1}^{n} P_i \alpha_{ik} \right) dP_k. \tag{29.15}$$

This additional work, by Section 20, is equal to the increase in the strain energy (29.4) and can thus also be written in the form

$$dW = dU = \frac{\partial U}{\partial P_k} dP_k. \tag{29.16}$$

Comparison of (29.15) and (29.16) then leads to the equation

$$\frac{\partial U}{\partial P_k} = \sum_{i=1}^{n} P_i \alpha_{ik}, \tag{29.17}$$

which will serve as the starting point for the next section.

Partial differentiation of relation (29.17) with respect to P_i leads to

$$\frac{\partial^2 U}{\partial P_i \, \partial P_k} = \alpha_{ik}, \tag{29.18}$$

and since this result must be true for arbitrary indices i and k, we also have

$$\frac{\partial^2 U}{\partial P_k \, \partial P_i} = \alpha_{ki}. \tag{29.19}$$

The left-hand sides of (29.18) and (29.19) are always continuous and therefore commutative. We therefore have the *theorem of Maxwell* (1831–1879)

$$\alpha_{ki} = \alpha_{ik},\tag{29.20}$$

according to which the influence numbers with interchanged indices are equal. In order to make this theorem intuitively more obvious, let us consider the body in Fig. 29.3, which is arbitrarily (but frictionlessly) supported. Two arbitrary points together with arbitrary directions through these are shown. If, in addition to the loads already present, a unit force is applied to point 1 along the direction 1, then point 2 undergoes an additional displacement α_{21} in direction 2. By (29.20), this is equal to the additional displacement α_{12} in direction 1 that point 1 would undergo, if a unit force were applied at point 2 in direction 2.

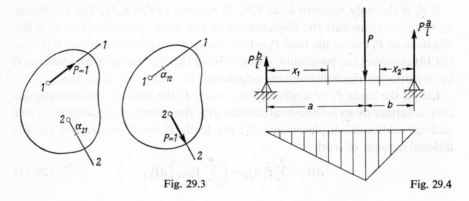

Fig. 29.3   Fig. 29.4

In the case of simple bending, the f_i are the displacements of the deflection curve under the loads. Figure 29.4 shows a simply supported prismatic beam that is loaded by P at an arbitrary section. The reactions can be determined by the moment conditions for the two supports. The moment diagram has the form of a triangle. With the notation of Fig. 29.4, the greatest bending moment is given by

$$M_{\max} = P\frac{ab}{l}.$$

Since it is impossible to write for the bending moment a single expression valid at every point of the beam, we subdivide the beam into two fields a and b. Let x_1 and x_2 be coordinates in each field measured from the respective support. For the elastic line we now have the differential equations

$$\zeta_1'' = -\frac{Pb}{lEI}x_1 \qquad (0 \le x_1 \le a),\tag{29.21}$$

$$\zeta_2'' = -\frac{Pa}{lEI}x_2 \qquad (0 \le x_2 \le b).\tag{29.22}$$

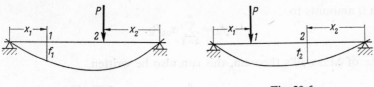

Fig. 29.5   Fig. 29.6

These are to be integrated separately and the constants of integration will be determined by the boundary conditions $\zeta_1(0) = 0$, $\zeta_2(0) = 0$, and the transition conditions $\zeta_1(a) = \zeta_2(b)$, $\zeta'_1(a) = -\zeta'_2(b)$, which guarantee that the elastic line and its tangent shall be continuous under the load P. The solution reads

$$\zeta_1 = \frac{Pbx_1}{6lEI}(l^2 - b^2 - x_1^2) \qquad (0 \leq x_1 \leq a),\tag{29.23}$$

$$\zeta_2 = \frac{Pax_2}{6lEI}(l^2 - a^2 - x_2^2) \qquad (0 \leq x_2 \leq b).\tag{29.24}$$

Consider now a beam (Fig. 29.5) that is loaded by P at station 2 with distance x_2 from the right-hand support. The displacement f_1 at station 1 with the distance $x_1 \leq l - x_2$ from the left-hand support is obtained by replacing b in (29.23) by x_2. This yields

$$f_1 = \frac{Px_2x_1}{6lEI}(l^2 - x_2^2 - x_1^2).$$

By exchanging the roles of the two stations (Fig. 29.6) it similarly follows from (29.24) that

$$f_2 = \frac{Px_1x_2}{6lEI}(l^2 - x_1^2 - x_2^2).$$

As required by Maxwell's theorem, the two displacements f_1 and f_2 are equal. The influence numbers for the two stations 1 and 2 amount to

$$\alpha_{12} = \alpha_{21} = \frac{x_1x_2}{6lEI}(l^2 - x_1^2 - x_2^2).\tag{29.25}$$

For a beam (Fig. 29.7) that is loaded at the stations $1, 2, \ldots, k, \ldots, n$ by the forces $P_1, P_2, \ldots, P_k, \ldots, P_n$, it follows from (29.14) that the displacement of

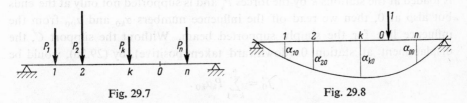

Fig. 29.7   Fig. 29.8

station 0 amounts to

$$f_0 = \sum_{k=1}^{n} \alpha_{0k} P_k .$$

Because of Maxwell's theorem, this can also be written

$$f_0 = \sum_{k=1}^{n} P_k \alpha_{k0} . \tag{29.26}$$

The influence numbers α_{k0} are the displacements that would arise at the stations k due to a unit force at station 0. By Fig. 29.8, these displacements can be read off from a single deflection curve, which is called the *influence line* for station 0. Thus, the problem has been reduced to the construction of this influence line.

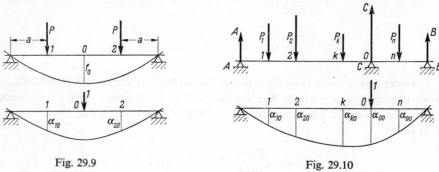

Fig. 29.9   Fig. 29.10

For the symmetrically loaded prismatic beam in Fig. 29.9, the influence number for stations 1 and 0, by (29.25), is

$$\alpha_{10} = \frac{al/2}{6lEI}\left(l^2 - a^2 - \frac{l^2}{4}\right) = \frac{a}{48EI}(3l^2 - 4a^2) .$$

Since α_{20} has the same value, (29.26) yields the greatest deflection

$$f_0 = \frac{Pa}{24EI}(3l^2 - 4a^2) , \tag{29.27}$$

occurring at the center.

By means of the superposition principle, the method of influence lines can also be used to solve statically indeterminate problems. If a beam (Fig. 29.10) is loaded at the stations k by the forces P_k and is supported not only at the ends but also at 0, then we read off the influence numbers α_{k0} and α_{00} from the influence line for the simply supported beam. Without the support C, the displacement at station 0 (downward taken positive), by (29.26), would be

$$f_0' = \sum_{k=1}^{n} P_k \alpha_{k0} .$$

On the other hand, under the force C alone, we would have a displacement

$$f_0'' = -C\alpha_{00}.$$

Actually, both the loads P_k and the reaction C are present, and since the middle support is rigid, the resultant displacement $f_0 = f_0' + f_0''$ at station 0 must vanish. Thus, for the determination of the reaction C, we have the equation

$$C = \frac{1}{\alpha_{00}} \sum_{k=1}^{n} P_k \alpha_{k0}.$$

Then the supporting forces A and B follow from the equilibrium conditions.

For the prismatic beam in Fig. 29.11, it follows from (29.27) that

$$f_0' = \frac{Pa}{24EI}(3l^2 - 4a^2),$$

and by (29.25)

$$\alpha_{00} = \frac{l^2/4}{6lEI}\left(l^2 - \frac{l^2}{4} - \frac{l^2}{4}\right) = \frac{l^3}{48EI}.$$

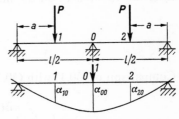

Fig. 29.11

Consequently $f_0'' = -Cl^3/48EI$. The condition $f_1' + f_1'' = 0$ yields

$$C = \frac{2Pa}{l^3}(3l^2 - 4a^2).$$

Exercises

1. A beam is subjected to general bending. Resolve the loading into two cases of simple bending and show that the strain energy is furnished additively by the contributions from these partial loadings.

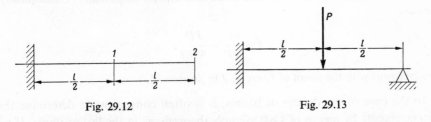

Fig. 29.12   Fig. 29.13

2. Determine the influence numbers α_{11}, α_{12}, and α_{22} for the cantilever beam in Fig. 29.12. Use these to determine the reactions when the cantilever is propped at the tip by a simple support and is loaded in the middle as shown in Fig. 29.13.

30. Castigliano's Theorems

In order to derive some further results related to Section 29, we retain the assumptions made therein. Thus, we limit ourselves to elastic bodies and assume also that the loads are so small that the displacement components can be represented as linear forms (29.14) of the loads. Then, when we interchange the indices i and k in (29.14), we obtain

$$f_k = \sum_{i=1}^{n} \alpha_{ki} P_i. \tag{30.1}$$

If in addition we take (29.17), while making use of Maxwell's theorem and reversing the indices on the influence numbers, we can write

$$\frac{\partial U}{\partial P_k} = \sum_{i=1}^{n} \alpha_{ki} P_i. \tag{30.2}$$

Comparison of (30.1) with (30.2) yields the *theorem of Castigliano* (1847–1884)

$$f_k = \frac{\partial U}{\partial P_k} \qquad (k = 1, 2, \ldots, n). \tag{30.3}$$

According to this theorem, the individual displacement components can be obtained by taking the partial derivatives of the strain energy with respect to the associated loads.

For the simply supported prismatic beam loaded in the center (Fig. 29.1), the strain energy, by (29.9), is

$$U = \frac{P^2 l^3}{96EI}.$$

By reason of symmetry, the greatest deflection f occurs at the center and thus corresponds to the displacement component associated with the single load P. Consequently, we have

$$f = \frac{\partial U}{\partial P} = \frac{P l^3}{48EI},$$

in agreement with the result of Exercise 2 in Section 23.

In the case of the flexure of beams, it is often convenient to determine the displacements by means of Castigliano's theorem, as in the last example. If no single load acts at the point where the displacement is sought, we introduce an auxiliary force there, and then in the result we finally set its magnitude equal to zero.

In order to determine the greatest deflection f at the center of the simply supported beam in Fig. 30.1, which is subjected to a uniformly distributed load P, we introduce the auxiliary force H. The reactions are then $(P + H)/2$. The bending moment in the left-hand field is given by

$$M = \frac{P + H}{2} x - \frac{P}{2l} x^2 \quad \left(0 \le x \le \frac{l}{2}\right), \quad (30.4)$$

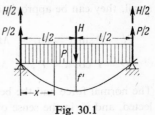

and, by (29.8), the total strain energy is

$$U = 2 \int_0^{l/2} \frac{M^2}{2EI} \, dx .$$

Fig. 30.1

According to Castigliano's theorem (30.3), the displacement f' at the center of the beam due to the loading P and the auxiliary force H is

$$f' = \frac{\partial U}{\partial H} = \frac{2}{EI} \int_0^{l/2} M \frac{\partial M}{\partial H} \, dx ,$$

where we have differentiated under the integral sign. Or by (30.4),

$$f' = \frac{2}{EI} \int_0^{l/2} \left(\frac{P + H}{4} x^2 - \frac{P}{4l} x^3\right) dx = \frac{1}{EI} \left[(P + H) \frac{l^3}{48} - P \frac{l^3}{128}\right] .$$

Setting $H = 0$, we obtain for the original problem

$$f = \frac{5Pl^3}{384EI} .$$

In all the problems on the strength of materials from Sections 22 to 28, we have restricted ourselves to straight bars. The methods used there, however, can also be applied to *curved bars*.

Figure 30.2 shows a helical spring made from a circular wire of radius r whose axis has the shape of a circular helix of radius R and pitch α. Let it be assumed that the ends A and B of the spring lie on the axis of the helix; at the same time let it be assumed that the number of turns n per length is so great that the deviation of the wire axis from the helix at either end can be neglected. The length of wire in the spring, if the pitch α is small, is to a first approximation given by

$$l = 2\pi nR . \quad (30.5)$$

If the spring as a whole is subjected to the tensile forces P, the loading of an arbitrary cross section of

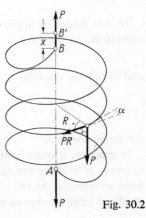

Fig. 30.2

the wire will consist in a force P parallel to the axis of the spring and a couple of moment PR directed azimuthally. The resolution of these two vectors according to Fig. 30.3 yields four stress resultants. Now if α is small, they can be approximated as follows:

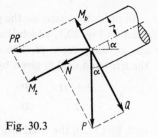

Fig. 30.3

$$N = P \sin \alpha = P\alpha, \qquad M_b = PR \sin \alpha = PR\alpha,$$

$$Q = P \cos \alpha = P, \qquad M_t = PR \cos \alpha = PR.$$

The normal force and the bending moment, being small stress resultants, can be neglected, and if, in the sense of Section 23, we drop the shearing force, only the torsion moment remains. The polar section modulus of the wire, by Section 28, is $Z_p = \pi r^3/2$. Thus, by (28.8), the design of the wire must be based on the requirement that

$$\tau_{\max} = \frac{M_t}{Z_p} = \frac{2PR}{\pi r^3} \leq \tau_{al}$$

or

$$P \leq \frac{\pi}{2} \frac{r^3}{R} \tau_{al}. \tag{30.6}$$

The strain energy of the wire in the spring is given by (29.12), and with (30.5) and $J = \pi r^4/2$, we find

$$U = \frac{P^2 R^2 \cdot 2\pi n R}{2G \cdot \pi r^4/2} = \frac{2n}{G} \frac{R^3}{r^4} P^2.$$

The elongation x of the spring follows from Castigliano's theorem (30.3):

$$x = \frac{\partial U}{\partial P} = \frac{4n}{G} \frac{R^3}{r^4} P.$$

To this degree of approximation, it is proportional to the loading. It is usual to express this in the form

$$P = cx \tag{30.7}$$

and to call the quantity

$$c = \frac{G}{4n} \frac{r^4}{R^3} \tag{30.8}$$

the *spring constant*.

In practice, it often happens that the load to be carried is prescribed and it is a question of making the spring as compliant as possible, namely of making c as small as possible. As (30.6) and (30.8) show, this can be most easily achieved by employing a large number of turns per length.

There are occasions when an elastic body is subjected not only to concentrated forces but also to couples with short arms. Figure 30.4 shows such a couple M_k acting in the vicinity of the point A_k. By section 3, it can be conceived as the limiting case of a small force P_k acting at a large distance a_k, and the displacement component f_k of its point of application is given by (30.3). Since a_k is large, the displacement of A_k can be neglected in comparison with f_k. The segment a_k then turns around A_k, and the angle of rotation φ_k, projected onto the plane of the couple M_k, is

$$\varphi_k = \frac{f_k}{a_k} = \frac{\partial U}{\partial (P_k a_k)},$$

i.e., it is given by

$$\varphi_k = \frac{\partial U}{\partial M_k}. \tag{30.9}$$

Thus, Castigliano's theorem is also valid for moments, and in this case it furnishes the projection of the angle of rotation on the plane of the couple.

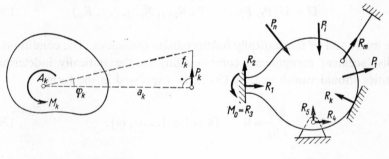

Fig. 30.4   Fig. 30.5

A suitable interpretation of Castigliano's theorem yields a powerful tool for the solution of *statically indeterminate problems*. If a body (Fig. 30.5) is loaded by the loads or moments $P_1, P_2, \ldots, P_n$ and is supported in a statically indeterminate manner, the equilibrium conditions (as well as possible symmetry conditions) do not suffice for determining the reactions. If m is the number of reactions $R_1, R_2, \ldots, R_m$ (already resolved into components and containing any possible couples), and $l < m$ the number of equations at our disposal, then the problem is $(m-l)$-fold statically indeterminate.

The reactions can be split up arbitrarily into two groups such that the first one contains l reactions which can be expressed in terms of the remaining reactions by means of the available equations, whereas the second group contains the $m-l$ remaining equations. The reactions in the first group are referred to as the *eliminable reactions*, and, with a suitable enumeration, they consist in the forces or moments

$$R_1, R_2, \ldots, R_l \qquad \text{(eliminable reactions).} \qquad (30.10)$$

The remaining reactions

$$R_{l+1}, R_{l+2}, \ldots, R_m \qquad \text{(statically indeterminate quantities)} \qquad (30.11)$$

are called the *statically indeterminate quantities*. The equilibrium of the body is already guaranteed by the eliminable reactions. The redundant supports, however, restrict the possible deformations in that the displacement components corresponding to the associated reactions are zero. Therefore one can consider the statically indeterminate quantities as additional loads, the magnitudes of which are such that the corresponding displacement components are zero. In this sense, we have a statically determinate problem whose strain energy, by (29.4), is a single-valued function

$$U = U(P_1, P_2, \ldots, P_n, R_{l+1}, R_{l+2}, \ldots, R_m) \qquad (30.12)$$

of the loads and of the statically indeterminate quantities. The conditions that the displacement components corresponding to the statically indeterminate quantities should vanish can, by (30.3), be expressed in the form

$$\frac{\partial U}{\partial R_k} = 0 \qquad (k = l + 1, \ldots, m). \qquad (30.13)$$

The relations (30.13) represent $m - l$ equations which are needed to augment the l equilibrium (and symmetry) conditions in order to determine the m reactions. Hence, statically indeterminate problems can be solved by means of *Castigliano's method* by (1) dividing the reactions into the two groups (30.10) and (30.11), (2) representing the total strain energy U in terms of the loads and statically indeterminate quantities, as indicated in (30.12), and (3) setting to zero the partial derivatives of U with respect to the statically indeterminate quantities, as in (30.13).

How the groups (30.11) and (30.12) are composed from the individual reactions is unimportant. However, it is essential that the first one contain l reactions and the second contain $m - l$, i.e., that the available equations are used to express as many reactions as possible in terms of the others and the loads. Only then are the arguments of U in (30.12) independent of each other, so that there is no possibility of error in formally calculating the partial derivatives (30.13).

Finally, it should be noted that we have hitherto assumed the supports to be rigid. When the supports are elastic, we can resort to the artifice of including the elastic parts in what is treated as the body and including their strain energies in expression (30.12).

Figure 30.6 shows a prismatic beam built-in at both ends and loaded in the center by P. Symmetry and equilibrium conditions provide the fixing forces $P/2$ and also the equality of the fixing moments M_0. The problem is thus simply statically indeterminate with the statically indeterminate quantity M_0. The bending moment in the left-hand field is

$$M = M_0 - \frac{P}{2} x \qquad \left(0 \leq x \leq \frac{l}{2} \right). \qquad (30.14)$$

The strain energy is

$$U = 2 \int_0^{l/2} \frac{M^2}{2EI} \, dx \,,$$

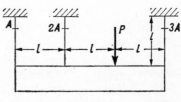

Fig. 30.6

and the additional relation necessary for the determination of M_0 is

$$\frac{\partial U}{\partial M_0} = \frac{2}{EI} \int_0^{l/2} M \, \frac{\partial M}{\partial M_0} \, dx = 0 \,.$$

Substituting (30.14), we obtain

$$\int_0^{l/2} \left(M_0 - \frac{P}{2} x \right) dx = M_0 \frac{l}{2} - \frac{P}{2} \frac{l^2}{8} = 0 \,,$$

and hence

$$M_0 = P \frac{l}{8} \,.$$

Exercises

1. An elastic prismatic cantilever beam (Fig. 30.7) is uniformly loaded. Determine the greatest deflection f by means of Castigliano's theorem.

2. A rigid beam of negligible weight is supported from three elastic wires, as shown in Fig. 30.8, and loaded by the force P. Determine the tensions in the wires with Castigliano's method.

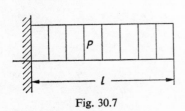

Fig. 30.7

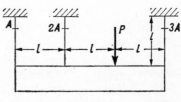

Fig. 30.8

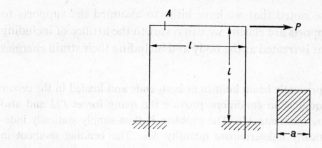

Fig. 30.9

3. Two elastic beams of square cross section are fixed at their lower ends. The upper ends are connected by a wire of the same material (elastic modulus E) and of cross-sectional area A (Fig. 30.9). A horizontal force P is applied to the upper end of the right-hand beam. Determine the tension in the wire.

Answers to Exercises

2.1. $A = 12.828$, lb* $B = 8.484$ lb*

2.3. $K_1 = \dfrac{1}{\sqrt{3}} K$,

$K_2 = \sqrt{\tfrac{2}{3}} K$,

$K_3 = \dfrac{2}{\sqrt{3}} K$

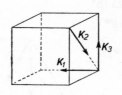

Graphically: force diagram in plan and elevation.

Exercise 2.3

2.4. $R = 2\pi\lambda$ (vertically downward, independent of distance h)

3.1.

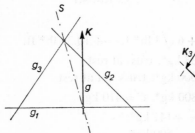

Exercise 3.1

3.2. Cable under tension, so plate remains at rest. $Z = 63$ lb*, $S = 10$ lb*

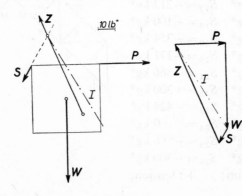

10 lb*

Exercise 3.2

3.3. $S_1 = 1.33$ kg* (compression),
$\quad S_2 = 0.66$ kg* (tension),
$\quad S_3 = 0.93$ kg* (tension)

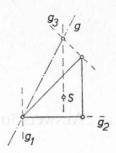

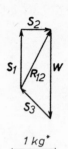

Exercise 3.3

4.1. $R = 2.35$ lb*, $R_{234} = 3.25$ lb*,
$\quad R_{145} = 2.25$ lb*
4.2. $R = 5.84$ kg*

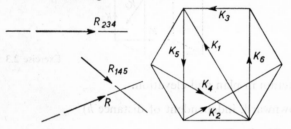

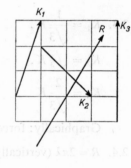

Exercise 4.1   Exercise 4.2

4.3. A couple of moment $+ 6\sqrt{3}$ lb* ft $= + 10.39$ lb* ft.
4.4. $A = 6350$ kg*, $B = 333$ kg*, truss at rest
$\quad A' = 6700$ kg*, $B' = 1000$ kg*, truss not at rest
5.1. $A = 640$ kg*, $B = 800$ kg*, $C = 410$ kg*
5.2.

$S_1 = -566$ kg*	$S_{14} = +141$ kg*
$S_2 = -100$ kg*	$S_{15} = -500$ kg*
$S_3 = 0$ kg*	$S_{16} = +354$ kg*
$S_4 = -566$ kg*	$S_{17} = -212$ kg*
$S_5 = +100$ kg*	$S_{18} = -100$ kg*
$S_6 = -141$ kg*	$S_{19} = -354$ kg*
$S_7 = 0$ kg*	$S_{20} = -171$ kg*
$S_8 = -424$ kg*	$S_{21} = -566$ kg*
$S_9 = -100$ kg*	$S_{22} = +300$ kg*
$S_{10} = -141$ kg*	$S_{23} = -424$ kg*
$S_{11} = +283$ kg*	$S_{24} = 0$ kg*
$S_{12} = -141$ kg*	$S_{25} = -566$ kg*
$S_{13} = -300$ kg*	$S_{26} = -300$ kg*

$-$: compression; $+$: tension:

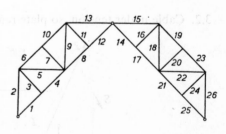

Exercise 5.2

6.1. $R = (0, -1, 0)\,\text{lb*}$, $M = (1, -1, -1)\,\text{lb* ft}$

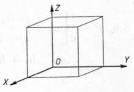

6.2. Central axis: $x = 1\,\text{ft}$, $z = 1\,\text{ft}$

   Force: $R = (0, -1, 0)\,\text{lb*}$

   Moment: $M = (0, -1, 0)\,\text{lb* ft}$

7.3. $K = \tfrac{1}{2}W\sin\alpha\sin\varphi$, $A_x = \tfrac{1}{2}W\left(\cos\alpha - \sin\alpha\cos\varphi\right)$,

   $B_x = -\tfrac{1}{2}W\left(\sin\alpha\cos\varphi + \cos\alpha\right)$, $A_y = W\cos\alpha$,

   $B_z = 0$ $A_z = \tfrac{1}{2}W\sin\alpha\sin\varphi$

8.1. (a) Force: $X = -4.61\,\text{lb*}$,

                 $Y = +6.0\ \ \text{lb*}$,

                 $R = \ \ \ 7.57\,\text{lb*}$,

                 $6x + 4.61y = 4$

   (b) Moment: $M = 4\,\text{lb* ft}$

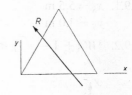

8.2. $A_x = \dfrac{W + 2P}{2} = 65\,\text{lb*}$, $A_y = \dfrac{W}{2} = 35\,\text{lb*}$,

   $D = \dfrac{W + 2P}{2}\sqrt{2} = 91.8\,\text{lb*}$

8.3. $P_1 = \tfrac{3}{4}W = 75\,\text{kg*}\,(\text{compression})$, $P_2 = \tfrac{1}{4}W = 25\,\text{kg*}\,(\text{tension})$,

   $P_3 = \dfrac{1}{2\sqrt{2}}W = 35.4\,\text{kg*}\,(\text{compression})$

8.4. $\varphi = \arctan\left(\dfrac{4l - 6r}{l - 6r}\right), 0 \le r \le \dfrac{l}{6}$ or $\dfrac{2l}{3} \le r \le l$

   $A = W\cos\varphi$, $B = W\sin\varphi$

8.5. $\tan\varphi = \dfrac{W_2\cot\alpha - W_1\cot\beta}{W_1 + W_2}$,

   $A = \dfrac{\sin\beta}{\sin(\alpha + \beta)}(W_1 + W_2)$, $B = \dfrac{\sin\alpha}{\sin(\alpha + \beta)}(W_1 + W_2)$,

   $N = \dfrac{\sin\alpha\sin\beta}{\sin(\alpha + \beta)}\sqrt{(W_1 + W_2)^2 + (W_2\cot\alpha - W_1\cot\beta)^2}$

8.6. $P = \dfrac{1}{c}\left[a_2 + \left(\dfrac{a_1 b_2}{b_1 + b_2} - a_2 \right) \dfrac{x}{l} \right] Q$

When $\dfrac{a_1}{a_2} = \dfrac{b_1 + b_2}{b_2}$,   we have $P = \dfrac{a_2}{c} Q$

Decimal balance: $\dfrac{a_2}{c} = \dfrac{1}{10}$ Centesimal balance: $\dfrac{a_2}{c} = \dfrac{1}{100}$

8.7. Built-in support: $A = P = 600 \text{ lb*}$, $M_A = (l + r) P = 7200 \text{ lb* ft}$
   Lower roller: $M = rS' = 1200 \text{ lb* ft}$, $S = J_V = P = 600 \text{lb*}$
   Left upper roller: $S = S' = P = 600 \text{ lb*}$, $H_V = H_H = P = 600 \text{ lb*}$
   Right upper roller: $S' = P = 600 \text{ lb*}$, $K_H = K_V = P = 600 \text{ lb*}$

9.1. $x_S = 5.5 \text{ m}$
   $y_S = 3.0 \text{ m}$

9.2. $\tfrac{3}{8} W \left(\pm 1 - \sqrt{3} \right) < P < \tfrac{3}{8} W \left(\pm 1 + \sqrt{3} \right)$

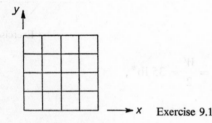

Exercise 9.1

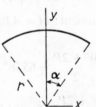

Exercise 10.1

10.1. $y_S = \dfrac{r}{\alpha} \sin \alpha$, $x_S = 0$

   semicircular arc: $y_S = \dfrac{2r}{\pi}$, $x_S = 0$

10.2. sector: $y_S = \dfrac{2r}{3\alpha} \sin \alpha$, $\alpha = \dfrac{\pi}{2} : y_S = \dfrac{4r}{3\pi}$

   segment: $y_S = \tfrac{4}{3} r \dfrac{\sin^3 \alpha}{2\alpha - \sin 2\alpha}$, $\alpha = \dfrac{\pi}{2} : y_S = \dfrac{4r}{3\pi}$

10.3. $z_s = h/3$

10.4. $z_s = \tfrac{3}{8} r$

10.5. $z_s = \tfrac{1}{3} h$

10.6. Center of gravity: $x_S = \dfrac{4a}{3\pi}, y_S = \dfrac{4b}{3\pi}$ Volume: $V = \dfrac{2\pi}{3} ab^2$

   Cable tensions: $S_1 = \dfrac{4}{3\pi} W, S_2 = \left(1 - \dfrac{8}{3\pi} \right) W, S_3 = \dfrac{4}{3\pi} W$

11.1. $K = 0$: Cylinder slides down.

No slipping if: $K_{\min} = W(\sin\alpha - \mu_0\cos\alpha) = 16.3\,\text{lb}^*$,
$$K_{\max} = W(\sin\alpha + \mu_0\cos\alpha) = 33.6\,\text{lb}^*$$

Will not tip over if: $K_{\text{upward}} \leq W\cos\alpha\left(\dfrac{2r}{h} + \tan\alpha\right) = +82.7\,\text{lb}^*$

$$K_{\text{downward}} \geq W\cos\alpha\left(-\frac{2r}{h} + \tan\alpha\right) = -32.7\,\text{lb}^*, \qquad \mu_0 < \frac{2r}{h}$$

11.2. $P = \dfrac{r}{R}\,\dfrac{b/\mu_1 - c}{a+b}\,Q$,

$$A_H = \frac{r}{R}Q,\, A_V = W + \left(1 + \frac{1}{\mu_1}\frac{r}{R}\right)Q,$$

$$B_H = \frac{r}{R}Q,\, B_V = \frac{r}{R}\left(\frac{b/\mu_1 - c}{a+b} - \frac{1}{\mu_1}\right)Q$$

11.3. $P = \dfrac{\mu_1 r_l + 2\mu_2}{r}\,W = 6.1\,\text{lb}^*$,

$$\sin\alpha = \frac{2}{3}\frac{r_l}{r}\mu_1, \qquad \alpha = 0°\,46', \qquad \mu_0 \geq \frac{\mu_1 r_l + 2\mu_2}{2r}.$$

11.4. $P = 2\dfrac{M}{d}\dfrac{1}{e^{\mu_1\alpha} - 1}\left(1 - \dfrac{a}{r}\right) - \dfrac{M}{d}\dfrac{a}{r}$, $\qquad B_x = 0, B_y = \dfrac{M}{r}\left(1 + \dfrac{2}{e^{\mu_1\alpha} - 1}\right)$,

$$A_x = 0, \qquad A_y = P - \frac{M}{r}\left(1 + \frac{2}{e^{\mu_1\alpha} - 1}\right), \qquad \frac{a}{r} < \frac{2}{1 + e^{\mu_1\pi}}$$

13.1. Lines of force: rays through O
Work (a) zero, (b) $-\lambda a^3/3$, (c) $-\lambda a^3/6$, (d) around closed contour $\lambda a^3/3$.
Field is therefore not conservative.

13.2. curl $K = 0$, $\quad V(r) = -\lambda r^3/3$
Lines of force: rays from O
Potential surfaces: concentric spheres

13.3. Lines of force: concentric circles around O parallel to x, y-plane
Potential surfaces: planes through the z-axis

$$\text{curl } K = \left(0, 0, -\frac{2\lambda}{r^2} + \frac{2\lambda r^2}{r^4}\right) = 0 \quad \text{if} \quad r \neq 0$$

The field is not uniquely defined at $r = 0$, so the region of definition is not simply connected. In fact, the work along circles around the z-axis is $2\pi\lambda$.

14.1. $P = \gamma\pi r^3/2$

14.2. $P = \gamma\pi r^3$, $\qquad x_p = 0$, $\qquad z_p = r/4$

14.3. $P = 2\gamma r^3/3$, $x_p = 0$, $z_p = (3\pi r/16)(1 - 64/9\pi^2)$

15.1. $I_x = \dfrac{BH^3 - bh^3}{12}$, $I_y = \dfrac{(H - h)B^3 + h(B - b)^3}{12}$, $C_{xy} = 0$,

$J_S = I_x + I_y$.

15.2. $\xi_S = +3a/8$, $\eta_S = +2b/5$

$I_\xi = 16ab^3/105$, $I_\eta = 2a^3b/15$, $C_{\xi\eta} = a^2b^2/12$, $J_O = 2ab(7a^2 + 8b^2)/105$,

$I_x = 8ab^3/175$, $I_y = 19a^3b/480$, $C_{xy} = -a^2b^2/60$,

$J_S = ab\left(\frac{133}{32}a^2 + \frac{24}{5}b^2\right)/105$

15.3. $I_x = I_1 = bh^3/12 = 256$ in^4, $I_y = I_2 = hb^3/12 = 144$ in^4,

$C_{xy} = 0$, $I_\xi = 184$ in^4, $I_\eta = 216$ in^4, $C_{\xi\eta} = -54$ in^4

15.4. $S\,(\xi_s = -a/6,\ \eta_s = -b/6)$

$I_\xi = ab^3/24 = 208.3$ in^4, $I_\eta = ba^3/24 = 52.1$ in^4, $C_{\xi\eta} = 0$,

$I_x = ab^3/36 = 138.9$ in^4, $I_y = ba^3/36 = 34.7$ in^4,

$C_{xy} = -a^2b^2/72 = -34.7$ in^4, $\varphi \approx 17°$, $I_1 = 149.4$ in^4, $I_2 = 24.2$ in^4,

15.5. $A = 3\pi r^2$, $S\,(x_s = 0,\ y_s = -r/3)$,

$I_x = 11\pi r^4/4$, $I_y = 15\pi r^4/4$, $C_{xy} = 0$, $J_O = 13\pi r^4/2$.

First principal axis parallel to x-axis,

second principal axis along the y-axis.

$I_1 = I_\xi = 29\pi r^4/12$, $I_2 = I_\eta = 15\pi r^4/4$, $I_g = 7.81\,r^4$

16.1. $h = \dfrac{c\sqrt{3}}{9}\,(\gamma_l/\gamma_b - 1)(4\sqrt{1 - \gamma_b/\gamma_l} - 3)$

Stability and depth of immersion x: $h > 0$ if   (a) $\lambda < 7/16$ and $x = c\sqrt{3}/8$, which is attainable, or (b) $\lambda > 7/16$ and $x = c\sqrt{3}/a2\,(1 - \sqrt{7}/4)$, which is not attainable.

16.2. $h = b^2/12c\lambda - (c/2)(1 - \lambda)$,   when $(b/c)^2 > 6\lambda(1 - \lambda)$ body stable.

When $\lambda < 1$ this means $b/c > \sqrt{6}/2$. In this case the condition is

$$\frac{1}{2} - \frac{1}{2}\sqrt{1 - \frac{2b^2}{3c^2}} \le \lambda \le \frac{1}{2} + \frac{1}{2}\sqrt{1 - \frac{2b^2}{3c^2}}, \quad \text{i.e.,} \quad h < 0.$$

17.2. $A = 6000$ lb*, $B = 12,000$ lb*, $M_{max} = 12,000$ lb* ft

17.3.

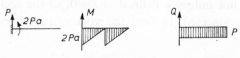

Exercise 17.3

18.1. $\sigma_1 = -930$ psi, $\sigma_2 = 430$ psi, $\tau = 632$ psi

18.2. $\sigma = 350$ kg*/cm^2, $\tau = 86.6$ kg*/cm^2, $\tau_{max} = 100$ kg*/cm^2 with normal stress $\sigma = 400$ kg*/cm^2, $\tau_{max_{max}} = 250$ kg*/cm^2 on an element through the 2-axis but inclined at an angle of $45°$ to the E plane.

18.3. The bounding circular arcs correspond to elements that pass through one of the principal axes. The greatest shear stress ($\tau_{max_{max}}$) acts on one of these elements that is inclined at angles of $45°$ to the other two principal axes.

19.1. $\varepsilon_1 = 2.0 \cdot 10^{-4}$,
$\varepsilon_2 = 0.8 \cdot 10^{-4}$,
$\varepsilon_3 = -0.9 \cdot 10^{-4}$

20.1. $\bar{U} = \dfrac{1}{2E}\{\sigma_x^2 + \sigma_y^2 - 2v\sigma_x\sigma_y + 2(1+v)\tau_{xy}^2\}$,

$\bar{U}_g = \dfrac{1}{6G}(\sigma_x^2 + \sigma_y^2 - \sigma_x\sigma_y + 3\tau_{xy}^2)$,

$\bar{U}_v = \dfrac{1-2v}{6E}(\sigma_x + \sigma_y)^2$

20.2. Uniaxial state of stress:

$$\bar{U} = \frac{1}{2E}\sigma^2, \qquad \bar{U}_g = \frac{1}{6G}\sigma^2, \qquad \bar{U}_v = \frac{1-2v}{6E}\sigma_1^2$$

State of pure shear:

$$\bar{U} = \frac{1}{2G}\tau^2, \qquad \bar{U}_g = \frac{1}{2G}\tau^2, \qquad \bar{U}_v = 0$$

State of hydrostatic stress ($\sigma_1 = \sigma_2 = \sigma_3 = s$):

$$\bar{U} = (1-2v)\frac{3s^2}{2E}, \qquad \bar{U}_g = 0, \qquad \bar{U}_v = (1-2v)\frac{3s^2}{2E}$$

21.1. Tresca: $\sigma_x^2 + 4\tau_{xy}^2 = \sigma_0^2$
Von Mises: $\sigma_x^2 + 3\tau_{xy}^2 = \sigma_0^2$

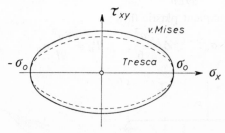

Exercise 21.1

21.2. The yield condition of von Mises is represented by a circular cylinder with axis through the origin and having the direction ratios $(1, 1, 1)$. The yield condition of Tresca is an inscribed hexagonal prism.

22.1. $A_1 \geq \dfrac{W}{\sqrt{3}\,\sigma_{al}} = 0.024 \text{ in}^2, \qquad A_2 \geq \dfrac{2W}{\sqrt{3}\,\sigma_{al}} = 0.048 \text{ in}^2$

$A_3 \geq \dfrac{W}{\sigma_{al}} = 0.042 \text{ in}^2, \qquad z = \dfrac{\sigma_{al}}{E}\left(\dfrac{l_1}{\sqrt{3}} + \dfrac{2l_2}{\sqrt{3}} + l_3\right)$.

22.2. $A = A_0 \exp(\gamma x/\sigma_{al})$, i.e., according to an exponential law.

22.3. $N_1 = P/7, \qquad N_2 = 2P/7, \qquad N_3 = 4P/7$
Wire 3 yields first: $P_0 = 7\sigma_0 A/4 = 26\tfrac{1}{4} \text{ kg}^*$.
Wire 2 yields next: $P^* = 2\sigma_0 A = 30 \text{ kg}^*$.

23.3. Section modulus $Z = a^3/3$,

$$P_{al} = \dfrac{8Z\sigma_{al}}{l} = 8,640 \text{ lb}^*, \qquad Z = \dfrac{lP_{al}}{8\sigma_{al(steel)}} = 6.48 \text{ in}^3$$

For 4 I 9.5 we have $Z = I'/e = 6.7 \text{ in}^3$ and the reserve of strength is sufficient to carry the additional weight of the steel beam also.

Exercise 23.3

23.4. $k = 16/3\pi = 1.70$

24.1. $A = 11P/16, \qquad B = 5P/16, \qquad M_0 = 3Pl/16.$
$M_{max} = M_0 = 3Pl/16$ at the built-in end.
Deflection curve:

$$\zeta = \dfrac{P}{96EI}(-5x^3 + 3l^2 x), \qquad 0 \leq x \leq \dfrac{l}{2}.$$

$$\zeta = \dfrac{P}{96EI}(11x^3 - 24l^2 x + 15l^2 x - 2l^3), \qquad \dfrac{l}{2} \leq x \leq l.$$

$$f_{max} = \dfrac{Pl^3}{48\sqrt{5}\,EI} = \dfrac{Pl^3}{12\sqrt{5}\,Ea4} \qquad \text{at} \quad x = l/\sqrt{5}$$

$$\alpha_{max} = \dfrac{-qPl^2}{352EI} = \dfrac{-27Pl^2}{59Ea^4} \qquad \text{at} \quad x = 8l/11.$$

Loading for incipient plastic flow:

$$\sigma_{max} = \dfrac{M_{max}}{Z} \leq \sigma_0, \qquad Z = \dfrac{a^3}{6}, \qquad P_0 = \dfrac{8a^3}{9l}\sigma_0$$

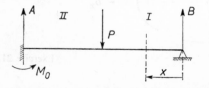
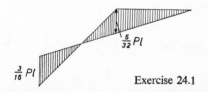

Exercise 24.1

24.2. $A = 17P/36,\quad B = P/18,$

$M_0 = 11Pl/144$

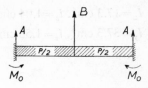

Maximum stress:

(a) at root of beam

$\sigma_b = 458\,P/l^2,$

Exercise 24.2

(b) in wire $\sigma_w = 556\,P/l^2$

Incipient plastic flow: $\sigma_w = \sigma_0,\quad P_0 = 18 \times 10^{-4} l^2 \sigma_0,\quad P^* = 42.10^{-4} l^2 \sigma_0$
$k' = 2.3$

25.1. $\sigma(z) = \dfrac{3P}{a^3}\,z,\qquad \tau(z) = \dfrac{3P}{a^2}\left(\dfrac{1}{4} - \dfrac{z^2}{a^2}\right).$

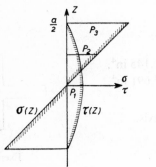

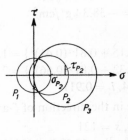

Exercise 25.1

25.2. $M_y = Pl/12,\qquad M_z = Pl/8,\qquad \sigma = -\dfrac{M_z}{I_z}\,y + \dfrac{M_y}{I_y}\,z.$

The endangered sections are at the fixed ends, and the maximum stress in the corner $y = -b/2,\ z = h/2$ is $\sigma = (Pl/4h^2b^2)\,(3h+2b) = (312/9)P$ in^{-2}, $P_{al} = 519$ lb*. Neutral axis: $\sigma = 0$, i.e., $27y - 8z = 0$.

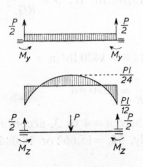

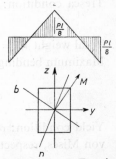

Exercise 25.2

26.1 $I_z = 17.3$ cm^4, $i_z = 1.04$ cm
     $I_y = 37.3$ cm^4, $i_z = 1.53$ cm

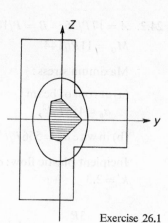

26.2. $\sigma(y) = -6.25\,(1 + 1.38y)$ kg*/cm^2
      Neutral axis: $y = -0.72$ cm
      $\sigma_{max} = 6.7$ kg*/cm^2 at $y = -1.5$ cm
      $\sigma_{min} = -27.9$ kg*/cm^2 at $y = +2.5$ cm

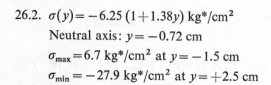

26.3.   (a) $f = 0.720$ cm at loaded end
      (b) Root section, where $M_{max} = 2.22$ kg*m
      (c) $y = -0.49$ cm, because $\sigma(y) = -6.25\,(1 + 2.05y)$ kg*/cm^2
      (d) $\sigma_{max} = +13.0$ kg*/cm^2
         $\sigma_{min} = -38.3$ kg*/cm^2

Exercise 26.1

27.1. $I_\eta = 4\,\{0.15 + 0.81 \cdot (0.41)^2\} = 1.145$ in^4,
      $I_\zeta = 4\,\{0.32 + 0.81 \cdot (0.66)^2\} = 2.691$ in^4,
      $i_\eta = 0.594$, $i_\zeta = 0.911$.
      Buckling in the direction of ζ-axis.
      $\lambda = 72$ in, $s = 121$
      $\Delta t = \pi^2/(\alpha s^2) = 56.2°C = 133°$ F.

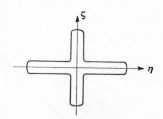

Exercise 27.1

27.3.   According to Euler formula $r = 0.78$ in, but then the slenderness ratio
      would be $s = l/R = 62 < 120$. From Tetmajer formula $r = 1.25$ in. to
      nearest quarter inch.

28.1.   Von Mises condition: $M_0 = \dfrac{\pi}{2} R^3 \dfrac{\sigma_0}{\sqrt{3}} = 18{,}137$ lb* ft, $\vartheta = \dfrac{\sigma_0 l}{RG} \dfrac{1}{\sqrt{3}} = 9°$.

      Tresca condition: $M_0 = \dfrac{\pi}{2} R^3 \dfrac{\sigma_0}{2} = 15{,}708$ lb* ft, $\vartheta = \dfrac{\sigma_0 l}{RG} \cdot \tfrac{1}{2} = 8°$.

28.2.   Total weight $W = \pi R^2 l\gamma = 633$ lb*
      Maximum bending moment $M = Wl/8 = 1420$ lb*in

$$\sigma_{max} = M/Z = \frac{l^2\gamma}{2R} = 2270 \text{ psi}$$

Yield condition: $\sigma^2 + n\tau^2 = \sigma_0{}^2$, where $n = 4$ or 3, according to Tesca,
von Mises, respectively. Accordingly, $M_0 = 15{,}662$ or $18{,}084$ lb* ft

28.3. $k = 1.27$

29.1. $\sigma = \dfrac{M_y}{I_y} \cdot z + \dfrac{M_z}{I_z}\, y$,

$$U = \int \frac{\sigma^2}{2E}\, dV = \int\limits_0^l \frac{M_y^2}{2EI_y}\, dx + \int\limits_0^l \frac{M_z^2}{2EI_z}\, dx\, .$$

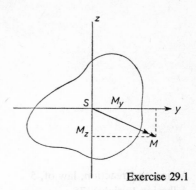

Exercise 29.1

29.2. $\alpha_{11} = l^3/(24EI)$, $\alpha_{12} = 5l^3/(48EI)$, $\alpha_{22} = l^3/(3EI)$,
$A = (11/16)\,P$, $B = (5/16)\,P$, $M = (3/16)\,Pl$.

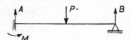

Exercise 29.2

30.1. $f = Pl^3/(8EI)$

30.2. $P_1 = 7P/53$, $P_2 = 16P/53$, $P_3 = 30P/53$ (from left to right)

30.3. $S = PAl^2/(3I + 2l^2 A) = 4PAl^2/(a^4 + 8Al^2)$.

Index

70
71
72
74

75
76
79

83